CHEMICAL ANALYSIS

A SERIES OF MONOGRAPHS ON
ANALYTICAL CHEMISTRY AND ITS APPLICATIONS

Volume XVIII

Organic Complexing Reagents: Structure, Behavior,

and Application to Inorganic Analysis

by D. D. Perrin

D1109353

CHEMICAL ANALYSIS

Other volumes in preparation

ORGANIC COMPLEXING REAGENTS:

Structure, Behavior, and Application to Inorganic Analysis

D. D. PERRIN

Department of Medical Chemistry
Institute of Advanced Studies
Australian National University, Canberra

INTERSCIENCE PUBLISHERS
a division of John Wiley & Sons, New York · London · Sydney

Preface

It is both pertinent and desirable, on the basis of our present knowledge, to discuss the principles involved in analytical chemical methods so that the latter may be placed securely upon a modern theoretical foundation. Such is the object of this book. In addition to providing a rationale for existing practices, I hope to point to possible avenues of exploration which could lead to more useful methods of analysis. Thus, the present approach can suggest ways in which complex-forming organic molecules could be "tailored" to confer greater inorganic species specificity. So, too, it can indicate which types of organic reagent are most suitable for use in precipitations, extractions, or other reactions of inorganic species and make it possible to predict likely properties (such as solubility and spectra) of reaction products.

It is probably true that no branch of chemistry has grown faster over the last thirty years than analytical chemistry or, in its practical applications, been better served by monographs and books. The monumental "Treatise on Analytical Chemistry" (at present in course of publication under the editorship of I. M. Kolthoff and P. J. Elving), E. B. Sandell's "Colorimetric Determination of Traces of Metals," and F. Feigl's "Spot Tests in Inorganic Analysis" are familiar examples.

Nevertheless, almost all analytical procedures and books, with the notable exception of F. Feigl's "Specific, Selective, Sensitive Reactions," have been concerned with experimental techniques, conditions, or requirements, rather than with information about the basic principles involved in the reactions and with the properties that confer analytical usefulness on the end products. To a large extent, current chemical methods of analysis are based on the practical application of characteristic properties found accidentally and refined empirically. This book is the result of the awareness of Doctors Kolthoff and Elving that this state of

v

affairs exists, and of their invitation to write a book dealing with these aspects of inorganic analysis with organic reagents.

The need for a fundamental approach to chemical analysis is evident from the important relation between theory and practice in every piece of research aimed at improving existing analytical methods, discovering new ones, or adapting known methods to special problems. A sound knowledge of the theoretical basis of chemical reactions used in analysis undoubtedly places the investigator in a far stronger position in developing new methods.

Complex formation exerts major effects in analytical chemistry, by increasing or decreasing solubilities of materials, by modifying their ease of oxidation or reduction, by altering the size of the ionic charge (which may even be removed or reversed), by leading to different crystalline forms, and by forming, or masking the formation of, colored products. The properties of such complexes are often strikingly different from those of the original species.

With the recent upsurge of interest in theoretical inorganic chemistry there has emerged a much better understanding of the nature of the forces binding inorganic substances and operating in complex formation between inorganic and organic species. This has stimulated and accompanied a great deal of investigation into the stereochemistry and physical chemistry of such complexes, including their thermodynamics and reaction kinetics, leading in turn to the emergence of such relations as the Irving-Williams stability sequence of the divalent metal ions from manganese to zinc.

It must be emphasized that no attempt has been made to give practical details. Instead, stress is laid throughout on basic principles, with the aim of providing a framework within which to view a large part of analytical chemistry. The inclusion of a chapter pointing out some of the key factors in the chemistry of elements and their ions should help to orient readers interested in analyses for particular species so as to make for more rapid appraisal of current chemical methods.

The aim, in brief, is to present a coherent account, based on modern theoretical inorganic chemistry, that will enable the reader to understand the choosing of reagents for particular determinations and the kinds of conditions under which the reactions can be carried out.

I am indebted to Professor A. Albert and Dr. C. J. Hawkins, who have read the manuscript, for their suggestions and criticisms, and to Mesdames C. Y. Greenhill and S. M. Schenk for preparing the typescript.

D. D. PERRIN

August 1964

Contents

Abbreviations

BAL	2,3-dimercapto-1-propanol
bipy	2,2′-bipyridine
DHG	N,N-di(2-hydroxyethyl)glycine
DTC	diethyldithiocarbamate
EDTA	ethylenediaminetetraacetic acid
en	ethylenediamine
NTA	nitrilotriacetic acid
NTE	2,2′,2″-nitrilotriethanol = triethanolamine
ox	oxine = 8-hydroxyquinoline
PAN	1-(2-pyridylazo)-2-naphthol
penten	tetrakis(aminoethyl)ethylenediamine
phen	1,10-phenanthroline
py	pyridine
SPADNS	2-p-sulfophenylazo-1,8-dihydroxynaphthalene-3,6-disulfonic acid
TG	thioglycollic acid
tren	2,2′,2″-triaminotriethylamine
trien	triethylenetetramine
TTA	thenoyltrifluoroacetone

CHAPTER 1

Introduction

It is convenient to define organic reagents used in chemical analysis as those carbon-containing substances which, by some form of interaction, enable other ions or molecules to be detected or determined. Such organic reagents find many important applications in the analytical chemistry of inorganic species.[1] Procedures such as complexometric titrations using ethylenediaminetetraacetic acid (EDTA) and selective determinations of metals spectrophotometrically with dithizone, or gravimetrically with 8-hydroxyquinoline, come readily to mind. Recent developments in theoretical chemistry, particularly those arising from the ligand-field theory of transition metal ions and their complexes, have led to a greatly increased understanding of factors in reactions that govern the stability of metal complexes, the nature of their absorption spectra, and other properties of interest to the analyst. This book attempts to present a picture of current chemical theory, more particularly as it relates to reaction between inorganic species and organic reagents. Applications to familiar analytical procedures will be discussed. To keep the account within reasonable limits, however, no attempt will be made to encompass practical details of the processes involved.

Unlike reactions in organic chemistry, most of those in inorganic chemistry involve dynamic equilibria, so that the positions of equilibria and the nature of the products are determined rapidly and directly by free-energy considerations. This is especially true of ionic reactions, and knowledge of the energies involved in such reactions is important in deciding whether, or how far, they can proceed. In some cases, however, including substitution reactions of complexes containing certain metal ions, rates are very slow although the processes involved are thermodynamically favorable. Reasons for this are given in Chapter 5.

Much of the most important group of reactions to be considered are those in which complexes are formed between hydrated metal ions and

1

organic molecules or ions, usually by coordination through one or more atoms of oxygen, nitrogen, or sulfur. Such complex formation is important in analytical chemistry in two ways. It may produce a species that has more useful characteristics for identification or estimation; and alternatively, the concentrations of particular cations can be reduced to levels below those at which they interfere in reactions designed to separate, or otherwise characterize, other molecules or ions.

Metal ions in aqueous solution are themselves complexes because they orient the water molecules immediately surrounding them, leading, especially in the transition and higher-valent metal ions, to definite complexes such as $Al(H_2O)_6^{3+}$ and $Cr(H_2O)_6^{3+}$. This is a consequence of the dipole moments of the water molecules, leading to their spatial orientation by the ionic charge on the metal ion.

For this reason, complex formation in solution is really a replacement process in which one or more of the solvent molecules surrounding an ion is replaced by other ions or molecules, to give species which usually have very different chemical and physical properties. Rates of exchange of water bound to metal ions show wide variation, ranging (for most ions) from exchange times of very much less than a millisecond to a half time $(t_{1/2})$ measured in days (for $Cr(H_2O)_6^{3+}$). The species with which a metal ion reacts to form a complex is known as a *ligand*. In most cases, the formation and dissociation of complexes proceeds rapidly by a succession of equilibrium reactions which, if M signifies a metal ion and L is a ligand, can be written

$$M + L \rightleftharpoons ML$$
$$ML + L \rightleftharpoons ML_2$$
$$ML_{n-1} + L \rightleftharpoons ML_n$$

so that, because of these stepwise equilibria, a series of complexes may coexist in the solution. Ligands may be anions (such as Cl^- or $NH_2CH_2COO^-$) or neutral molecules (such as NH_3 or 1,10-phenanthroline), so that complexes may be cations, neutral molecules, or anions.

For a substance to function as a ligand it must have at least one pair of electrons it can "donate" towards a metal ion. The maximum number of such ligands that are bound by a metal ion is equal to its *coordination number*.

Where, as in this series, each complex contains only one metal ion, the quantity $\bar{n}$, Bjerrum's *formation function*, is independent of metal ion concentration and provides a quantitative measure of the extent of formation of the complexes. This is because $\bar{n}$, which is defined as the average number of ligand molecules bound per metal ion, depends on the ligand concentration.

However, the actual concentrations of the individual complexes are determined by the stepwise equilibrium ratios,

$$K_1 = \frac{[ML]}{[M][L]}, \quad K_2 = \frac{[ML_2]}{[ML][L]}, \quad \ldots, \quad K_n = \frac{[ML_n]}{[ML_{n-1}][L]}$$

which are known as *formation constants*, and the overall constant $\beta_n = [ML_n]/[M][L]^n$, which is the *overall stability constant* of the complex ML_n. Methods used in obtaining such constants are described elsewhere,[2] and extensive collections of formation and overall stability constants are available.[3] They show that many factors influence the stability of complexes (in respect of their dissociation into their components), including the nature of the atoms concerned in bond formation, the base strength of the ligand, the stereochemistry of the complexes themselves, and contributions due to resonance. It is the interrelation of these factors that determines the extent to which any reagent shows selectivity towards inorganic species.

One of the greatest effects arises from the formation of complexes in which the ligand is attached to the metal by two or more atoms to form a *chelate compound*. Typical examples include the *bis* complexes of ethylenediamine and of glycine with copper (II) (structures (I) and (II)).

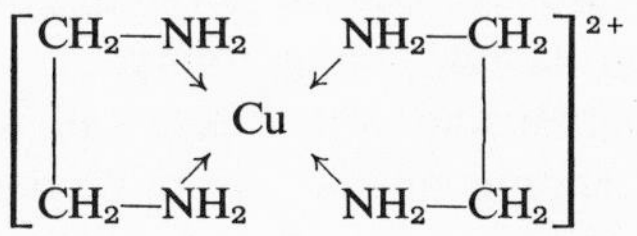

I 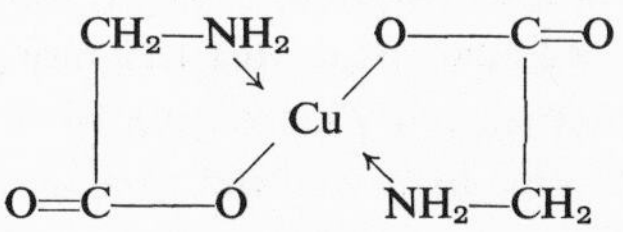   II

Whereas (I) is a divalent cation, (II) is a neutral molecule. If five- or six-membered rings are formed in this way, the complex shows a greatly increased stability, an effect further enhanced if the ligand is *multidentate* (so that the complex contains two or more such rings). Ethylenediamine and the dianion of salicylic acid are examples of bidentate ligands. Qualitatively, this *chelate effect* can be explained by saying that, the more points of attachment there are between a ligand and a metal ion, the more difficult it will be for the metal ion to break all the bonds and move away

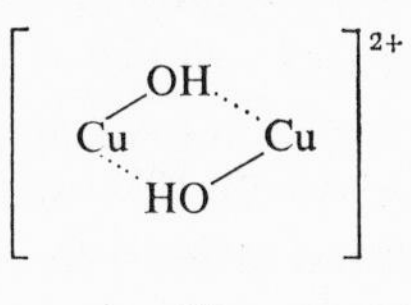

III

before they can re-form.   Polynuclear complex formation can sometimes occur, giving complexes of the type M_mL_n.   Examples are fairly common where partial hydrolysis of metal ions is involved, if this leads to *olation* in which metal ions are joined by bridging —OH groups, as in the hydroxo complex ion (III).   The mathematical analysis of such systems is complicated because equilibria depend on the metal ion concentration as well as on the ligand concentration.

Where concentrations instead of activities are used in their calculation, stability constants vary to some extent with the experimental conditions, reflecting particularly the effects of changes in ionic strength on the activity coefficients of the species concerned.   For the present discussion these effects will be ignored.

Some complexes, such as those involving Cr(III) and Co(III), form and dissociate slowly.   These "robust" complexes, and the reasons for their existence, are discussed in Chapter 5.   Their slowness of reaction prevents their analytical determination by titration procedures.

A ligand is usually an anion or a neutral molecule with basic properties so that, at sufficiently low pH values, it becomes extensively protonated, with consequent reduction in its complex-forming ability.   Thus phenols (pK_a 10) are weak acids that form complexes via the phenolate ion. This leads to a progressive decrease in their complexing abilities at pH values less than 10.   On the other hand, thiocyanate ion, derived from a strong acid, is almost pH-independent in its complexing ability.

The stability constants of any particular ligand with a series of metal ions fall in a well-defined sequence, depending on the nature of the coordinating groups, so that the analytical ideal of a specific reagent for any individual metal is unlikely to be realized.   The number of types of group involved in chelated-ring formation is strictly limited by the requirement that the atoms bonded to the metal in the complex be able to "donate" a pair of electrons to the union.   In practice, this almost restricts the choice to N, O, and S.   The nitrogen may be present as a primary, secondary, or tertiary amine; a nitro, nitroso, azo, or diazo group; or as a nitrile or an acid amide.   Oxygen may coordinate as phenolate or carboxylate ion, (neutral) alcoholic OH, or ether-oxygen, or as —C═O of ketones, aldehydes, and carboxyl groups.   Similarly, sulfur bonding may be through ionized thiol and thiocarboxylate anions, through thioethers and thioketones, and through disulfide groups.   The main types of reactive group are listed, with the chelating agents in which they occur, in Table 1.1.

Some examples of the types of chelate ring to which these groups give rise are shown in rings (IV) to (IX).   Ring (IV) occurs in metal complexes of 8-hydroxyquinoline and its derivatives and in 4-hydroxybenzothiazole. Ring (V) is found in α,α'-bipyridyl, 1,10-phenanthroline, and α,α',α''-terpyridyl complexes. The ring (VI) is present in metal

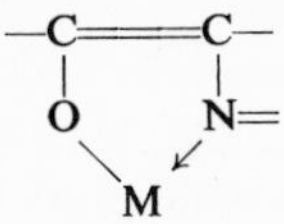

complexes of dimethylglyoxime and other dioximes, whereas (VII) occurs in complexes of pyrocatechol and its derivatives. Ethylenediamine and glycine give structures (VIII) and (IX), respectively.

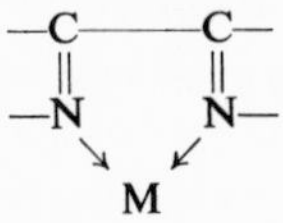

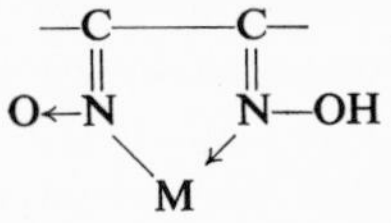

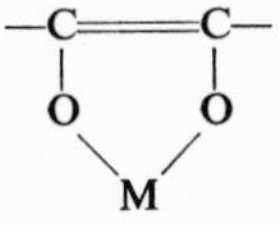

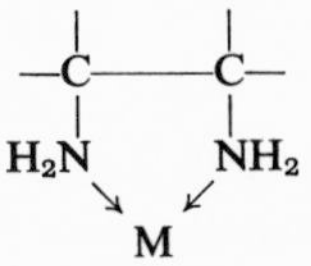

TABLE 1.1

The Main Complex-Forming Groups in Analytical Reagents

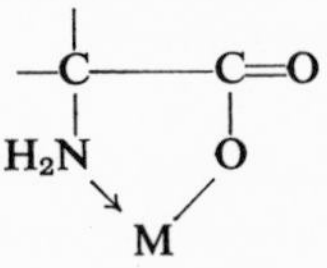

Group	Examples
Tertiary N	α,α'-Bipyridine, 4-hydroxybenzothiazole, 8-hydroxyquinaldine, 8-hydroxyquinoline, PAN, 1,10-phenanthroline, picolinic acid, quinaldic acid, α,α',α''-terpyridyl
(Usually phenolic) —O⁻	Acetylacetone, alizarin, chloranilic acid, cupferron, eriochrome black T, glyoxal-bis(2-hydroxyanil), 4-hydroxybenzothiazole, 8-hydroxyquinaldine, 8-hydroxyquinoline, kojic acid, 9-methyl-2,3,7-trihydroxy-6-fluorone, morin, murexide, α-nitroso-β-naphthol, nitroso-R-salt, PAN, pyrocatechol, rhodizonic acid, salicylaldoxime, salicylic acid, SPADNS, tiron
—S⁻	4-Chloro-1,2-dimercaptobenzene, diphenylthiocarbazone, dithiol, mercaptobenzothiazole, rubeanic acid, thionalide
—C—O⁻ ‖ O	Aluminon, anthranilic acid, EDTA, glycine, mandelic acid, metalphthalein, oxalic acid, picolinic acid, quinaldic acid, salicylic acid
—C—S⁻ ‖ S	Sodium diethyldithiocarbamate, zinc dibenzyldithiocarbamate

(Continued)

TABLE 1.1 (*Continued*)

The Main Complex-Forming Groups in Analytical Reagents

Group	Examples
$-C{=}O$	Acetylacetone, alizarin, aluminon, chloranilic acid, kojic acid, morin, rhodizonic acid, thionalide
$-C{=}S$	Thiourea
$-C{=}N$ OH	Dimethylglyoxime, α-furildioxime, nioxime, salicylald-oxime
$-C{=}N-O^-$	α-Benzoinoxime, dimethylglyoxime, α-furildioxime, ni-oxime
$-N{=}O$	Cupferron, α-nitroso-β-naphthol, nitroso-R-salt
$-N-N^-$	Diphenylcarbazone, diphenylthiocarbazone
$-N{=}N$	Diphenylcarbazone, diphenylthiocarbazone, eriochrome black T, PAN, SPADNS
$-C{=}N$	Glyoxal-bis(2-hydroxyanil), murexide.
(Neutral)—OH	α-Benzoinoxime, mandelic acid
$-NH_2$	Anthranilic acid, ethylenediamine, glycine, triaminotri-ethylamine, triethylenetetramine
$-NH$	Thionalide, triethylenetetramine
$-N$	EDTA, metalphthalein, triaminotriethylamine
$-As{=}O$ with O^- and O^-	Arsonic acids

These groups differ in their relative complexing abilities with different metal ions—for example, the difference between the stability constants of the ethylenediamine complexes of Cu(II) and Zn is much greater than for the corresponding oxalato complexes—but these differences are of degree rather than of kind, so that reagents are rarely specific. Nor, for most analytical purposes, are reagents sufficiently selective to be used directly.

Metal ions, in turn, fall into three reasonably sharp classifications, as shown by the examples in Table 1.2. These three groups comprise:

1. Ions in which the electronic distributions approximate to those of the inert-gas atoms, He, Ne, A, Kr, Xe, and Rn. Examples include Na^+, Ca^{2+}, and Al^{3+}.

2. Ions in which the d or f orbitals are only partially filled. These are the transition metal ions.

3. Ions with filled d orbitals, such as Ag^+, Zn^{2+}, and Ga^{3+}.

TABLE 1.2

Division of Metals in Terms of Electronic Structure

1. Those metals giving ions resembling the inert gases

Li	Be	B	
Na	Mg	Al	
K	Ca	Sc	Zr(IV)
Rb	Sr	Y	Hf(IV)
Cs	Ba	La, Ce-Lu	Th(IV)

2. Metals with ions having partly filled d or f orbitals

Ti	V	Cr	Mn	Fe	Co	Ni	Cu(II)
Nb	Mo	Tc	Ru	Rh	Pd	Ag(II)	
Ta	W	Re	Os	Ir	Pt	Au(III)	
Rare earths and actinides							

3. Metals whose ions have filled d orbitals

Cu(I)	Zn	Ga	Ge	As	
Ag(I)	Cd	In	Sn	Sb	Te
Au(I)	Hg	Tl	Pb	Bi	Po

Some overlapping occurs. For example, in many of their complexes Fe(III) and Mn(II) show properties more closely resembling "inert-gas" ions.

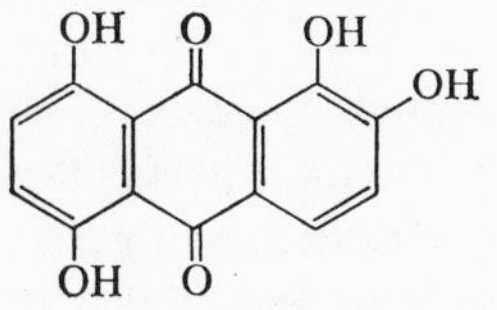

X 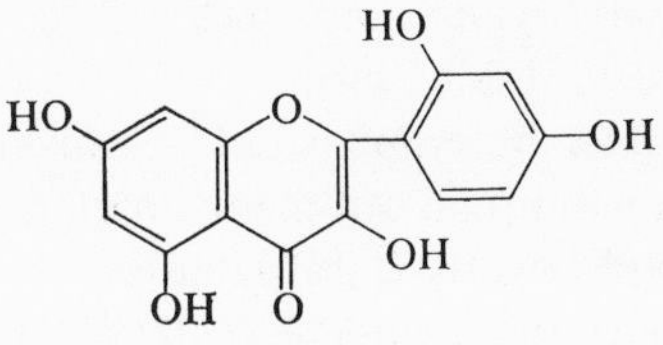   XI

Ions in the first group react preferentially with oxygen-containing anionic ligands such as carboxylate ions and the anions of quinalizarin (X) and morin (XI), in which the important parts of the ligands are the groupings (XII) or (XIII). Thus, quinalizarin is used in alkaline solution for the colorimetric determination of Be, Mg, B, and Al; it also reacts with Sc

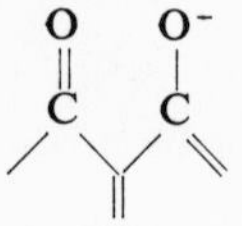

XII 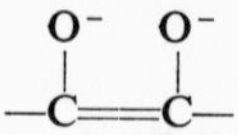   XIII

and the rare earths but, in neutral or weakly acid solutions, many other metal ions, including Zr and Th, also give colors. Similarly, in acid solutions morin is used to estimate Zr, Th, Sc, and Al, whereas in strongly alkaline solutions it is almost specific for Be.

Transition-metal ions form more stable complexes with ligands containing polarizable portions such as amino groups and heterocyclic nitrogen atoms. There is some overlap in properties between the ions to the right of the transition-metal series and the earliest of those with filled d shells, so that ethylenediamine also forms strong complexes with Zn, Cd, and Hg.

The third group in Table 1.2 also prefers highly polarizable ligands, especially if the latter have suitable vacant orbitals into which some of the d electrons can be "back-bonded." This condition favors sulfur-containing ligands, so that a reagent such as thionalide (XIV) forms insoluble complexes with Cu, Ag, Au, Cd, Hg(II), Tl, Sn(II), Pb, As, Sb, Bi, Pt, and Pd. Here again, some overlap with the higher members of the transition metals is evident.

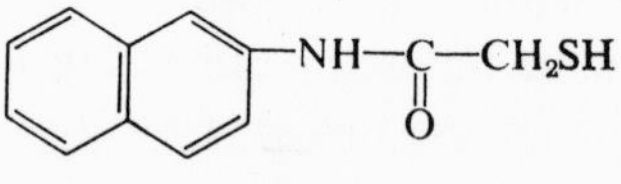

XIV

A reagent such as dithizone, where metal binding takes place through nitrogen and sulfur groups, has an even broader "spectrum" of metal reactivity, which embraces a large part of the transition metal and the "filled d orbital" series.

It must be emphasized, however, that although these considerations indicate in broad outline the preferred types of ligand for particular classes of metal ions they are by no means exclusive. Instead, all ligands might be expected to interact with all metal ions, to an extent that depends largely on the nature of the donor groups on the ligand. To achieve the degree of selectivity desired in analytical work it is usually necessary to exploit differences in two or more physical or chemical properties. Some of the more common properties that are used in this way include:

1. The production of a characteristic color. This may be:
   (i) for the direct spectrophotometric estimation of the species giving rise to the color.
   (ii) for detecting an endpoint, e.g. by means of an indicator in acid-base or oxidation-reduction titrations, or by adsorption of an indicator onto a precipitate.
2. Differences in solubility. This may be made the basis of a gravimetric method or used volumetrically, or trace constituents may be separated by coprecipitation.
3. The use of "masking" reagents to prevent a species other than the one being studied from participating in a reaction.
4. Differences in distribution between solvents at controlled pH values.
5. Differences in ion-exchange and chromatographic behavior.
6. Differences in volatility.
7. Oxidation or reduction to other valence states.

All these properties of inorganic species can be profoundly modified by the use of suitable organic reagents. Sometimes, too, modification of a reagent improves its analytical usefulness. For example, in dilute mineral acid solutions, zirconium and hafnium (also Ti, Th, Sn, and Al) form intensely colored but sparingly soluble "lakes" with alizarin (XV) and other hydroxyanthraquinones such as purpurin (1,2,4-trihydroxyanthraquinone) and quinalizarin (X) as well as morin (XI) and quercetin (which differs from morin only in the position of one of the hydroxyl groups on the phenyl side chain). Insertion of a sulfonic acid group into alizarin confers water solubility without otherwise affecting the reaction, which is the basis of colorimetric methods for estimating these metals. This book attempts to elucidate the factors that give rise to these effects.

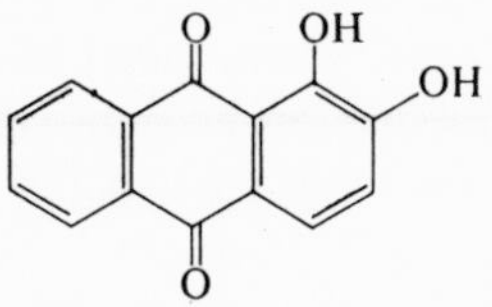

XV

Our understanding of the factors governing such properties has, in recent years, been materially assisted by developments in theories of

10 ORGANIC COMPLEXING REAGENTS

chemical bonding. In particular, we have been assisted by the union of two treatments which superficially are quite different. On the one hand, the sizes, shapes, and directions of orbitals were held to be very important in determining whether or not chemical combination could occur. Apparently opposed to this was the suggestion that molecules were held together by nondirected, nonspecific electrostatic forces. The combination of these two approaches, to give the ligand-field theory, is described in Chapter 2.

It is hoped that this theoretical background will, in turn, increase the possibilities of predicting with some confidence the kinds of substances most suitable for particular determinations, the experimental conditions that should be used, and the nature and magnitude of the effects of modifying the structures of the reagents.

References

1. See, for example, Sandell, E. B., *Colorimetric Determination of Traces of Metals,* Interscience, New York, 3rd ed., 1959; Feigl, F., *Spot Tests in Inorganic Analysis,* Elsevier Publishing Co., Amsterdam, 5th ed., 1958; Feigl, F., *Chemistry of Specific, Selective and Sensitive Reactions,* Academic Press, New York, 1949; and Welcher, F. J., *Organic Analytical Reagents,* Van Nostrand, New York, 4 vols., 1947–1948.
2. Rossotti, F. J. C., and H. Rossotti, *The Determination of Stability Constants,* McGraw-Hill Book Co., New York, 1961.
3. Bjerrum, J., G. Schwarzenbach, and L. G. Sillén, eds., *Stability Constants of Metal-Ion Complexes; Part I: Organic Ligands; Part II: Inorganic Ligands,* Chemical Society, London, 1957–1958.

CHAPTER 2

Chemical Bonds

The complete mathematical solution of the Schrödinger wave equation
for the hydrogen atom, permitting as it does the accurate prediction of the
spectrum and other physical properties of this species, represents one of
the greatest achievements in physical chemistry.[1] It also provides the
foundation for much of our present understanding of chemical bonding,
stereochemistry, and spectra. A grasp of some of the fundamental
properties and consequences of this wave equation is essential to much
that is discussed elsewhere in this book.

2.1 Atomic Orbitals

The Heisenberg uncertainty principle and the wave character of the
electron prohibit the exact location, at any instant, of the position of an
electron in any atom. All that can be obtained from the wave equation
is information about the average time spent by an electron in any small
element of space. By constructing contours of the space within which
electrons spend, say, 99% of their time, the volumes they occupy can be
visualized. These volumes are known as "orbitals," and any orbital
can contain a maximum of two electrons. Chemical-bond formation results
from the overlap of filled and unfilled orbitals of different atoms, molecules, or ions, resulting in a greater spreading out in space ("delocalization") of the electrons concerned. The electron density in any region of an
orbital is proportional to the square of the wave function, ψ.

A further, crucial factor that must be taken into account is the mathematical sign that the wave function takes in any totally enclosed part of an
orbital. This sign (*which has nothing to do with electronic charge*) is
somewhat analogous to "phase." Where parts of overlapping orbitals
have the same sign for ψ, so that the wave functions are "in phase," chemical
bonding can occur; if they are of opposite sign, then the orbital resulting

11

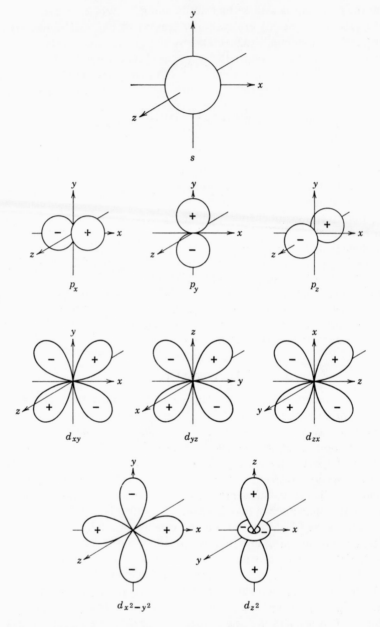

Fig. 2.1.   Shapes of atomic orbitals.   The p orbitals lie along each of the x, y, and z axes.   The lobes of the d_{xy}, d_{yz}, and d_{zx} orbitals lie in the corresponding planes, in directions bisecting the axes.   The $d_{x^2-y^2}$ and d_{z^2} orbitals lie along the x and y, and z axes, respectively.

from their overlap is said to be "antibonding." Where overlap is such that equal contributions are made by regions of like and unlike signs, they are "nonbonding." Qualitatively, the greater the overlap of two bonding orbitals the stronger the resulting chemical bond. This can be pictured as increasing the concentration of the bonding electrons between the nuclei so as to decrease nuclear repulsions and increase the mutual electrostatic attractions between the electrons on the nuclei.

The shapes of the atomic orbitals of hydrogen are known precisely, and the orbitals of all other atoms are believed to be qualitatively similar. The only atomic orbitals that are important in theoretical chemistry are, in order of increasing complexity, those classified as s, p, d, and f, corresponding to the azimuthal quantum numbers 0, 1, 2, and 3. The f orbitals need to be considered only for the lanthanide and actinide elements. With this exception, all chemical bonding can be discussed in terms of the distribution of electrons among s, p, and d orbitals. These orbitals are represented diagrammatically in Fig. 2.1.[2] The s-type atomic orbitals are spherically symmetrical, and, for any specified principal quantum number, only one such orbital is possible. There are three p-type atomic orbitals, which are perpendicular to each other, the boundary surface of

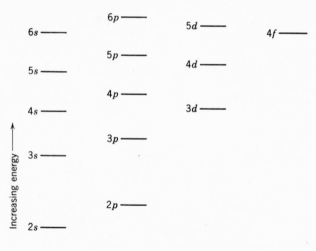

Fig. 2.2.   The approximate sequence of energy levels of atomic orbitals.

each orbital resembling the two halves of a dumbbell. Because all three of the p orbitals correspond to the same energy value, they are described as "triply degenerate." Similarly, although d_{z^2} has a different shape, the equivalence of the five d orbitals makes them "fivefold degenerate," and the f orbitals are "sevenfold degenerate."

Whereas the wave function of an s orbital remains everywhere the same, in p, d, and f orbitals the lobes vary in sign. Thus, in a p orbital, if one lobe is designated positive, the other lobe is negative. Similarly, in d orbitals, there is an alternation of sign in passing from a lobe to its neighbors. The shapes and signs of atomic orbitals are such that the net overlap between any two of them on the same atom is always exactly zero.

The orbitals are designated by their principal quantum number, e.g. $1s$ or $3p$, and, in general, the energies associated with atomic orbitals fall in the sequence shown in Fig. 2.2, where $2p$ represents $2p_x$, $2p_y$, $2p_z$; $3d$ represents $3d_{xy}$, $3d_{yz}$, $3d_{zx}$, $3d_{x^2-y^2}$, $3d_{z^2}$; etc.

This energy sequence, and the restriction that not more than two electrons (which must be of opposite spins) can occupy the same orbital (the Pauli exclusion principle), lead directly to the ground-state (lowest-energy) electronic configurations of most of the elements in the periodic table. Some examples are given in Table 2.1. A further refinement of electronic distribution is provided by Hund's rule: If two orbitals of equal energy are available to accommodate two electrons, the preferred electronic configuration will have only one electron in each of the orbitals, and the electrons will have parallel spins. This explains, for example, why oxygen and Fe^{3+} are paramagnetic and why, in the latter, there are five unpaired electrons.

The principal quantum number governs the overall size of the atomic orbital, so that the boundary layer of a $2s$ orbital lies inside that of a $3s$ orbital, while the $1s$ orbital is still closer to the nucleus. With increasing nuclear charge each of the completed "shells" $1s^2$, $2s^22p^6$, $3s^23p^6$ moves closer towards the nucleus (compare, for example, the isoelectronic series Na^+, Mg^{2+}, Al^{3+}, Si^{4+} in Table 2.2), but this does not offset the increasing size of the outer orbitals so that bond formation by the latter, depending as it does on electron density within regions of orbital overlap, is weakened.

The tendency of atoms to complete these "shells" by covalent-bond formation is the basis of the *octet rule*, which is a useful guide to the valencies of elements. This accounts for the valencies of 4, 3, 2, and 1 shown by C, N, O, and F, respectively. Boron is limited to a valency of 3 because this is its total number of valence electrons, but it completes the $2s^22p^6$ octet by "accepting" a pair of electrons from an atom with a lone pair of electrons to form a dative bond, giving species such as BF_3NH_3. The ability of phosphorus, sulfur, and heavier atoms to show higher-valence states arises from the fact that the energy needed to promote, say, a $3s$ electron in phosphorus into a vacant $3d$ orbital is not prohibitively large. It is, indeed, commonly more than offset by the energy liberated in the formation of the two additional bonds, so that in such cases low-lying d_π orbitals (i.e. d orbitals concerned in π-bond formation) are more important in multiple bonding than are p_π orbitals. Similarly, electron

TABLE 2.1

Ground States of Some Representative Atoms and Ions

H	$1s^1$
He, Li^+, Be^{2+}	$1s^2$
Li	$[He]2s^1$
C	$[He]2s^22p_x^12p_y^1$
N	$[He]2s^22p_x^12p_y^12p_z^1$
O	$[He]2s^22p_x^22p_y^12p_z^1$
Ne, Na^+, Mg^{2+}, O^{2-}, F^-	$1s^22s^22p^6$
S	$[Ne]3s^23p_x^23p_y^13p_z^1$
Fe	$[Ar]3d_{xy}^23d_{yz}^13d_{zx}^13d_{x^2-y^2}^13d_{z^2}^14s^2$
Ce	$[Xe]4f^15d^16s^2$
Mn^{2+}, Fe^{3+}	$[Ar]3d_{xy}^13d_{yz}^13d_{zx}^13d_{x^2-y^2}^13d_{z^2}^1$
Ti^{3+}	$[Ar]3d^1$
V^{3+}	$[Ar]3d^2$
V^{2+}, Cr^{3+}	$[Ar]3d^3$
Cr^{2+}, Mn^{3+}	$[Ar]3d^4$
Fe^{2+}, Co^{3+}	$[Ar]3d^6$
Co^{2+}	$[Ar]3d^7$
Ni^{2+}	$[Ar]3d^8$
Cu^{2+}	$[Ar]3d^9$
Mo^{3+}	$[Kr]4d^3$
Rh^{3+}	$[Kr]4d^6$
Ir^{3+}, Pt^{4+}	$[Xe]4f^{14}5d^6$

removal from such orbitals is facilitated.[3] It is the electrons at or near the surface of atoms and ions that are the most important in determining their chemical and physical properties.

The special properties of the transition metal ions are directly attributable to their incompletely filled d orbitals; the rare earths owe their superficial similarities to the possession of incompletely filled f orbitals which play only a relatively small part in chemical bonding. This difference is due to the spatial location of these orbitals. In ions of the

TABLE 2.2

Atomic[a] and Cationic[b] Radii, in Angstrom Units

	Atom	Ions (and Valence)
Ac	1.88	1.18(III)
Ag	1.44	1.26(I), 0.89(II)
Al	1.43	0.51(III)
Am		1.07(III), 0.92(IV)
As	1.25	0.58(III), 0.46(V)
At		0.62(VII)
Au	1.44	1.37(I), 0.85(III)
B	0.79	0.23(III)
Ba	2.17	1.34(II)
Be	1.11	0.35(II)
Bi	1.55	0.96(III), 0.74(V)
Br	1.14	0.62(I), 0.47(V), 0.39(VII)
C	0.77	
Ca	1.97	0.99(II)
Cd	1.49	0.97(II)
Ce	1.83	1.07(III), 0.94(IV)
Cl	0.99	
Co	1.25	0.72(II), 0.63(III)
Cr	1.25	0.80(II),[c] 0.63(III), 0.52(VI)
Cs	2.65	1.67(I)
Cu	1.28	0.96(I), 0.72(II)
Dy	1.75	0.92(III)
Er	1.73	0.89(III)
Eu	1.99	0.98(III)
F	0.64	
Fe	1.24	0.74(II), 0.64(III)
Fr		1.80(I)
Ga	1.22	0.62(III)
Gd	1.79	0.97(III)
Ge	1.23	0.73(II), 0.53(IV)
H	0.37	
Hf	1.56	0.78(IV)
Hg	1.50	1.10(II)
Ho	1.74	0.91(III)

16

TABLE 2.2 (*Continued*)

Atomic^a and Cationic^b Radii, in Angstrom Units

Atom		Ions (and Valence)
I	1.33	
In	1.63	0.81(III)
Ir	1.36	0.92(II),[c] 0.68(IV)
K	2.27	1.33(I)
La	1.87	1.14(III)
Li	1.52	0.68(I)
Lu	1.72	0.85(III)
Mg	1.60	0.66(II)
Mn	1.37	0.80(II), 0.66(III), 0.60(IV), 0.46(VII)
Mo	1.36	0.70(IV), 0.62(VI)
N	0.70(single bonds)	
Na	1.86	0.97(I)
Nb	1.43	0.74(IV), 0.69(V)
Nd	1.81	1.04(III)
NH_4^+		1.43
Ni	1.25	0.69(II)
Np	1.31	1.10(III), 0.95(IV), 0.71(VII)
O	0.66(single bonds)	
Os	1.34	0.88(II),[c] 0.69(VI)
Pa	1.61	1.13(III), 0.98(IV), 0.89(V)
Pb	1.75	1.20(II), 0.84(IV)
Pd	1.38	0.80(II), 0.65(IV)
Pm		1.06(III)
Po	1.67	0.67(VI)
Pr	1.82	1.06(III), 0.92(IV)
Pt	1.39	0.80(II), 0.65(IV)
Pu	1.51	1.08(III), 0.93(IV)
Ra		1.43(II)
Rb	2.48	1.47(I)
Re	1.37	0.72(IV), 0.56(VII)
Rh	1.35	0.80(II),[c] 0.68(III)
Ru	1.33	0.81(II),[c] 0.67(IV)
S	1.04(single bonds)	
Sb	1.45	0.76(III), 0.62(IV)

(*Continued*)

TABLE 2.2 (*Continued*)

Atomic[a] and Cationic[b] Radii, in Angstrom Units

Atom		Ions (and Valence)
Sc	1.61	0.81(III)
Se	1.16	0.50(IV), 0.42(VI)
Si	1.18	0.42(IV)
Sm		1.00(III)
Sn	1.41	0.93(II), 0.71(IV)
Sr	2.15	1.12(II)
Ta	1.43	0.68(V)
Tb	1.76	0.93(III), 0.81(IV)
Tc	1.35	0.56(VII)
Te	1.43	0.70(IV), 0.56(VI)
Th	1.80	1.02(IV)
Ti	1.45	0.85(II),[c] 0.76(III), 0.68(IV)
Tl	1.70	1.47(I), 0.95(III)
Tm	1.72	0.87(III)
U	1.39	1.05(III), 0.97(IV), 0.80(VI)
V	1.31	0.88(II), 0.74(III), 0.63(IV), 0.59(V)
W	1.37	0.70(IV), 0.62(VI)
Y	1.78	0.92(III)
Yb	1.94	0.86(III)
Zn	1.33	0.74(II)
Zr	1.59	0.79(IV)

[a] Half of atom-atom bond length, usually in metal, from *Tables of Interatomic Distances and Configuration in Molecules and Ions*, Special Publication No. 11, The Chemical Society, London, 1958.
[b] For sixfold coordination. From Ahrens, L. H., *Geochim. Cosmochim. Acta.* **2**, 115 (1952).
[c] Largely estimated. Brewer, L., L. A. Bromley, P. W. Gilles, and N. L. Lofgren, in *Chemistry and Metallurgy of Miscellaneous Materials*, L. L. Quill, ed., McGraw-Hill Book Co., New York, 1950, pp. 165 ff.

transition elements, the partially filled 3d, 4d, or 5d orbitals have quite large fractions of their total volumes near the outsides of the ions so that they are well placed to take part in, or otherwise influence, chemical-bond formation. The general similarities of transition metal ions to one another arise mainly from the fact that they are all formed by the loss of the one or two outermost s electrons from their metal atoms, with, in some cases, the loss of one or more additional electrons from the d orbitals. On the other hand, the 4f orbitals in the rare earth elements are located much more deeply inside the atoms or ions, so that electrons in these orbitals are, to a large extent, screened by electrons in the 5d orbitals and exert relatively little effect on bond formation. This leads to even greater similarities among the rare earth cations. In the actinide elements the 5f orbitals appear to be less well shielded so that their properties tend to be intermediate between those of the transition metals and those of the rare earth elements.

The similarity in chemical properties between members of the lanthanide (rare earth) series and the corresponding actinides ($4f^n$ and $5f^n$, respectively) serves as a valuable basis for prediction in cases where only trace amounts are available or where radiation hazard precludes detailed chemical investigation.

2.2 Theoretical Treatments of Chemical Bonding

Three distinct theoretical treatments are available for discussing the nature of bonding in cordination compounds. All are approximate, and the question of which treatment to use in any particular instance is at least partly subjective and partly conditioned by the nature of the information sought.

SIMPLE ELECTROSTATIC THEORY

At a distance greater than several times its radius, an ion can be represented as a point source having the same net charge. Under these conditions, interactions between ions should vary directly with the products of their charges and inversely with the distance separating them.

In the series $U^{4+} > U^{3+} > UO_2^+$, the order of stability of complexes with anions is as shown, in qualitative agreement with this expectation, but UO_2^{2+} lies between U^{4+} and U^{3+}.

Electrostatic forces predominate in cations with "inert-gas" configurations ($1s^2$; $1s^2 2s^2 2p^6$; $1s^2 2s^2 2p^6 3s^2 3p^6$), so that the simple theory applies successfully to cations of the alkali metals, alkaline earth metals, and aluminium. The ratio of the radii of cation and anion is also important in this theory because, if the disparity in size is too great, sufficient anions may not be able to fit closely around the cation. Thus the small, highly charged Al^{3+} ion forms fairly strong complexes with F^-, but very weak ones with the much larger I^- ion. Another factor here is that in I^- the electronic charge is distributed over a much larger volume so that the ion-ion interaction in the Al complex would be less than expected on the basis of point-charge predictions. The stability sequence $F^- > Cl^- > Br^- > I^-$ is common among salts where bonding is likely to be predominantly ionic.

Atomic and ionic radii are given in Tables 2.2 and 2.3. In general, the radii of the heavier transition metal ions are greater than for lighter members in the same group. However, the filling of the $4f$ orbitals in the lanthanide (rare earth) elements leads to the steady and progressive *lanthanide contraction* in atomic and ionic radii, so that there is little difference in radii between corresponding second and third transition metal elements and ions, such as Pd^{2+} and Pt^{2+}.

Electrostatic repulsions of four pairs of electrons (whether or not they are concerned in bond formation) disposed around a central nucleus are least if a tetrahedral stereochemistry is adopted. Similarly, two pairs would require a linear structure, and six pairs would give an octahedral one. Double-bonded structures, such as $H_2C{=}CH_2$, would be predicted to have bond angles of about 120°, while valence bond and molecular orbital theories agree that the molecule should be planar. These theories and the electrostatic approach lead, in general, to similar stereochemical expectations for nontransition elements. The less the electron pair repulsion, the smaller the bond angle should be. These repulsions would also be expected to lie in the order: bonding-bonding < bonding-nonbonding < nonbonding-nonbonding. Bonding-bonding repulsion is further diminished if the electronegativity of the central atom is low so that the bonding electrons are further away from it. These considerations account for some of the finer differences in observed bond angles of many organic and inorganic compounds.

This "purely ionic" treatment can be refined by taking account of all electrostatic attractions and repulsions, not only of electric charges, but also of induced and permanent electric dipoles in reacting species. As ions approach more closely towards one another, so that their atomic structure becomes more important, the theory must be increasingly modified if it is to account for experimental observations. Thus, filled electron shells exert van der Waals' repulsions, and, in addition, the effective ionic charge of a cation increases as anions or polar molecules approach it. The latter phenomenon, which leads to increased electrostatic attraction, is due to a reduction in the screening effect of the orbital electrons. It is much more significant in cations of the transition metals, and of metals such as zinc and cadmium, than in the "inert-gas" type of cation. This is because, in the transition and "palladium-type" metal ions (which have, respectively, partly and completely filled d shells) the outermost electrons occupy d orbitals and are much more easily polarized.

TABLE 2.3

Anionic Radii,[a] in Angstrom Units

F^-	1.36	Cl^-	1.81	Br^-	1.95	I^-	2.16
O^{2-}	1.40	S^{2-}	1.84	Se^{2-}	1.98	Te^{2-}	2.21
CO in CO_3^{2-},	1.31;	NO in NO_3^-,	1.21.				

[a] From L. Pauling, Ref. 6, p. 514.

Also, from considerations of the shapes of orbitals it is obvious that an electron in a d orbital is less effective in screening outer electrons from interaction with the nucleus than, say, an electron in an s orbital, which is spherically symmetrical. The importance of the effects increases with the principal quantum member of the cation and the complex-forming ability of the ligand.[4]

Thus, in a series such as Zn^{2+}, Cd^{2+}, Hg^{2+} the electrostatic contribution to bonding decreases, and covalent bonding increases, progressively with increasing ionic radius. On the other hand, in a series of trivalent ions such as Ga^{3+}, In^{3+}, and Tl^{3+} the increased electronic charge and slightly decreased radii ensure that the cations are not readily deformable and that they obey bonding predictions based on electrostatic theory.

This treatment suggests that, because ligands are either anions or polar molecules, the higher the charge and the smaller the radius of the cation (i.e. the greater the ionic potential, defined as the ratio of cation charge to its crystal radius), the greater should be the stability of its complexes. This is useful as a rough guide, but it is seriously limited by its failure to take account of the polarizability (deformability) of the cations, which leads to greater interaction with ligands. The more polarizable the cation and the ligand, the more tendency there is to covalent-bond formation resulting from orbital overlap. Hence, because the polarizability of a cation increases as its charge is reduced, the simple electrostatic approach is most likely to fail with transition- and palladium-type univalent cations, especially with highly polarizable ligands. It becomes quite inadequate for discussing zerovalent states, such as the π-olefinic iron tetracarbonyl complexes.

Increased polarization interaction explains why the ammoniates of the transition metals are more stable than the hydrates. Ammonia, although it has a lower permanent dipole moment than water, has a much higher polarizability, and hence total dipole, in the presence of these ions.   Conversely a semiquantitative electrostatic treatment[5] has shown, in agreement with observation, that for univalent "inert-gas"-type cations of greater size than lithium the hydrates should be more stable than the ammoniates.   Thus, although their crystal radii are almost the same, Cu^+ forms a stable ammine in aqueous solution but Na^+ does not.

Where the ligand is a neutral molecule, the electrostatic treatment predicts the strength of metal complex formation on the basis of the interaction between the ionic charge of the metal ion and the dipole of the ligand. Such ion-dipole interaction is much weaker than the forces between pairs of ions so that, although it is important in the formation of hydrated metal ions of the "inert-gas" type, it is quite inadequate to explain the strong complexes formed with some neutral ligands, especially by some transition metal ions.

The electrostatic approach can be modified by introducing the concept of *electronegativity*.   Complex formation between a metal ion and a ligand can be pictured as drawing electrons from the ligand towards the metal ion, and, the greater the extent to which this occurs, the stronger might the metal-ligand bond be expected to be.   Electronegativity is a measure of the electron-attracting ability of an ion or an atom in a molecule.   Pauling[6] used an empirical relation with the energy of a bond to obtain the electronegativities of the bonded atoms.   Closely similar values are given using a purely electrostatic treatment and effective nuclear charges.[7]   Mulliken's scale of electronegativity values is based on "valence state" ionization potentials of metal ions[8].   The (stepwise) ionization potential is the energy required to remove an electron from an atom or an ion: Values are listed in Tables 2.4.

These values apply to the isolated gaseous atom.   The energies for the higher-valence states are much greater than are likely to be involved in those cases where covalent-bond formation occurs.   For example, the 3702 kcal needed to convert S^{4+} to S^{6+} bears little relation to the energy required to convert SO_3^{2-} to SO_4^{2-}.   Part of this difference comes from the greatly increased electrostatic work involved in removing an electron from an ion with a large positive charge.   Ionization potentials are useful, however, in comparing metal ions in the same valence states and in providing information about the relative energies likely to be involved in their oxidation or reduction.   Ionization potentials, by their nature, give some measure of the electronegativity of an ion (except that electronic configurations in complexes may differ from those in ions), and many roughly linear correlations between such potentials for a series of metal ions and logarithms of their stability constants with a common ligand have been reported.[9]

TABLE 2.4

Ionization Potentials of Elements[a]

(Energy in kilocalories, for successive removal of electrons)	
Ac	159, 279
Ag	175, 495, 803
Al	138, 434, 656, 2767
As	226, 430, 654, 1155, 1444
Au	212, 473
B	191, 580, 875
Ba	120, 231
Be	215, 420
Bi	168, 385, 589
Ca	141, 274
Cd	207, 390
Ce	151, 341, 398, 847
Co	181, 393, 772
Cr	156, 380, 714, 1153
Cs	90, 579
Cu	178, 468, 849
Fe	182, 373, 707
Ga	138, 473, 708
Ge	182, 367, 789, 1054
Hf	160, 344
Hg	241, 432
In	133, 435, 646
Ir	208, 374
K	100
La	129, 264, 442
Li	124, 1744
Mg	176, 347
Mn	171, 361, 777
Mo	164, 372, 626, 1070, 1411, 1568
Na	118, 1091
Nb	159, 330, 577, 883, 1153
Ni	176, 419, 819

(*Continued*)

TABLE 2.4 (*Continued*)

(Energy in kilocalories, for successive removal of electrons)

Os	201, 392
Pb	171, 347, 736, 976
Pd	192, 448, 759
Po	194
Pt	208, 428
Ra	122, 234
Rb	96
Re	182, 383
Rh	172, 417, 716
Ru	170, 387, 656
S	239, 540, 807, 1091, 1672, 2030
Sb	199, 381, 583, 1017, 1292
Sc	151, 295, 571
Se	225, 496, 738, 992
Si	188, 377, 772, 1045
Sn	169, 337, 703, 939
Sr	131, 254
Ta	182, 374
Tc	168, 352
Te	208, 429, 715, 876
Ti	157, 313, 634, 997
Tl	141, 471, 687
V	155, 338, 676, 1107, 1499
W	184, 408
Y	147, 282, 473
Zn	217, 414
Zr	158, 303, 530, 792

[a] Mainly from C. E. Moore, "Atomic Energy Levels," Vol. 4, *Natl. Bur. Std. (U.S.), Circ.* 467 (1958).

24

VALENCE BOND THEORY

This treatment, as developed by Pauling,[6] has been of great importance in the qualitative discussion of a wide range of organic and inorganic chemical topics. Its popularity has undoubtedly lain in the simplicity of the "chemical" picture it provides, but this in turn makes it of very limited application for quantitative calculations. The valence bond theory distinguishes two types of metal complex, which may conveniently be designated as "ionic" and "covalent." Other classifications sometimes used refer to them as "outer" and "inner" complexes, or "high-spin" and "low-spin" complexes. (The latter description is based on magnetic properties.) In both cases, a number of atomic orbitals on the metal ion (equal to the number of ligands in the complex) are assumed to be hybridized and then used in bond formation. This treatment parallels the familiar hybridization of the $2s$, $2p_x$, $2p_y$, and $2p_z$ orbitals on carbon to give four equivalent orbitals distributed tetrahedrally about it. If among the transition metal ions the d orbitals used in bond formation are postulated to have the same principal quantum number as the s and p orbitals, the complex is designated as "covalent." Otherwise it is "ionic."

In covalent-bond formation the important energy term is not the

TABLE 2.5

Stereochemistries for Some Orbital Hybridizations

Coordn. No.	Bond Orbitals[a]	Stereochemistry
2	sp	linear, e.g. $HgCl_2$
3	sp^2	triangular (planar), e.g. BF_3
4	sp^3	tetrahedral, e.g. CH_4
4	$d^3s(d_{xy}, d_{yz}, d_{zx}, s)$	tetrahedral
4	$dsp^2(d_{x^2-y^2}, s, p_x, p_y)$	square planar, e.g. $Ni(CN)_4{}^{2-}$
5	$sp^3d(s, p_x, p_y, p_z, d_{z^2})$	trigonal bipyramid, e.g. PCl_5
5	$dsp^3(d_{x^2-y^2}, s, p_x, p_y, p_z)$	square pyramid
6	$d^2sp^3(d_{x^2-y^2}, d_{z^2}, s, p_x, p_y, p_z)$	octahedral, e.g. $Co(CN)_6{}^{3-}$

[a] If orbitals are to be hybridized in this way, they must be of comparable energy. This is generally the case if the s and p orbitals are from the next higher principal quantum number than d (e.g. $3d$, $4s$, $4p$).

ionization potential (corresponding to the removal of an electron to infinity from an atom or ion) but the energy needed to promote an electron into another orbital which is then involved in bonding. For example, in the formation of $HgBr_2$ one of the $6s^2$ electrons of mercury ([Xe] $4f^{14}5d^{10}6s^2$) has to be promoted into one of the vacant $6p$ orbitals. The half-filled s and p are then hybridized, and addition of the bromine atoms gives a linear, covalently bonded structure. Covalent-bond formation can be expected in cases where the bond energies are appreciably greater than the promotional energies. These promotional energies are clearly much less than the corresponding ionization energies, although there is usually a rough proportionality between them, except at the beginning of a related series such as Li-Cs, where promotional energies are much less than expected.

The most important stereochemistries, and the bond orbitals that must be hybridized to produce them, are given in Table 2.5. Thus, to produce the six equivalent hybrid orbitals pointing along the x, y, and z axes that are needed to form an octahedral complex it is necessary to take the atomic orbitals having the greatest components in these directions: They are $d_{x^2-y^2}$, d_{z^2}, s, p_x, p_y, and p_z. Similarly, a square planar configuration results from hybridization of $d_{x^2-y^2}$, s, p_x, and p_y. In all cases, each of the hybrid orbitals is assumed to overlap, along the direction in which it points, with a suitable orbital from a ligand molecule, so as to form a σ bond. Such *sigma bonds* are similar to the single bonds of organic chemistry and have maximum electron density along the bond axis.

Pauling suggested that the bond-forming powers of s, p, and d orbitals were proportional to their angular wave functions along the bond directions, namely $1:\sqrt{3}:\sqrt{5}$, and the relative strengths of bonds were given by the products of these values for the two types of orbital involved. This approximation is valid only if the radial wave functions are of similar size. In practice, it is better to calculate the overlap integrals using approximate wave functions such as the *Slater orbitals*, which take account of empirically estimated effective nuclear charges.

It will be readily seen that, in such octahedral complexes, the unused d_{xy}, d_{yz}, and d_{zx} orbitals point in directions between ligand molecules and hence cannot form σ bonds. If they can overlap with suitably placed orbitals on the ligands ("π orbitals"), however, a different kind of bond can be formed. This is known as a π *bond* and is analogous with the second half of an olefinic double bond. A third type of bond, the δ *bond*, can result if two atoms are sufficiently close together that all four lobes of a d orbital on one of them can overlap with the four lobes of a d orbital on the other. The three types of bond are illustrated in Fig. 2.3.[10]

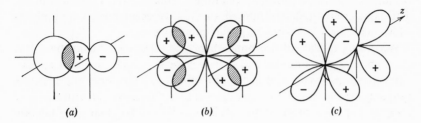

Fig. 2.3. Some examples of σ, π, and δ bonds between atoms. (a) A σ bond resulting from overlap of s and p orbitals. (b) Two π bonds due to p_π–d_π overlap, as in phosphonitrilic chlorides. (c) A δ bond formed by sideways overlap of suitably placed d orbitals on two atoms approaching each other along the z axis.

Orbitals commonly important in tetrahedral, square planar, and octahedral complexes are listed in Table 2.6.

TABLE 2.6

Orbitals Commonly Used in Tetrahedral, Square Planar, and Octahedral Complexes

Complex	For σ-Bond Formation	For π-Bond Formation
Tetrahedral	s, p_x, p_y, p_z	$d_{x^2-y^2}$, d_{z^2}
Square planar	$d_{x^2-y^2}$, s, p_x, p_y	d_{xy}, d_{yz}, d_{zx}
Octahedral	$d_{x^2-y^2}$, d_{z^2}, s, p_x, p_y, p_z	d_{xy}, d_{yz}, d_{zx}

Although the $4f$ orbitals lie too deep in the lanthanides to play any significant part in chemical bonding, it is likely that $5f$ orbitals ought to be considered in complexes of the earlier members of the actinide series. In making calculations of the likely stereochemistries resulting from orbital hybridizations it is probably a good approximation to assume that f and p orbitals give rise, in combination with other orbitals, to the same spatial distributions. Theoretical predictions give the stereochemistry for hybridization of sf as linear, sf^3 as tetrahedral, sf^2d as square planar, and d^2sf^3 as octahedral.

Whether a complex of a transition metal ion is "covalent" or "ionic" was in many cases decided on the basis of their magnetic behavior, the former group comprising complexes where the number of unpaired electrons was less than in the free metal ion. It is now suggested that, in fact, both groups involve covalent bonding, but whereas the former uses "inner" d orbitals, for example d^2sp^3, the latter use "outer" d

orbitals of the same principal quantum number as the s and p orbitals. The noncommittal description of the two types of complex simply as "low-spin" and "high-spin" appears preferable.

According to the valence bond theory, another factor contributing to the stabilities of molecules and ions is *resonance*. This concept may be summarized by saying that if, for any substance, more than one structure fulfilling certain conditions can be written, the actual structure will be intermediate and more stable. The conditions are that the different structures involve no great changes in bond distances and that the number of unpaired electrons does not change. Resonance is invoked to explain the same effects as the idea of electron delocalization does in molecular orbital theory. Although the descriptive value of the valence bond treatment of metal complexes is high, its predictive value is limited. The molecular orbital theory, although intuitively less simple, possesses more flexibility and shows greater promise of quantitative development.

Molecular Orbital Theory

Whereas the valence bond method brings together complete atoms, ions, and ligands and then allows them to interact, the molecular orbital method proceeds by placing in position all the nuclei (or nuclei + inner shells) and then allotting all the electrons concerned in bond formation to molecular orbitals. Thus in a metal complex the orbitals can, in principle, extend over all the atoms present. To reduce the mathematical complexity of this approach, molecular orbitals are assumed to be made up of linear combinations of atomic orbitals (the LCAO approximation). In the particular case that a molecular orbital derives almost entirely from one atomic orbital, the electrons in the molecular orbital are, effectively, non-bonding. Similarly, where a molecular orbital is formed mainly from two atomic orbitals and contains two electrons, it approximates to a conventional chemical bond. Where, however, more than two atomic orbitals contribute significantly, the resulting, more extended molecular orbital cannot be readily represented by conventional chemical structures.

A further difference from the valence bond approach is the basic postulate of the molecular orbital method that the combination of two orbitals to form two new orbitals that are less localized will make one of the new orbitals more stable, and the other less stable, than either of the original orbitals. The more stable one is a "bonding" orbital and the other is an "antibonding" one, but both are available to contain electrons if required. (The valence bond method takes no account of antibonding orbitals.) Figure 2.4 represents pictorially the molecular orbitals resulting from the combination of six atomic orbitals ($d_{x^2-y^2}$, d_{z^2}, s, p_x, p_y, p_z) on a transition

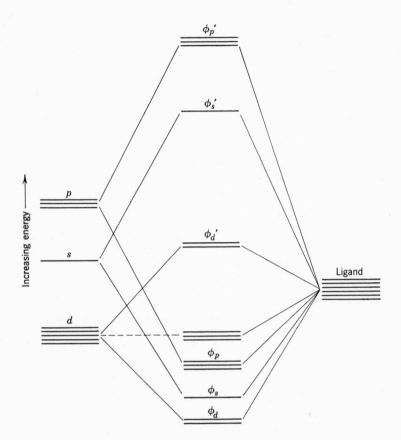

Fig. 2.4. The molecular orbital treatment of regular octahedral complex formation. (Diagrammatic only.) Bonding and antibonding molecular orbitals are
designated ϕ and ϕ', respectively. The three unlabeled lines represent the d_{xy}, d_{yz},
and d_{zx} atomic orbitals.

metal ion with six suitably located ligand orbitals to form a regular
octahedral complex. If desired, the diagram could have been extended
to take account of any π-bond formation by d_{xy}, d_{yz}, and d_{zx} with π
orbitals of the ligands.

The molecular orbital treatment also takes account of unshared pairs
of electrons and hence of their contributions to the observed stereochemistries. This explains, for example, why the bond angle of 107°
in NH_3 (approaching that for sp^3 hybridization) falls to 94° in PH_3
(corresponding to an increased p character in the bonding orbitals, with
some contribution from suitably directed d orbitals).

Orbitals used in forming molecular orbitals cannot be selected arbitrarily. For example, it is essential that the symmetry of orbitals on metal and ligand match.[11] The electrons originally in the atomic orbitals used in complex formation are fed into the molecular orbitals (two per orbital), beginning with those of lowest energy (i.e. the lowest lines in Fig. 2.4). In the diagram, the first six molecular orbitals are bonding, the next three are nonbonding, and the remainder are antibonding. When two electrons are placed in an orbital, more energy is required for the second one than for the first; the difference between them is known as the "energy of pairing." If, in the molecular orbital diagram, the energy separation between two orbitals is less than the energy of pairing, the orbitals will be occupied singly. Otherwise, both electrons will go into the lower orbitals and the upper one will be empty.

In general the molecular orbital approach is used throughout this book, and particular aspects of the theory are developed as required. To facilitate this discussion for transition metal ions some familiarity with ligand-field theory is essential.

LIGAND-FIELD THEORY

In the electrostatic fields of ligands disposed around transition metal ions the d orbitals of the metal no longer remain equal in energy. If all the d orbitals are occupied fully by electrons, this effect produces no overall energy change. Otherwise, when some of the orbitals are unfilled,

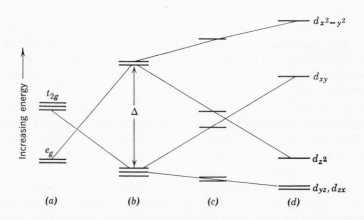

Fig. 2.5. Approximate crystal-field splittings of d orbital energy levels for some of the commoner complex structures. (a) Tetrahedral, (b) octahedral, (c) square pyramidal, (d) square planar. Except for $d_{x^2-y^2}$, the order of orbital energies in (c) and (d) depends on other factors and is not invariably the same.

electrons tend to be forced from orbitals directed towards ligands (e.g. $d_{x^2-y^2}$ and d_{z^2} in an octahedral complex) into orbitals lying between the ligands (in this case, d_{xy}, d_{yz}, d_{zx}), so that the system gains in stability. Figure 2.5 shows the crystal-field splitting produced in this way for some of the more common complex structures. In tetrahedral and octahedral complexes the five d orbitals split into two groups, comprising triply degenerate d_{xy}, d_{yz}, d_{zx} (also known as the t_{2g}, γ_5, or $d\epsilon$ group) and the doubly degenerate $d_{x^2-y^2}$, d_{z^2} (the e_g, γ_3, or $d\gamma$ group). Whereas the t_{2g} group is favored in octahedral complexes, the e_g group is energetically preferred in tetrahedral ones.

Depending on the value of Δ, the crystal-field splitting (commonly referred to as $10Dq$), two cases can be distinguished. If the crystal field is weak, Δ is less than the energy needed for pairing electrons in the d orbitals, and all the d orbitals will be occupied singly by electrons before any pairing takes place. In this case the number of unpaired electrons will be the maximum possible, and the metal ion will be in a "high-spin" state. On the other hand, if Δ is greater than the pairing energy, electrons will pair in the lower orbitals before the higher orbitals are occupied, so that a "low-spin" state is obtained. The main factors governing the value of Δ are the nature of the ligand and the charge on the metal ion. Table 2.7 gives the crystal-field stabilization energies for "weak-field" and "high-field" tetrahedral and octahedral complexes. It should be noted that in tetrahedral complexes the spins and energies differ in the two cases only if three, four, five, or six d electrons are concerned. Similarly, in octahedral complexes distinction can be made only for four, five, six, or seven d electrons.

By combining the electrostatic effect with the molecular orbital approach, a more complete treatment is possible. This is known as the *ligand-field theory*. It takes account, for example, of the effect of π-bond formation, using vacant p_π or d_π orbitals on the ligands. In octahedral complexes, the t_{2g} orbitals are depressed further with respect to the e_g orbitals. Conversely, if the π orbitals of the ligands are already filled this energy separation is decreased.

This theory can be usefully employed to discuss the stabilities of the transition metal complexes, their reaction mechanisms, electron-transfer reactions, stereochemistry, magnetic properties and, in some cases, their absorption spectra. Also, although little has so far been done in this way, the theory should be useful in explaining the chemistry of the rare earths and the actinides. The rare earth elements comprise the group Ce to Lu, which have as their outermost electrons either $5d^16s^2$ or $5d^06s^2$. They differ only in the number of $4f$ electrons they contain. Their characteristic valency is 3, but Ce $(\cdots 4f^25s^25p^66s^2)$, Pr $(\cdots 4f^35s^25p^66s^2)$, and Tb

$(\cdots 4f^9 5s^2 5p^6 6s^2)$ can exhibit tetravalency; and Sm $(\cdots 4f^6 5s^2 5p^6 6s^2)$, Eu $(\cdots 4f^7 5s^2 5p^6 6s^2)$, and Yb $(\cdots 4f^{14} 5s^2 5p^6 6s^2)$ can be divalent. The stability of Ce^{4+}, Tb^{4+}, Eu^{2+}, and Yb^{2+} can be ascribed to the fact that the f orbitals are completely empty (in Ce^{4+}), half filled (in Tb^{4+} and Eu^{2+}), or filled (in Yb^{2+}). Ions of the types f^n and f^{n+7} show marked resemblances, as do d^n and d^{n+5} in the transition metal ions. Similarly, Gd^{3+}, with its half-filled f orbitals, resembles Mn^{2+} (d^5). However, because electrons in the $4f$ orbitals are deep seated and quite strongly shielded by electrons in the outer orbitals, they take little part in chemical bonding, so that the complex-forming ability of the rare earth elements is best treated in terms of electrostatic theory.

Electronic structures of the ions of metals beyond Ra are somewhat uncertain. The $6d$ and $5f$ orbitals are comparable in energy, so that, for example, Np may have the structure $5f^5$ rather than $5f^4 6d^1$. Their common valency is 3, and they also show marked chemical resemblances to one another. The $5f$ orbitals are less effectively shielded, and the properties of those "actinide elements" are intermediate between those of the transition elements and the rare earths.

TABLE 2.7

Crystal-Field Stabilization Energies and Numbers of Unpaired Electrons for Tetrahedral and Octahedral Complexes

Examples		Tetrahedral		Octahedral	
		Weak Field	Strong Field	Weak Field	Strong Field
d^1	Ti^{3+}	$0.6\Delta(1)$	$0.6\Delta(1)$	$0.4\Delta(1)$	$0.4\Delta(1)$
d^2	Ti^{2+}, V^{3+}	1.2 (2)	1.2 (2)	0.8 (2)	0.8 (2)
d^3	V^{2+}, Cr^{3+}	0.8 (3)	1.8 (1)	1.2 (3)	1.2 (3)
d^4	Cr^{2+}, Mn^{3+}	0.4 (4)	2.4 (0)	0.6 (4)	1.6 (2)
d^5	Mn^{2+}, Fe^{3+}, Os^{3+}	0 (5)	2.0 (1)	0 (5)	2.0 (1)
d^6	Fe^{2+}, Co^{3+}, Ir^{3+}	0.6 (4)	1.6 (2)	0.4 (4)	2.4 (0)
d^7	Co^{2+}, Rh^{2+}	1.2 (3)	0.8 (3)	0.8 (3)	1.8 (1)
d^8	Ni^{2+}, Pd^{2+}, Pt^{2+}	0.8 (2)	0.4 (2)	1.2 (2)	1.2 (2)
d^9	Cu^{2+}	0.4 (1)	0 (1)	0.8 (1)	0.6 (1)

The values of Δ differ for tetrahedral and octahedral complexes. They are greater for the latter; the theoretical ratio is about 9/4. In addition, the crystal-field splitting due to eight ligands arranged at the corners of a cube is similar to that for the tetrahedral case. In the strong-field tetrahedral

d^3, d^6 and octahedral d^4, d^7 complexes, the stabilization energies are partly offset by the energy required to pair up two of the electrons. Similarly, for strong-field tetrahedral d^4, d^5 and octahedral d^5, d^6, twice the pairing-up energy is required.

References

1. For fuller discussion, see Coulson, C. A., *Valence*, 2nd edition, Oxford University Press, London, 1961; and Pauling, L., and E. B. Wilson, *Introduction to Quantum Mechanics*, McGraw-Hill Book Co., New York, 1935.
2. For a more precise description of their shapes, see White, H. E., *Introduction to Atomic Spectra*, McGraw-Hill Book Co., New York, 1934, p. 62.
3. For energies associated with s, p, and d electrons, see Slater, J. C., *Phys. Rev.*, **98**, 1039 (1955).
4. For estimates of "effective" nuclear charge, see Slater, J. C., *Phys. Rev.*, **36**, 57 (1930).
5. Arkel, Van, A. E., and J. H. de Boer, *Rec. Trav. Chim.*, **47**, 593 (1928).
6. Pauling, L., *The Nature of the Chemical Bond*, 3rd ed., Cornell University Press, Ithaca, New York, 1960.
7. Allred, A. L., and E. G. Rochow, *J. Inorg. Nucl. Chem.*, **5**, 264 (1958).
8. Pritchard, H. O., and H. A. Skinner, *Chem. Rev.*, **55**, 745 (1945).
9. See, for example, Uitert, Van, L. C., W. C. Fernelius, and B. E. Douglas, *J. Am. Chem. Soc.*, **75**, 2736 (1953). Chapman, D., *Nature*, **174**, 887 (1954).
10. For further discussion of π bonding see Chatt, J., and A. A. Williams, *J. Chem. Soc.*, **1952**, 3061; Chatt, J., and R. G. Wilkins, *ibid.*, **1952**, 273; Nyholm, R. S., and L. N. Short, *ibid.*, **1953**, 2670; Hieber, W., R. Nast and J. G. Floss, *Z. Anorg. Allgem. Chem.*, **283**, 188 (1956); and for δ bonding see Jaffé, H. H., and G. O. Doak, *J. Chem. Phys.*, **21**, 156, 196, 258 (1953); **22**, 1462 (1954); Jaffé, H. H., *J. Phys. Chem.*, **58**, 185 (1954); Craig, D. P., A. Maccoll, R. S. Nyholm, L. E. Orgel, and L. E. Sutton, *J. Chem. Soc.*, **1954**, 332.
11. For discussion, see Orgel, L. E., *An Introduction to Transition Metal Chemistry*, Methuen, London, 1960, p. 27.

CHAPTER 3

Stereochemistry and Stability
of Metal Complexes

The number of groups disposed around a metal ion, and the stereo-chemistry of the resulting complexes, are important factors in determining the stability and reactivity of metal complexes. Some of the probable stereochemistries of ions and complexes in solution are given in Table 3.1.

Stepwise formation constants of metal complexes usually follow the simple relation that $\log (K_n/K_{n+1})$ is positive and approximately constant. Unusual and abrupt changes may indicate differences in stereochemistry, in the π bonding between metal ion and ligand, or a change from a high-spin to a low-spin state. For example, $HgCl_2$ is linear, but $[HgCl_4]^{2-}$ is tetrahedral, so that there is a change from sp to sp^3 hybridization in going from $HgCl_2$ to $[HgCl_3]^-$ and the value of K_2/K_3 is anomalously high.

The break in the series between $(FeCl_3)aq$ and $FeCl_4^-$ probably represents a change from octahedral to tetrahedral symmetry, while the opposite change probably occurs between $Cd(NH_3)_4^{2+}$ and $Cd(NH_3)_5^{2+}$, and between $Zn(en)_2^{2+}$ and $Zn(en)_3^{2+}$. In the Cr(II) and Cu(II) ethylene-diamine complexes the corresponding step is perhaps due to the removal of Jahn-Teller stabilization and a change from a distorted octahedral or planar structure to a more nearly regular octahedron. π Bonding, which should affect mainly the ΔH term, is likely to be reponsible for the big difference between $\log K_1$ and $\log K_2$ in the complexes of Ag(I) with iodide ion. Filled d orbitals on the metal, if back-bonded into vacant orbitals on one ligand, are less available for bonding with another ligand. Conversely, for the Ag(I) ammine complexes, $\log K_2$ is greater than $\log K_1$, so that possibly the complex $[Ag(NH_3)_2]^+$ has a linear, sp-hybridized structure, while in the 1:1 complex the ammonia replaces one of the water molecules in a tetrahedral or octahedral aquo complex. The big increase

34

TABLE 3.1

Common Stereochemistries of Metal Ions in Their Complexes

Metal Ion	Coordn. No.	Stereochemistry
Cu(I),[a] Ag(I),[b] Au(I),[b] Hg(I), Hg(II)	2	Linear
Cu(I),[c] Li(I), Be(II), Mg(II) (?), B(III), Zn(II), Cd(II), Hg(II), Pb(IV), Sn(IV)	4	Tetrahedral
Co(II), Ni(II), Cu(II), Ag(II), Pd(II), Pt(II), Au(III)	4	Planar
Mg(II)(?), Ca(II), Sr(II), Ba(II), Ti(IV), V(III), V(IV), Cr(III), Mn(II), Mn(III), Fe(II), Fe(III), Co(II), Co(III), Ni(II), Ni(IV), Pt(IV), Cd(II), Zn(II), Al(III), Sc(III), Y(III), lanthanides, Si(IV), Sn(II), Sn(IV), Pb(II), Pb(IV), Ru(III), Rh(III), Os(III), Ir(III), Cu(II)[d]	6	Octahedral
Zr(IV), Hf(IV), Mo(IV), W(IV), U(IV), actinides	8	Various stereochemistries possible

[a] If ligands are strongly basic, highly polarizing, or easily polarized.
[b] Can also show coordination number of 4, but less readily than Cu(I).
[c] If ligands accept π electrons from the metal or if bonding is ionic.
[d] Distorted octahedral, with 4 short bonds and 2 long (weaker) bonds, or, rarely, 2 short bonds and 4 long ones. In the limit it becomes square planar.

in stability in passing from bis to tris ferrous complexes with 1,10-phenanthroline and 2,2′-bipyridine is due to the change from high-spin (paramagnetic) to low-spin (diamagnetic) state with a large gain in stability.

Because of the differences in d electronic distributions, it is reasonable to look upon high-spin and low-spin states of a metal ion as being, effectively, those of two different kinds of species. Comparison of stabilities of metal complexes of, say, a series of metal ions with a given ligand is valid only where corresponding spin states are involved. Thus, the Irving-Williams series (Mn < Fe < Co < Ni < Cu > Zn, for divalent ions) is valid for comparisons only of high-spin complexes. It fails, for example, with tris-o-phenanthroline complexes because of the anomalously high stability of the ferrous complex, in which the metal is low-spin.

As the metal ion radius increases with the atomic number, so does the coordination number, in general agreement with expectations from the radius-ratio rule. (The coordination number of a metal ion in its complexes or salts is the number of atoms to which it can be considered to be chemically bonded at any one time.) For example, the maximum coordination number for Li, Be, B, C, N, O, and F in any covalently bonded complexes would be expected to be 4, corresponding to the four pairs of electrons filling the $2s$ and $2p$ orbitals. However, O and more particularly F do not usually reach this limit because of the difficulty of "donating" more than one pair of electrons from either of these donor atoms for dative-bond formation.

Table 3.1 indicates that a large fraction of known metal complexes exist as linear, tetrahedral, or octahedral structures, depending on whether the ligands occupy 2, 4, or 6 of the coordination sites around a metal ion. These are the structures to be expected on electrostatic grounds if ligands are to be placed in such a way as to minimize their mutual repulsions. Alternatively, they can be readily accounted for by either the valence bond or the ligand-field theory. Among the transition metal ions, however, other shapes, especially square planar and distorted octahedral, are commonly met. Their formation is best explained in terms of ligand-field theory.

This theory points out that, in complexes of transition metal ions, the metal's d orbitals no longer remain equal in energy. If all of the d orbitals were occupied equally by electrons there would be no net overall energy change. Otherwise, the system gains in stability to an extent that varies with the number of d electrons present, the particular ligand and metal ion, and the geometrical shape of the complex. If the gain in ligand-field stabilization energy is great enough to offset the increased repulsion, a transition metal ion can form, for example, square planar complexes instead of tetrahedral ones, or distorted octahedral complexes that approximate to square planar. The significance of ligand-field effects is probably most easily brought out by discussing some particular examples among the metal ions.

3.1 Examples of Ligand-Field Effects

COPPER (II)

The key to the stereochemistry of Cu(II) complexes is provided by the $(3d)^9$ configuration of the metal ion. Most of these complexes are distorted octahedral in which four coordination sites (in the plane x, y) are filled by ligands close to the metal, and two other ligands are positioned at a greater distance above and below the metal. This altered structure is probably due to the operation of the *Jahn-Teller effect* which arises when a complex has two or more total energy levels that are equal in the ground state, leading to a distortion of the system to give a single, lower, energy level of greater stability. (Compare the concept of resonance and canonical forms.) Assume, momentarily, that six ligands are disposed in a regular octahedral structure around a Cu^{2+} ion, and the $3d$ orbital which contains only one electron is $3d_{x^2-y^2}$. If, now, we distort the structure so as to bring the ligands in the x, y plane closer, at the same time moving the ligands on the z axis further away, we make each of the two electrons in the d_{z^2} orbital more stable by an amount almost the same as that by which the electron in $d_{x^2-y^2}$ is made less stable, so that there is a net gain in stability. If the ligands on the z axis are removed to a sufficient distance, the structure approximates to square planar. In any case, as stability constant measurements show, they are very much more weakly held than ligands in the other four coordination sites. Often, in crystals isolated from solution, the fifth and sixth sites are occupied by water molecules which x-ray analysis shows to be rather distant from the metal ion. A similar distortion towards planarity occurs in $[CuCl_4]^{2-}$, one of the few (distorted) tetrahedral complexes formed by Cu^{2+}.

Nickel (II) and Platinum (II)

Since both of these metal ions are d^8 systems, they are to be expected to favor square planar complexes in strong ligand fields, e.g. $Ni(CN)_4^{2-}$ and $Ni(SCN)_4^{2-}$. Tetrahedral Ni(II) complexes are uncommon and are likely to be formed only when the ligand field is too weak to force spin pairing and the steric requirements of the ligands require such an arrangement. The theoretical argument is similar to that for Cu^{2+}. The $d_{x^2-y^2}$ orbital is now vacant, and the d_{z^2} orbital is filled, so that any tendency to octahedral complex formation is opposed. However, in weak ligand fields, complexes of nickel (II) are predicted to undergo an elongation, rather than a compression towards planarity.[1] There is still doubt in many individual cases whether nickel (II) complexes are planar or tetrahedral, but the latter are unlikely in aqueous solution.[2] Weak-field, six-coordinate nickel (II) complexes should be regularly octahedral.

Cobalt (II), d^7

In low-field, high-spin, octahedral cobalt (II) complexes, five of the $3d$ electrons are present in the t_{2g} orbitals (d_{xy}, d_{yz}, d_{zx}), and there is one electron in each of the e_g orbitals ($d_{x^2-y^2}$, d_{z^2}). Although electrons in e_g orbitals tend to weaken bond formation between the metal and ligands, these cobalt (II) complexes should be close to regular octahedral in structure. The existence of tetrahedral complexes such as $[CoCl_4]^{2-}$, $[CoBr_4]^{2-}$, and $[Co(NCS)_4]^{2-}$ is due in part to the fact that the ligand-field stabilization energy for a d^7 electron system in a weak ligand field is not very different for tetrahedral (1.2Δ) or octahedral (0.8Δ) configurations. Taking Δ for the tetrahedral complex as being about four-ninths of the value of Δ in the octahedral complex, this leaves the latter with a slightly greater ligand-field stabilization energy. However, the difference may not be sufficient to offset the tendency towards a tetrahedral configuration, which is the electrostatically preferred way of disposing four charged groups around a central ion. The convenient classification of blue Co(II) complexes as tetrahedral and of pink or violet ones as octahedral is not very reliable,[2] and it has been suggested that the hundredfold greater intensity of absorption bands in tetrahedral complexes is a better criterion. On the other hand, in high-field, low-spin octahedral cobalt (II) complexes the t_{2g} orbitals will be filled, leaving one electron to be accommodated in the two e_g orbitals, and leading to Jahn-Teller distortion towards planarity in the same way as for copper (II). The overall effect is likely, however, to be smaller, and six-coordinate complex formation should still occur.

Iron (II) and Cobalt (III), d^6

Iron (II) and cobalt (III) present no unusual features. In low ligand fields they form octahedral complexes with four unpaired electrons, while in high fields their complexes are diamagnetic, the t_{2g} orbitals being filled and the e_g orbitals empty.

Iron (III) and Manganese (II), d^5

In weak ligand fields, each of the t_{2g} and e_g orbitals contains one electron, so that there is no ligand-field stabilization. Iron (III) and manganese (II) complexes may be expected to have tetrahedral and octahedral configurations. In strong ligand fields electron pairing occurs to give stable octahedral complexes in which the e_g orbitals are vacant and the five electrons are accommodated in the t_{2g} orbitals. Stronger fields than usual are needed to achieve this low-spin state because of the special stability of half-filled d-electron shells (for which the exchange energy has a maximum value). Anions with weak ligand fields form tetrahedral complexes, such as $FeCl_4^-$, probably for electrostatic reasons.

Chromium (II) and Manganese (III), d^4

High-spin octahedral complexes of chromium (II) and manganese (III) contain one electron in each of the t_{2g} orbitals, with the remaining electron in one of the e_g orbitals. In tetrahedral complexes it is one of the t_{2g} orbitals that is unfilled. In both cases, conditions are such as to lead to Jahn-Teller distortion, so that in $[MnF_6]^{3-}$ the metal ion has four fluoride ions as near neighbors, with the two fluoride ions further away.

COPPER (I)

Copper (I) ion contains ten $3d$ electrons and usually forms four-coordinate, tetrahedral structures, such as $CuCl_4^{3-}$. However, with strongly basic, highly polarizing, or easily polarized ligands, copper (I) forms two-coordinate, linear complexes, that have been explained[3] by postulating an admixture of s and d_{z^2} orbitals, because the lowest d^9s state is only 2.7 ev above the d^{10} level. This makes it possible for the two electrons in the d_{z^2} orbital to be placed in the $(s-d_{z^2})$ hybrid orbital, removing charge from the z axis and transferring it to the xy plane, so as to enable strong bond formation along the z axis, provided the metal ligand bond has a high degree of covalent character. An alternative explanation has been offered by assuming that two-coordinate complexes are formed by ligands that are strong δ donors but weak π acceptors, and four-coordination occurs if the ligands are strong π acceptors, the tetrahedral configuration resulting from strong back-donation of π electrons.[4]

3.2 Polarizability and Covalent Character

Nyholm[5] considers that the greater the percentage covalency of metal-ligand bonds the more important it becomes that the metal has orbitals that are suitable both stereochemically and energetically. The main factor governing the ease with which these orbitals can be hybridized to give equivalent bonds is their energy separation. His approach differs from that of Dunitz and Orgel because it leads to the expectation that if the sp separation is large, sp hybridization (two-coordinate complex) is likely, whereas as it is reduced sp^2 (three-coordination) and finally sp^3 (four-coordination) bonding becomes more likely. It is possible that Nyholm's approach is better if the residual charge on the metal atom is small; whereas, if the metal ion is appreciably positive, the alternative picture is more satisfactory.

Coordination numbers greater than six are not common, and occur, with few exceptions, among compounds of the second and third series of transition elements, the rare earths and the actinides. Examples include the cyanide complexes $[Mo(CN)_8]^{4-}$, $[Mo(CN)_8]^{3-}$, $[W(CN)_8]^{3-}$, and $[Re(CN)_8]^{2-}$. Their occurrence is attributed to the larger size of the cation, permitting the packing of more ligands around it, and also to the availability of a greater number of orbitals.

The most important factor deciding the coordination number of a metal ion has been suggested [2,6] to be the polarizability of the ligand. Provided the ligands can be accommodated around the metal ion, as many will be coordinated as are needed, in accordance with the Pauling electroneutrality principle, to reduce the charge on the metal ion nearly to zero. Where the ligand is not readily polarized there is relatively little donation of

TABLE 3.2

Predicted Stereochemistries of Metal Complexes

No. of d Electrons in Cation	(i) High-Spin State	
	Four-Coordinate	Six-Coordinate
0, 5, 10	Regular tetrahedral	Regular octahedral
1, 6	Almost regular tetrahedral	Almost regular octahedral
2, 7	Regular tetrahedral	Almost regular octahedral
3, 8	Distorted tetrahedral	Regular octahedral
4, 9	Square planar	Tetragonal[a]
	(ii) Low-Spin State	
3	Almost regular tetrahedral	[b]
4	Regular tetrahedral	Almost regular octahedral
5	Distorted tetrahedral	Almost regular octahedral
6	Distorted tetrahedral	Regular octahedral
7	Square planar	Tetragonal
8	Square planar	Tetragonal

[a] Octahedral, distorted along one axis.
[b] A six-coordinate low-spin state for d^1, d^2, d^3, or d^9 is not possible, nor is a four-coordinate low-spin state for d^1, d^2, or d^9.

charge from ligand to metal, and a higher coordination number is to be expected. This explains $[FeF_6]^{3-}$ and, with the more polarizable Cl^-, $[FeCl_4]^-$. So, too, because H_2O is less polarizable than Cl^-, we find $[Co(H_2O)_6]^{2+}$ and $[CoCl_4]^-$. A more theoretical explanation in terms of orbital contraction has been proposed.[7] The higher coordination members in cyanide complexes, e.g. $Fe(CN)_6^{3-}$ and $Fe(CN)_6^{4-}$, can be explained by back-bonding of d electrons from the metal, so that its oxidation state is somewhat increased. An increase in oxidation state of a metal ion would be expected to lead to an increase in coordination number, as in $[AgCl_2]^-$, $[CdCl_4]^{2-}$, and $[InCl_6]^{3-}$. Coordination numbers might be less for bulky ligands because of the difficulty of packing them around the metal ion.

Table 3.1 shows that four-coordinate square planar and tetrahedral, and six-coordinate octahedral structures represent a large part of the observed stereochemistries in metal complexes. For transition metal ions the foregoing discussion can be generalized to a good approximation by using a crystal-field approach. From considerations of crystal-field stabilization energies, the stereochemistries given in Table 3.2 would be expected. Some examples are given in Table 3.3.

TABLE 3.3

Some Examples of Complexes with Stereochemistries Approximating to Those Given in Table 3.2

(i) High-Spin State

No. of d Electrons in Cation	
3	$Cr(CN)_6^{3-}$
4	$Cr(CN)_6^{4-}$
5	$MnCl_4^{2-}$, $FeCl_4^-$, FeF_6^{3-}
6	$Fe(H_2O)_6^{2+}$, CoF_6^{3-}
7	CoI_4^{2-}, $Co(H_2O)_6^{2+}$
8	$Ni(H_2O)_6^{2+}$
9	$Cu(NH_3)_4^{2+}$, $Ag(bipy)_2^{2+}$
10	$ZnCl_4^{2-}$, $CdCl_4^{2-}$, $Cu(CN)_4^{3-}$, $Hg(CN)_4^{2-}$, $Zn(H_2O)_6^{2+}$, $Cd(NH_3)_6^{2+}$

(ii) Low-Spin State

5	$Mn(CN)_6^{4-}$, $Fe(CN)_6^{3-}$, CoF_6^{2-}, $Ru(CN)_6^{3-}$, RhF_6^{2-}, $Os(CN)_6^{3-}$, $IrCl_6^{2-}$
6	$Fe(phen)_3^{2+}$, $Fe(CN)_6^{4-}$, $Co(CN)_6^{3-}$, NiF_6^{2-}, $Ir(CN)_6^{3-}$, $PtCl_6^{2-}$, $Rh(CN)_6^{3-}$, PdF_6^{2-}
7	$Co(NO_2)_6^{4-}$
8	$Ni(CN)_4^{2-}$, $Pd(CN)_4^{2-}$, $Au(CN)_4^-$, $Ni(diars)_3^{2+}$

Table 3.2 applies well if the bonding is largely ionic, but the shapes are modified if the structures are mainly covalent, especially if π bonding is important. In the ions $[CuCl_4]^{2-}$ and $[CuBr_4]^{2-}$, predicted to be tetrahedral, there is appreciable distortion towards a square planar structure.[8]

3.3 Steric Effects

Although the most stable complexes are likely to be those formed when vacant orbitals of the cation point in directions that overlap filled ligand orbitals (or vice versa) without serious distortion, such structures may be impossible for steric reasons. For example, if unidentate ligands are large, the physical difficulty of fitting them around a central ion will handicap complex formation if many ligand molecules are involved. The situation becomes much more complicated if the ligand can fill more than one coordination site round the metal ion.

Much information about the permitted stereochemistry in metal complexes with organic ligands can be obtained from the use of commercially available atomic models. Alternatively, particularly if the ligand is planar, an approximate structure can often be drawn using the cationic radii in Table 2.2, the average bond lengths listed in Table 3.4, and the usual bond angles.

TABLE 3.4

Average Bond Lengths[a] in Angstrom Units

N—H	1.01–1.07	N—O	1.19–1.36	N=O	1.11–1.22
O—H	0.96–0.98	P—O	1.39–1.63	P—S	1.86
S—H	1.33–1.35	S—O	1.41–1.45	S—S	2.04
C—C	1.54, 1.47(in C=C—C=C), 1.37(in C≡C—C≡C)				
CC(aromatic)	1.40	C=C	1.34	C≡C	1.20
C—H	1.09	C—N	1.47, 1.32(in amides)		
CN(heterocyclic)	1.35	C≡N	1.16		
C—O	1.43, 1.36(phenols, carboxylic acids, esters)				
CO(heterocyclic)	1.37	C=O	1.23, 1.15(p-quinones)		
C—S	1.81	CS(heterocyclic)	1.73	C=S	1.71

[a] From *Tables of Interatomic Distances and Configurations in Molecules and Ions*, Special Publication No. 11, The Chemical Society, London, 1958.

Steric hindrance to coordination can result from rather small changes in ligand structure. 1,10-Phenanthroline, which is used in the estimation of ferrous ion, and 2,9-dimethyl-1,10-phenanthroline, a reagent for cuprous ion, provide good examples. The tris-1,10-phenanthroline ferrous complex (but not the mono or bis) is low-spin and has a high stability constant. It is also intensely colored. The corresponding cuprous complexes lack ligand-field stabilization and are less stable. On the other hand, in 2,9-dimethyl-1,10-phenanthroline, the methyl groups prevent the formation of the tris ferrous complex, because of steric hindrance, and the bis complex is high-spin and colorless. However, the methyl groups do not interfere in the formation of the tetrahedral copper (I) bis complex, but actually increase the stability of the complex because they raise the basicity of the ligand. A similar effect is observed following 6,6'-dimethyl or 6,6'-diamino substitution in 2,2'-bipyridine. The difference in size of the metal ions may also be important: Cu(I) ion has the greater radius, so that the ligands approach one another less closely and steric hindrance is decreased. Similarly, the smaller radius of Al^{3+} may explain the nonformation of complexes with 2-methyl-8-hydroxyquinoline and with similarly substituted acridines, which react with ions of larger radii such as Cr^{3+}, Fe^{3+}, Ga^{3+}, Cu^{2+}, and Zn^{2+}.[9] Insertion of a 2-phenyl group into 8-hydroxyquinoline prevents the formation of tris complexes with Al(III) and Cr(III). Thus 2-methyl-8-hydroxyquinoline differs from 8-hydroxyquinoline by giving no precipitate with aluminium. Its use also facilitates the solvent extraction and estimation of gallium and indium in the presence of aluminium.

An interesting steric effect of a different type is provided by 3,3'-disubstitution in 2,2'-bipyridine. Bulky groups in these positions destroy the planarity of the ligand molecule, reducing resonance stabilization and introducing strain into the metal-ligand bonds.[10] A similar effect is observed when acetylacetone is substituted in the 3-position by isopropyl or *sec*-butyl groups. These ligands do not form the usual colored complexes with Fe(III) or Cu(II), probably because steric interaction between the isopropyl group on the 3-position and the methyl group on positions 2 or 4 upsets the planarity of the ring, inhibiting resonance and preventing complex formation.[11] If the isopropyl group is moved away from the acetylacetone chain by interpolating a methylene group, normal complex formation occurs.

In ligands such as the porphyrins and phthalocyanines the size of the central cavity has an important effect on the stability of the complex. Large ions such as Hg^{2+} and Pb^{2+} may be unable to fit into the center of the porphyrin nucleus,[12] whereas with small ions the stability of the complex would be expected to diminish with decreasing cation radius because the rigidity of the porphyrin nucleus would progressively reduce the extent of bond overlap between metal ion and ligand. These comments on stability are relative: Such complexes, and others involving multidentate ligands, are much more stable than complexes with unidentate ligands. This "chelate effect" is partly attributable to differences in entropy changes and partly to the very much greater energy required to break all the metal bonds in the multidentate complexes in a time that is short relative to the time needed to form them. In addition to the effect of the size of the cavity on complex formation in porphyrins and phthalocyanines, their geometry imposes a square planar configuration on their metal complexes. They may, however, by additional coordination, approach octahedral symmetry.

Another example of a geometrical factor is in complex formation of Ag(I) with the polymethylenediamines. Ordinarily, chelates involving the formation of five-membered rings have greater stability constants than the corresponding complexes of different ring size. However, the six-, seven-, and eight-membered ring structures formed by Ag(I) with trimethylenediamine, tetramethylenediamine, and pentamethylenediamine are all more stable than the five-membered ethylenediamine complex.[13] This is probably because, with increasing ring size, the bonds to Ag can approach more closely the linear structure expected for a coordination number of 2.

Similarly, the ligand β,β',β''-triaminotriethylamine is able to form a quadridentate complex having a tetrahedral structure, but the preference of Cu(II) is for planar or distorted octahedral complexes, so that its triaminotriethylamine complex is less stable than would otherwise be expected.[14] Triethylenetetramine, on the other hand, can readily form square planar complexes, and its copper complexes are much more stable.

3.4 Stability Constants of Metal Complexes

The magnitude of the stability constants of complexes formed in aqueous solution by particular metal ions with specified ligands are important in analytical chemistry. So, too, are the differences in these values for other metals with the same ligands, because they provide indications of the levels at which interference by such species is likely to be encountered in analytical methods.

One of the earliest attempted qualitative classifications was due to Sidgwick,[15] who divided metals into three groups depending on their relative abilities to combine with oxygen (usually through a normal covalent bond) or nitrogen (usually through a coordinate covalent bond). The three groups were:

1. Bonding to oxygen more strongly than to nitrogen:

$$Mg, Ca, Sr, Ba, Ga, In, Tl, Zr, Th, Si, Ge, Sn,$$
$$V^{4+}, V^{5+}, Nb^{5+}, Ta^{5+}, Mo^{5+}, U^{6+}, Fe^{3+}, Co^{2+}$$

2. Bonding to oxygen and nitrogen comparable in strength:

$$Be, Cr^{3+}, Fe^{2+}, Ru, Rh, Pd, Os, Ir, Pt$$

3. Bonding to oxygen less strongly than to nitrogen:

$$Cu^+, Ag^+, Au^+, Cu^{2+}, Cd, Hg, V^{3+}, Co^{3+}, Ni^{2+}$$

This classification is readily explained in terms of polarization interaction if it is observed that whereas the first group comprises ions that are mainly either of the "inert-gas" type or low in d electrons, the third group has filled, or nearly filled, d electron levels. The greater polarizability of lone-pair electrons on nitrogen than on oxygen, and the greater deformability of metal ions with filled d shells, can be pictured as leading to greater orbital interpenetration and hence to the formation by the third group of stronger bonds with nitrogen than with oxygen.

Polarizability effects increase as the charge on the metal ion decreases, so that the biggest difference between related subgroups in the periodic table is found for Group IA (Li^+, Na^+, K^+, Rb^+, Cs^+) and Group IIB (Cu^+, Ag^+, Au^+), whereas the tetravalent ions of Groups IVA and IVB are very similar in their complexing properties and belong with the cations binding oxygen more strongly than nitrogen. The occurrence of Fe(III) in the first group although the other trivalent transition metal ions are found in groups 2 and 3 can be explained in terms of differences in ligand-field stabilization energies (LFSE), which are higher with nitrogen-containing than with oxygen-containing ligands. In weak fields, LFSE = 0 for Fe(III), so that in this case the additional stabilization favoring nitrogen is absent. Sidgwick also grouped O > S for Be, Cu(II), Au(III), and S > O for Cu(I), Ag(I), Au(I), and Hg.

Some division within these groups is also possible. For example, in the series Al^{3+}, Ga^{3+}, In^{3+}, and Tl^{3+} the more electropositive cations, Al^{3+} and Ga^{3+}, will have a greater tendency to form electrostatically bound complexes, whereas the relatively less electropositive ions, In^{3+} and Tl^{3+}, will have a relatively greater tendency towards covalent-bond formation so that they will form complexes more readily with polarizable ligands, such as the heavier halide ions.

A recent more extensive correlation has been made of the relative affinities of ligand atoms for various molecules and cations.[16] Cations generally fall into two definite classes (a) and (b), depending on whether they form their most stable complexes with the first or second ligand atom of the pairs N,P; O,S; and F,Cl. Although different valency states of the same metal can behave very differently, in their common valency states most metals bind more strongly to N, O, and F. On the other hand, metals preferring P, S, and Cl include Cu(I), Rh(I), Pd(II),

Ag(I), Pt(II), Hg(II), most of the transition metals in their lower-valent, and all in their zerovalent, states. Differences in stability in Co(II), Ni(II), and Cu(II) complexes are less well defined, so that F binds slightly more strongly than Cl, S slightly more than O, and perhaps P slightly more than N. The most important single factor appears to be the back-double-bonding that can occur between metal d_π electrons and the vacant 3d orbitals on P, S, and Cl. This becomes greater the lower the valence state of the metal ion and the lower the ionization potential of the metal ion, and it also becomes greater if the ligand is neutral rather than an anion, especially where the metal ion has full or nearly full d orbitals. In As, Se, and Br the 4d orbitals are more diffuse, so that this kind of orbital overlap makes a smaller contribution to the stability of complexes.

The observed complex formation by thiourea, $(NH_2)_2CS$, in which coordination to the metal is through the sulfur atom, is consistent with this interpretation. It forms colorless and only slightly soluble complexes with Ag, Cu(I), Hg(II), and Tl but also gives colored complexes such as $[Bi(NH_2CSNH_2)_3]^{3+}$ and $[Os(NH_2CSNH_2)_6]^{3+}$. Thiourea and its derivatives have been used in this way for the detection of a number of metal ions.[17] However, complex formation with Ru is reported to involve the loss of a proton from an NH_2 group of each molecule of thiourea that is coordinated.[18,19] Copper (II) ion is reduced by thiourea to the bis complex ion $[Cu(NH_2CSNH_2)_2]^+$.

In the absence of steric and conjugative effects, class (a) cations show coordinating affinities in the sequences $N \gg P > As > Sb$; $O \gg S$; $F \gg Cl > Br > I$; and for a series of similar ligands NR_3, R_2O, and RF, $N \geqslant O \geqslant F$. With class (b) the orders are $N \ll P > As > Sb > Bi$; $O \ll S$; $F \ll Cl < Br < I$; and $N \gg O \gg F$. Differences in the series $P > S > Cl$ are less pronounced because of back-double-bonding, increased polarizability and reduced lone-pair electron repulsions with filled d_π orbitals on the metals. The higher-valent states of Hg, Tl, Sn, and Pb should show greater back-double-bonding tendencies than their lower-valent states because, in the latter, the valence electrons occupy s orbitals, thereby screening electrons in the d orbitals and making them less available for back-double-bonding.

A limited, but valuable, sequence first pointed out by Irving and Williams[20] puts the stability constants of complexes of the bivalent metals of the first transition series in the order $Mn < Fe < Co < Ni < Cu > Zn$, independent of the nature of the ligand involved. Theoretical reasons for this sequence are given in Chapter 4. The greatest increases in log β (where β is the "overall" stability constant of a complex) in passing from Mn(II) to Cu(II) occur in ligands with nitrogen donor atoms (for example, log β_2 for ethylenediamine changes from 4.8 to 19.6 from Mn to Cu). Nitrogen-oxygen-type ligands show a smaller change (e.g. log β_2 for glycine increases from 5.5 to 15.2 from Mn to Cu). Oxygen-type ligands show much less change. (The corresponding figures for oxalic acid are 5.3 and 8.5.) Differences in rate of change of log β can be ascribed to differences in ligand-field strengths. The stabilities of zinc complexes commonly lie between those of cobalt and nickel.

Many other stability constant sequences have been reported. They lack any general application but serve as useful empirical guides in assessing the probable relative abilities of different cations to coordinate with specific ligands. Some examples are given in Table 3.5. In practice, it is more useful to go directly to tables of stability constants.[21] These tables show that, in general, the stability constants of complexes of the alkali and alkaline earth metals decrease as the size of the cation increases.

In size and charge Tl^+ resembles K^+ and Rb^+, but because Tl^+ is more deformable than K^+ (as is expected for an ion with a filled d shell) it forms more stable complexes with organic ligands. For the same reason $K_{TlBr} > K_{TlCl} > K_{TlF}$. Among the complexes of trivalent lanthanide ions with 1,2-diaminocyclohexane-N,N,N′,N′-tetraacetic acid, ethylenediaminetetraacetic acid, and nitrilotriacetic acid there is a linear relation between log K_1 and the reciprocal of the radius of the metal ion.[22] Also, as expected, stability constants are lower for the alkali metals than for the alkaline earth metals. Similarly, rare earth metals show a progressive decrease in complex stability with increasing size of the cation. The quantity z^2/r, where z is the charge and r is the radius of the metal ion, roughly correlates values of log K_1 for complexes of metal ions with different charges, provided the complexes are mainly electrostatic in bonding.

The stability constants of complexes of a metal with a series of structurally similar ligands often show a roughly linear dependence on the basic strengths of the ligands, log $\beta \simeq a \cdot pK_a + b$. This is because the factors involved in forming a σ bond between ligand and metal ion are similar to those concerned in protonation of the ligand, so that the greater the basic strength of an amine the greater the stability constant of the metal complex. The quantity b has been suggested as a measure of the π-bond character of the metal-ligand bond.[23] More detailed analysis of this relation for Cu(II) with substituted salicylaldehydes supports this interpretation but suggests that the value of b depends on the position in which the molecule is substituted. This was interpreted as showing variations in π-electron interactions.[24] Similarly, if in an aromatic system the conjugation is extended by annelation of more rings, or by ring closure, e.g. by changing from salicylaldehyde to 2-hydroxy-1-naphthaldehyde, or from 2,2′-bipyridine to 1,10-phenanthroline, this is likely to lead to

TABLE 3.5

Some Empirical Stability Constant Sequences for Metal Complexes

Sequence	Ligand Type
Pd(II) > Cu(II) > Ni(II) > Pb(II) > Co(II)	O–O [a]
Zn > Cd > Hg(II)	O–O [a]
Pd(II) > Cu(II) > Ni(II) > Co(II) > Zn > Cd > Fe(II) > Mn(II) > Mg	N–N [b]
Cu(II) > Ni(II) > Fe(II) > Zn > Mg	N [c]
Cu(II) > Be > Cd > Pb(II) > Ni(II) > Zn > Co(II) > Mg > Ca > Ba	O [d]
Cu(II) > Be > Ni(II) > Zn > Co(II) > Pb(II) > Mn(II) > Cd > Mg	O–O [e]
Cu(II) > Ni(II) > Zn > Pb(II) > Cd > Mg	O [f]
Cu(II) > Ni(II) > Zn > Pb(II) $\approx$ Co(II) > Mn(II) > Mg > Ca > Sr > Ba	N–O [g]
Mg > Ca > Sr > Ba > Ra	N–O [h]
Pt(II) > Pd(II) > Hg(II) > UO_2(II) > Be > Cu(II) > Ni(II) > Co(II) > Pb(II) > Zn > Cd > Fe(II) > Mn(II) > Ca > Sr > Ba	(i)
Ag(I) > Tl(I) > Li > Na > K > Rb > Cs	O–O [j]
Fe(III) > Ga(III) > Al > Sc > In(III) > Y(III) > Pr(III) > Ce(III) > La(III)	O–O [k]

[a] Salicylaldehyde.　Mellor, D. P., and L. E. Maley, *Nature*, **159**, 370 (1947).

[b] Ethylenediamine.　Mellor, D. P., and L. E. Maley, *Nature*, **161**, 436 (1948).

[c] Pyridine.　Pfeiffer, P., H. Thielert, and H. Glaser, *J. Prakt. Chem.*, **152**, 145 (1939).

[d] Nitroacetic acid.　Pedersen, K. J., *Acta Chem. Scand.*, **3**, 676 (1949).

[e] Acetonedicarboxylic acid.　Prue, J., *J. Chem. Soc.*, **1952**, 2331.

[f] Ethyl 2-oxocyclopentacarboxylate.　Pedersen, K. J., *Acta Chem. Scand.*, **2**, 385 (1948).

[g] Glycine.　Monk, C. B., *Trans. Faraday Soc.*, **47**, 297 (1951).

[h] Aspartic and glutamic acids.　Lumb, R. F., and A. E. Martell, *J. Am. Chem. Soc.*, **75**, 690 (1953).

[i] Not stated.　Basolo, F., and R. G. Pearson, *Mechanisms of Inorganic Reactions*, John Wiley and Sons, New York, 1958, p. 16.

[j] Dibenzoylmethane.　Fernelius, W. C., and L. G. Van Uitert, *Acta Chem. Scand.*, **8**, 1726 (1954).

[k] Acetylacetone.　Izatt, R. M., W. C. Fernelius, C. G. Haas, and B. P. Block, *J. Phys. Chem.*, **59**, 170 (1955).

energetically much more favorable ligand orbitals for π bonding with metal ions. On the other hand, the σ-electron density at the basic centers, and hence the pK_a of the ligand, will not be very different. Thus the plots of log K versus pK_a for complexes of transition metal ions with substituted bipyridines and 1,10-phenanthrolines will lie on different lines and the latter will have the greater slope.

3.5   Thermodynamics of Complex Formation

Most reactions involving complex formation are rapid and reversible, so that the extent to which a reaction proceeds will be governed by differences in thermodynamic quantities for the initial and final states.

The stability constant of a complex is quantitatively related to the free energy of the reaction for its formation from its components:

$$-\Delta G = 2.303RT \log K$$

Using the relation $-\Delta G = -\Delta H + T\Delta S$, where ΔH is the corresponding heat, or enthalpy, and ΔS is the entropy, change, we can write:

$$\log K = \frac{\Delta S - \Delta H/T}{2.303R} \tag{1}$$

Usually ΔS and ΔH do not vary greatly with temperature.

From equation (1) it follows that complex formation will be most favored in reactions for which the entropy change is positive (the system becomes more disorganized or contains more particles) and the enthalpy change is negative (heat is evolved).

At first sight, entropy change on complex formation would always be expected to be negative because of the reduction in the number of free particles when ligand ions or molecules are disposed around the central metal ion. However, the effect of the solvent must also be considered. Because metal ions orient water molecules in their neighborhood, there is a tendency to form definite hydrates which might be thought of as little "icebergs," in which the water is "frozen." This effect leads to a disordered (or "thawed") region in the solution outside the sheath of water molecules.[25] The resulting entropy changes comprise a loss of 5.3 entropy units (equal to the entropy of crystallization of water) for every "frozen" water molecule, together with an unknown term for the solvent disorientation. These changes are additional to the contribution, predicted by the Born equation, due to the interaction of the ion with the polarized dielectric medium, water. This term varies as the square of the charge and inversely as the radius of the cavity into which the ion fits. When a metal ion and an anionic ligand come together to form a complex, there will be a decrease in the number of ions in solution, a partial neutralization and attenuation of charge in the system, and a decrease in the number of water molecules held in the solvation sheaths of the ions. The last effect appears to be the most important one from the point of view of entropy change; therefore, in any reaction between a cation and an anion to form a complex, an entropy change favorable to the reaction is likely. The entropy change will probably be less positive, or more negative, when the cation-ligand interaction is more purely electrostatic and approximates ion pair formation.

An alternative approach is to consider some generalizations regarding entropies of some inorganic species. The entropy of a hydrated monatomic ion is given by

$$\bar{S}^\circ = \tfrac{3}{2}R \ln M + 27 - \frac{270|z|}{r_e^2}$$

where M is the atomic weight of the ion, z is the number of charges on the ion, and r_e, in Angstrom units, is its effective radius.[26] The alternative relation[27]

$$\bar{S}^\circ = \tfrac{3}{2}R \ln M + 15.7 - \frac{11.6z^2}{r}$$

where r is the Pauling ionic radius, fits better to the form expected from the Born equation. Both of these equations for $\bar{S}^\circ$ fit results for many ions with a standard deviation of about ± 4–5 e.u. The entropy of a hydrated oxyanion of formula XO_n^{-z} is well represented by[28]

$$\bar{S}^\circ = 43.5 - 46.5(z - 0.28n)$$

Furthermore, the entropies of many hydrated inorganic ions can be obtained within the accuracy of available experimental data from the equation[29]

$$\bar{S}^\circ = 49 - \frac{99|z|}{r_{12}} + 16.7n,$$

where r_{12} is the interatomic distance (cation-ligand) for the complex, z is its net ionic charge, n is the number of coordinated water molecules replaced by ligand anions, and $16.7 = S^\circ_{H_2O}$. Exceptions have been pointed out.[30]

These equations also suggest that, in any reaction between a cation and an anion to form a complex, the entropy change should favor the reaction, and also that this entropy change should be larger the greater the charges and the smaller the radii of both the cation and the anion. Experimentally, positive entropy changes are usually found[31,32] and are qualitatively in agreement with those conclusions. For example, at 25°C, the entropy change for $Fe_{aq}^{3+} + X_{aq}^- \rightleftharpoons FeX_{aq}^{2+}$, is $+23.0$, $+35.0$, and $+49.0$ e.u. (cal/°C), where X is respectively Br^-, Cl^-, and F^-.[33] Similarly for $M_{aq}^{n+} + Cl^- \rightleftharpoons MCl_{aq}^{(n-1)+}$, the entropy changes when $M^{n+} = Ag^+$, Cd^{2+}, Sn^{2+}, Cr^{3+}, and Fe^{3+} are 6.0,[34] 8.0,[35] 14.0,[36] 23.3,[37] and 35.0[33] e.u., in that order.

When the ligand is unidentate and uncharged, there is no reduction in the number of ions in solution, nor is there any charge neutralization. The ligand will be less hydrated than if it was an anion, and change in solvent orientation about the metal ion on complex formation will also be less. As a result of these differences, the entropy change will be less favorable than with charged ligands. In fact, on the usual molar scale it is often negative,[32] and hence opposing the reaction, but in most cases the effect is small.

These considerations suggest that, to a large extent, the entropy changes on complex formation are due to the different degree of hydration in the complex relative to its components and to the differences in the extent of the disordered solvent region.

When the ligand forms a multidentate chelate complex there is a loss of configurational entropy, but there should be a greater displacement of water from the hydration spheres of the reactants.   The resulting entropy change is greater than for the formation of the comparable nonchelate complex.   It is also, as expected, greater for a charged than for a neutral chelating agent, the effect increasing with the charge on the ligand.   For example, ΔS for the formation of the EDTA complexes of Ni, Cu, and Zn is 56 e.u.,[38] whereas for the corresponding bis complexes with acetylacetone, 8-hydroxyquinoline, and ethylenediamine it lies in the ranges 12–31, 15–21, and 3–8 e.u., respectively. (The contribution of entropy differences to the "chelate effect" is discussed more fully in Section 3.6.)

There is also a general trend in values of entropy changes for complex formation with the standard entropies of the metals and ligands taking part,[39] indicating that the same factors influence all three entropy terms. Nevertheless, there is still insufficient reliable information about entropy changes on complex formation to permit any quantitative predictions to be made.

The same comment is also largely true when applied to the heat changes under the same conditions.   In aqueous solution, usual ranges for stepwise addition are: $-\Delta H \sim 0$ to ± 5 kcal/mole, for ionic ligands, increasing to 10 kcal where covalent bonding is likely, e.g. Ag(I) or Hg(II) with CN^- or I^-; $-\Delta H \sim 0$ to 5 kcal/mole for neutral unidentate ligands; $-\Delta H$ up to 20 kcal for neutral multidentate ligands.   (An uncertainty of 5 kcal in ΔH produces an uncertainty of 3.6 in any value of log K at 25° that may be calculated from the thermodynamic data.)

These values of $-\Delta H$ are the small heat changes that accompany replacement of water by other ligands. Grinberg and Yatsimirskii[40] suggested from consideration of a thermodynamic cycle that the heat change for replacement of water molecules by another ligand in the gas phase gave a measure of $-\Delta H$ for the same process in solution. This approach enabled them to predict that $-\Delta H$ for hexammine formation would lie in the sequences $Na < Mg < Al$, $Mg > Ca > Sr$, and $Ca < Mn < Co < Ni < Cu > Zn$.

A major factor contributing to the value of ΔH for transition metal ions is the ligand-field stabilization energy. Energy separations between levels in an octahedral field are about 30 kcal/mole for bivalent aquo ions and about 60 kcal/mole for trivalent aquo ions of the first transition metal series. In high-spin complexes, LFSE values lead to the prediction that values of $-\Delta H$ will vary with the number of d electrons in the metal ion as follows: $d^\circ < d^1 < d^2 < d^3 \approx d^4 > d^5 < d^6 < d^7 < d^8 \approx d^9 > d^{10}$, except that $d^3 < d^4$ and $d^8 < d^9$ if there are four or less coordinated donor atoms or if the Jahn-Teller stabilization effect (~ 8 kcal/mole in the aquocopper (II) ion) is relatively high. This again indicates the "natural" stability sequences $Fe < Co < Ni < Cu > Zn$ for the divalent ions in their complexes.

In view of the uncertainties inherent in any attempts to predict ΔS or ΔH for any complex-forming reaction, it might appear quite unprofitable to discuss the corresponding free-energy differences. Nevertheless, if complexes of two similar metals with a wide range of ligands are compared useful predictions can be made. Thus the plot of $\log K(NiL)$ versus $\log K(ZnL)$ for 72 different ligands, covering a logarithm scale of 19 units, gave a good linear regression,[41] indicating the operation of similar factors in both cases. In the special case of the complexes of lanthanides with polycarboxylic acids, the free-energy changes depend essentially on entropy changes, so that the logarithms of the stability constants of their EDTA complexes gave a straight line when plotted against the standard entropies of the lanthanide ions.[42] On the other hand, the entropy changes accompanying complex formation in the series manganese (II) to copper (II) are either essentially constant or else related to the corresponding heat changes, so that the free-energy sequence is the same as for $-\Delta H$. Similarly, among complexes of the alkaline earth metal ions, $-\Delta H$ and $+\Delta S$ often vary in the same direction, so that the sequence $Mg > Ca > Sr > Ba$ is usually found. If the entropy effect predominates, the free-energy sequence is $F > Cl > Br > I$; otherwise, it is reversed.

In aqueous solvent mixtures such as dioxan-water or ethanol-water metal complexes have higher stability constants than they do in water. This fact is due largely to reduced interaction between solvent and metal ion because of the lower dielectric constant. Less work is required to remove a solvent molecule from the neighborhood of a metal ion and replace it by a ligand molecule. However, this effect is usually less than would be suggested by the measured (bulk) dielectric constant because of the tendency for the water molecules to fill, preferentially, the solvent sheath around the metal ion.

3.6 The Chelate Effect

Chelated complexes, most often involving five- or six-membered ring formation, are usually more stable than the corresponding complexes involving monodentate ligands. The few known exceptions can be explained in terms of steric strain, usually as a consequence of the preferred stereochemistry of the metal ion. The preference of Ag(I) and Cu(I) (if the ligand is a strong base) for linear coordination introduces considerable strain if these metals are to be chelated by the two ends of an ethylenediamine molecule. (In fact, it is unlikely that Cu(I) forms chelates with ethylenediamine or the glycine anion. Both ligands probably behave as monodentate substituted primary amines.)

This enhanced stability can be expressed quantitatively by comparing, say, the value of $\log K_1$ for a 1:1 metal complex with ethylenediamine with $\log \beta_2$ for the corresponding bis complex with methylamine. It is in part an entropy effect, but ligand-field stabilization is also important because ligand-field strengths of multidentate chelates are greater than those of monodentate ones. This, in turn, suggests that the enthalpy (ΔH) change on chelation is greater and that the metal-ligand bond distances are shorter. Thermodynamic functions obtained for metal complexes with ammonia and ethylenediamine [43] support this interpretation. Adamson [44] pointed out that the entropy change associated with the chelate effect was quite small if results were expressed on the thermodynamically preferred mole-fraction scale rather than the customary molar-concentration one. Under these conditions, ΔS may have small negative values. They possibly arise from the loss in configurational entropy on chelation, e.g. the flexible ethylenediamine chain becomes more rigid. [45]

Qualitatively, one would expect the chelate effect to become more important the more dilute the solution. This may be seen by comparing the complex behavior of very dilute solutions of uni- and bidentate ligands. In the first case, attachment of a ligand to a metal ion does not enrich the solution around the 1:1 complex with ligand, whereas in the second case, attachment of one end of a bidentate ligand ensures the proximity of a second complexing group.

Provided stereochemical requirements are met, the chelate effect increases with the number of chelate rings formed in the complex. Stability constants for bivalent Mg, Co, Ni, Cu, Zn, and Cd complexes with the bi, ter-, and quadridentate chelating agents, glycine, iminodiacetic acid, and nitrilotriacetic acid[46] provide a useful example.

References

1. Orgel, L. E., *An Introduction to Transition Metal Chemistry*, Methuen, London, 1960, p. 65.
2. Gill, N. S., and R. S. Nyholm, *J. Chem. Soc.*, **1959**, 3997.
3. Dunitz, J. D., and L. E. Orgel, *Adv. Inorg. Radiochem.*, **2**, 1 (1960).
4. James, B. R., and R. J. P. Williams, *J. Chem. Soc.*, **1961**, 2007.
5. Nyholm, R. S., *Proc. Chem. Soc.*, **1961**, 273.
6. Gill, N. S., P. J. Pauling, and R. S. Nyholm, *Nature*, **182**, 168 (1958).
7. Craig, D. P., and E. A. Magnusson, *Discussions Faraday Soc.*, **26**, 116 (1958); *J. Chem. Soc.*, **1956**, 4895.
8. Morosin, B., and E. C. Lingafelter, *Acta Cryst.*, **13**, 807 (1960).
9. Irving, H., E. J. Butler, and M. F. Ring, *J. Chem. Soc.*, **1949**, 1489.
10. Cagle, F. W., and G. F. Smith, *J. Am. Chem. Soc.*, **69**, 1860 (1947).
11. Martell, A. E., and M. Calvin, *Chemistry of the Metal Chelate Compounds*, Prentice-Hall, New York, 1952, p. 175.
12. Barnes, J. W., and G. D. Dorough, *J. Am. Chem. Soc.*, **72**, 4045 (1950).
13. Schwarzenbach, G., B. Maissen, and H. Ackermann, *Helv. Chim. Acta*, **35**, 2333 (1952); Schwarzenbach, G., H. Ackermann, B. Maissen, and G. Anderegg, *Helv. Chim. Acta*, **35**, 2337 (1952).
14. Schwarzenbach, G., *Helv. Chim. Acta*, **35**, 2344 (1952).
15. Sidgwick, N. V., *J. Chem. Soc.*, **1941**, 433; *The Electronic Theory of Valency*, Oxford University Press, London, 1927.
16. Ahrland, S., J. Chatt, and N. R. Davies, *Quart. Rev. (London)*, **12**, 265 (1958).
17. Yoe, J. H., and L. G. Overholser, *Ind. Eng. Chem. (Anal. Ed.)*, **14**, 435 (1942); Mahr, C., *Angew. Chem.*, **53**, 257 (1940); Gilchrist, R., *J. Res. Natl. Bur. Std.*, **6**, 421 (1931); Whitmore, W. F., and F. Schneider, *Mikrochem.*, **17**, 279 (1935).
18. Yaffe, R. P., and A. F. Voigt, *J. Am. Chem. Soc.*, **74**, 2503 (1952).
19. For a study of thiourea-type reagents for the colorimetric determination of ruthenium, see Steiger, B., *Mikrochem.*, **16**, 193 (1934); and for platinum metals see Knight, S. B., R. L. Parks, S. C. Leidt, and K. L. Parks, *Anal. Chem.*, **29**, 571 (1957); and Geilmann, W., and R. Neeb, *Z. Anal. Chem.*, **152**, 96 (1956).
20. Irving, H., and R. J. P. Williams, *Nature*, **162**, 746 (1948).
21. Bjerrum, J., G. Schwarzenbach, and L. G. Sillén, eds., *Stability Constants of Metal-Ion Complexes; Part I: Organic Ligands; Part II: Inorganic Ligands*, Chemical Society, London, 1957–1958.
22. Schwarzenbach, G., and E. Freitag, *Helv. Chim. Acta*, **34**, 1492 (1951); Schwarzenbach, G., and R. Gut, *Helv. Chim. Acta*, **39**, 1589 (1956); Schwarzenbach, G., R. Gut, and G. Anderegg, *Helv. Chim. Acta*, **37**, 936 (1954).
23. Jones, J. G., J. B. Poole, J. C. Tomkinson, and R. J. P. Williams, *J. Chem. Soc.*, **1958**, 2001.
24. Clarke, K., R. A. Cowen, G. W. Gray, and E. H. Osborne, *J. Chem. Soc.*, **1963**, 245.

25. Frank, H. S., and M. W. Evans, *J. Chem. Phys.*, **13**, 507 (1963).
26. Latimer, W. M., and R. E. Powell, *J. Chem. Phys.*, **19**, 1139 (1951).
27. Laidler, K. J., *Can. J. Chem.*, **34**, 1107 (1956).
28. Connick, R. E., and R. E. Powell, *J. Chem. Phys.*, **21**, 2206 (1953).
29. Cobble, J. W., *J. Chem. Phys.*, **21**, 1446 (1953).
30. Scaife, D. B., and H. J. V. Tyrrell, *J. Chem. Soc.*, **1958**, 392.
31. Bell, R. P., and J. H. B. George, *Trans. Faraday Soc.*, **49**, 619 (1953); King, E. J., *J. Chem. Ed.*, **30**, 72 (1953); Nancollas, G. H., *Discussions Faraday Soc.*, **24**, 108 (1957); Rabinowitch, E., and W. H. Stockmayer, *J. Am. Chem. Soc.*, **64**, 335 (1942).
32. Williams, R. J. P., *J. Phys. Chem.*, **58**, 121 (1954).
33. Evans, M. G., and N. Uri, *Symposia Soc. Exptl. Biol.*, **5**, 130 (1951).
34. Jonte, J. N., and D. S. Martin, *J. Am. Chem. Soc.*, **74**, 2052 (1952).
35. King, E. L., *J. Am. Chem. Soc.*, **71**, 319 (1949).
36. Vanderzee, C. E., *J. Am. Chem. Soc.*, **74**, 3552, 4806 (1952).
37. Rossini, F. D., D. D. Wagman, W. H. Evans, S. Levine, and I. Jaffé, "Selected Values of Chemical Thermodynamic Properties," *Natl. Bur. Std. Circ. No. 500* (1952).
38. Care, R. A., and L. A. K. Staveley, *J. Chem. Soc.*, **1956**, 4571.
39. Williams, R. J. P., *Proc. Symposium on Coordination Chem.*, 1953, Danish Chemical Society, Copenhagen, 1954, p. 68.
40. Grinberg, A. A., and K. B. Yatsimirskii, *Bull. Acad. Sci. USSR, Div. Chem. Sci.*, **1952**, 239; K. B. Yatsimirskii, *J. Gen. Chem. Moscow*, **24**, 1485 (1954).
41. Rossotti, F. J. C., in *Modern Coordination Chemistry*, J. Lewis and R. G. Wilkins, eds., Interscience, New York, 1960, p. 33.
42. Foreman, J. K., and T. D. Smith, *J. Chem. Soc.*, **1957**, 1752.
43. Spike, C. G., and R. W. Parry, *J. Am. Chem. Soc.*, **75**, 2726, 3770 (1953).
44. Adamson, A. W., *J. Am. Chem. Soc.*, **76**, 1578 (1954).
45. Bent, H. A., *J. Phys. Chem.*, **60**, 123 (1956).
46. Chaberek, S., and A. E. Martell, *J. Am. Chem. Soc.*, **75**, 2888 (1953).

CHAPTER 4

Effects of Complex Formation
on Oxidation-Reduction Potentials

Oxidation-reduction processes involve the more or less complete transfer of one or more electrons from one ion or molecule to another. If such a process is thermodynamically reversible, it impresses a characteristic electrical potential upon any inert electrode (such as gold or bright platinum) that may be present in the system. The oxidation-reduction potential E obtained in this way for the two valence states of the metal (e.g. ceric-cerous, or ferric-ferrous) forming the couple,

$$M^{n+} + (n - m)e \rightleftharpoons M^{m+}$$

is given by

$$E = E_M{}^0 + \frac{2.3026RT}{(n - m)F} \log \frac{a_{M^{n+}}}{a_{M^{m+}}}$$

where $E_M{}^0$ is a constant, the standard oxidation-reduction potential of the pair of metal ions, and the a's are the activities of the species concerned.

4.1 Factors Determining Magnitudes of Potentials

Standard oxidation-reduction potentials of some transition metal ion couples have been calculated from other properties of the ions concerned.[1] The semiquantitative agreement (within about 0.4 v) with experimental values suggests that the magnitude and sign of such a couple is determined mainly by the following.

1. The value of the nth ionization potential of the metal.

56

2. The difference between the ligand-field stabilization energies (LFSE) of the two hydrated ions.

3. The difference in the electrostatic free energies for the hydration of the metal ions, considered as being generated in the gas phase and transferred to the solution. (This, in turn, depends on the ionic radii and charges, being greater the smaller the radius and the larger the charge.)

These are also the factors that govern the stability sequence in many metal ion complexes. For example, in the Irving-Williams series of divalent cations, the sequence is Mn < Fe < Co < Ni < Cu > Zn. The corresponding overall ionization potentials are $532 < 556 < 583 < 596 < 646 > 631$ kcal, and the ionic radii are $0.80 > 0.74 > 0.72 > 0.69 < 0.72 < 0.74$ Å. Similarly, differences in LFSE for divalent ions favor Mn < Fe < Co < Ni, and Cu > Zn, but Ni > Cu; this difference would become important only in very strong ligand fields.

The often decisive influence of stepwise ionization potentials is shown in Table 2.4. These values can be used in this context only as a guide, because they include an electrostatic contribution that is much greater than when complex formation occurs. Nevertheless, they provide useful qualitative information if corresponding valence states for different metal ions are compared. For example, an energy of 1228 kcal is required to remove the first three electrons from a gas atom of aluminium, and for titanium the figure is 1104 kcal. On the other hand, the energies for removal of the fourth electron from aluminium and titanium are 2767 and 997 kcal, respectively. This difference is so great that the species Al(IV) is of no chemical significance. Similarly, for Li to Li^+ and Li^+ to Li^{2+} the figures are 124 and 1744 kcal, respectively, compared with values for barium of 120 and 231 kcal. Among the transition metal ions, the much higher energy of $Cu^{2+} \rightarrow Cu^{3+}$ (849 kcal) than of $Fe^{2+} \rightarrow Fe^{3+}$ (707 kcal) accounts for the nonexistence of simple Cu(III) salts, and the difference between $Sn^{2+} \rightarrow Sn^{4+}$ (1642 kcal) and $Pb^{2+} \rightarrow Pb^{4+}$ (1712 kcal) helps explain the greater ease of oxidation of the former.

Thus the oxidation-reduction potentials of metal ions are seen to be governed by other, fundamental properties, all of which depend directly on the electronic structures of the elements concerned. For example, for the heavier transition elements, higher oxidation states are usually much more stable than for the corresponding elements of the first transition series. Similarly, low-spin complexes are more easily produced in the former than in the latter. This is because the splitting of d orbitals by a given ligand lies in the sequence $5d > 4d > 3d$, whereas (for spatial reasons) the energy needed to pair electrons in these orbitals varies in the reverse order.

4.2 Some Analytical Applications

Now it can readily be shown that the standard oxidation-reduction potential E_L^0 of any pair of metal complexes containing the same number of ligands is

$$E_L^0 = E_M^0 - \left[\frac{2.3026RT}{(n-m)F}\right] \log(\beta_{M^{n+}} - \log \beta_{M^{m+}})$$

where the β's are the stability constants of the appropriate ligand-metal complexes. This means that the effect of complex formation on metal ion oxidation-reduction potentials can be discussed directly in terms of the differences in stability constants of the metal complexes in the valence states concerned. Quite large effects are sometimes produced. For example, when ferrous ion is present as the ethylenediaminetetraacetic acid (EDTA) complex ($E_0 = 0.117$ v as against 0.771 v for the free metal ions) its reducing power is intermediate between stannous and titanous chlorides.[2] This is true also of the cuprous complex, and indicates the possible application of such complexes as reductimetric reagents.

The sharp drop in potential in the ferrous-ferric system at the endpoint of the titration of ferric ion with EDTA enables the oxidation-reduction dye, variamine blue B, to be used as indicator. The color change is from faint yellow (reduced) (XVI) to intense violet-blue (oxidized) (XVII) at pH 2–3.[3]

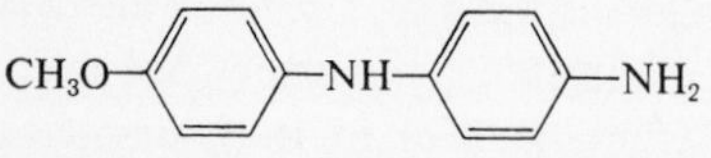

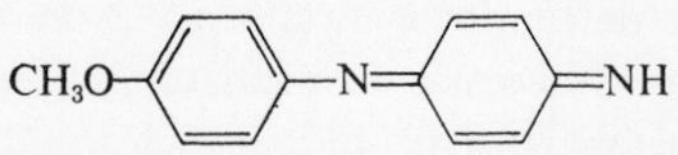

Similarly, copper (II) solutions can be titrated potentiometrically using EDTA.

Both the ferrous and the cuprous EDTA complexes are oxidized by iodine, whereas normally Fe^{3+} and Cu^{2+} are reduced by iodide, with the liberation of iodine. Hence the ferrous-EDTA complex can be used, for example, instead of thiosulfate ion as a titrant for iodine (although starch is not then recommended as indicator) because EDTA complex formation quantitatively reverses the reaction:

$$2Fe^{3+} + 2I^- \rightleftharpoons 2Fe^{2+} + I_2$$

which can ordinarily be used for the determination of ferric ion.

In the same way, cobalt (II) can be titrated with iron (III) in the presence of α,α'-bipyridine[4] and 1,10-phenanthroline[5] using a potentiometric method. For reasons discussed later in this chapter, there is preferential stabilization (relative to the aquo ions) of the Co(III) and the Fe(II) states, so that sharp endpoints can be obtained.

Addition of mercuric ion to form the stable complex HgI_4^{2-} can force the oxidation-reduction reaction

$$As_2O_3 + 2I_2 + 2H_2O \rightleftharpoons As_2O_5 + 4H^+ + 4I^-$$

to the right, even in acid solution, by removing almost all of the free iodide ion.   Similarly, complex formation between Pd(II) and thiosulfate ion so greatly diminishes the concentration of Pd^{2+} ions as to mask it against reduction by some of the more usual reducing agents.   Sulfite ion is much less easily oxidized by permanganate ion if mercuric ion is added to form the stable anion, $Hg(SO_3)_2^{2-}$.   In acid solutions, Mo(VI) combines with oxalic acid, so that permanganate oxidation (or calcium precipitation) of oxalic acid is no longer observed.

Similar considerations apply to metals in contact with solutions of their ions.   In all cases, the electrode potentials are lowered by complex formation in a way that can be predicted quantitatively from stability constant values.   Familiar examples include the effect of the presence of ammonia on the electrode potential of silver and the use of cyanide solutions in electrodeposition.   These effects find application in analytical chemistry: undesirable metal ions can be removed by electrodeposition while, if necessary, the concentration of free metal ions of the species to be determined is reduced by suitable masking agents to levels well below those necessary to secure significant deposition.   Conversely, the species sought can be plated out while undesirable species in the solution are masked.   For example, copper can be selectively deposited from solutions also containing antimony and bismuth if tartrate is added.   Differences in the stability of their cyanide complexes enable zinc to be separated in this way from iron.

4.3 Ligand-Field Stabilization Energies

One of the most important factors determining the magnitude of electrode potentials for transition metals is the difference in ligand-field stabilization energy between the two valence states, resulting from differences not only in the charges on the metal ions but also in the number of d electrons they contain.

From a detailed analysis of the visible and near-infrared absorption spectra of transition metal ions and their complexes, the energy level separations associated with the d orbitals in these systems can be calculated (see Chapter 8).   Table 4.1 lists the values Δ of such ligand-field splitting

TABLE 4.1

Values[a] of the Ligand-Field Splitting, Δ, and the LFSE of Some Hydrated Transition Metal Ions

Ion	Δ, kcal	No. of d Electrons	LFSE, kcal
Ti^{3+}	57.8	1	23
V^{3+}	50.4	2	43
V^{2+}	35.9	3	43
Cr^{3+}	49.5	3	59
Cr^{2+}	39.6	4	24
Mn^{3+}	59.8	4	36
Mn^{2+}	22.2	5	0
Fe^{3+}	38.9	5	0
Fe^{2+}	29.6	6	11
Co^{3+}	52.6[b]	6	(~ 20 for high spin)
Co^{2+}	26.5	7	21
Ni^{2+}	24.2	8	29
Cu^{2+}	35.9	9	22
Rh^{3+}	76.8[b]	6	

[a] Calculated from Holmes, O. G., and D. S. McClure, *J. Chem. Phys.*, **26**, 1686 (1957), and Jørgensen, C. K., thesis, Copenhagen, 1957, taking 1000 $cm^{-1} \equiv 2.846$ kcal.

[b] Low-spin complexes.

for some hexahydrated transition metal ions, and also the LFSE of the ions themselves. For the first row of the transition metal ions, Δ does not vary greatly, lying within the limits 32 ± 8 kcal for the divalent ions, and 50 ± 10 kcal for the trivalent ions. The result for Rh^{3+} suggests that the transition metal ions of the second row have values of Δ about 50% greater than those of the first row.

Fajans[6] and Tsuchida[7] observed that replacement of one ligand in a transition metal complex by another often shifted the spectrum in a constant direction, independent of the metal ion present. On this basis, ligands could be arranged in a definite order, known as the *spectrochemical series*. The following is the sequence of increasing energy level separations in their complexes for some of the more common ligands:[8]

$I^- < Br^- < CO_3^{2-} < SCN^- \approx Cl^- < NO_3^- < F^- \approx$
$(C_6H_5)PO \approx N_3^- < urea \approx OH^- \approx -NCO^- \approx HCOO^- <$
$(C_2O_4)^{2-} \approx H_2O < NCS^- < glycine^- \approx EDTA^{4-} < pyridine <$
$NH_3 < ethylenediamine < 2,2'\text{-bipyridine} < 1,10\text{-phenanthroline} <$
$NO_2^- \ll CN^-$

In this series SCN^- is bonded to the metal ion through sulfur, whereas for NCS^- bonding is through nitrogen.   Other ligands include diethyldithiophosphate between Cl^- and F^-, malonate about equal to water, and   diethylenetriamine   and   tris(aminoethyl)amine   about   equal   to ethylenediamine.[9]   This series can be generalized in terms of the ligand atom directly concerned in metal bonding, as follows:

$$I < Br < Cl < S < F < O < N < C$$

which corresponds to the order of decreasing ionic radii.

Values of Δ can be expressed to a useful approximation as the product of factors for the ligand and the metal ion concerned.   In octahedral complexes the first of these factors varies from 0.76 for Br^- through 1.00 for H_2O to 1.7 for CN^-, whereas the second factor shows a 4.5-fold increase from Mn(II) to Pt(IV), in the sequence

Mn(II) < Ni(II) < Co(II) < Fe(II) < V(II) < Fe(III) < Cr(III) $\approx$
V(III) < Co(III) < Mn(IV) < Mo(III) < Rh(III) $\approx$
Ru(III) < Pd(IV) < Ir(IV) < Re(IV) < Pt(IV)

The average ligand field of a complex MX_2Y_2 is given approximately by the numerical average of MX_4 and MY_4 so long as there are no distinctly different splittings of their absorption spectral bands.

The high position occupied in this series by CN^-, pyridine, and usually ligands such as 2,2'-bipyridine and 1,10-phenanthroline is due to the ability of suitably placed d orbitals on the metal to combine with unoccupied π orbitals on the ligand to form a low-energy bonding molecular orbital which these d electrons then occupy ("back-double-bonding," or "dative π bonding").   By increasing the positive charge on the metal and hence the electrostatic interaction with the ligands, this process increases the value of Δ and helps to stabilize the complex.

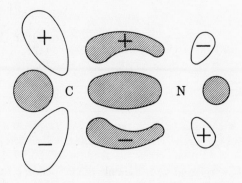

Fig. 4.1.   Orbitals used in bond formation by cyanide ion.

The ability of the CN$^-$ ion to act as an electron donor in σ-bond formation, or to form π bonds in its capacity of electron acceptor, is clearly shown in Fig. 4.1, where the shaded and unshaded areas represent filled and empty molecular orbitals, respectively.[10]

By contrast, some of the lower values of Δ in the series are associated with ligands in which the π orbitals are filled, leading to electron repulsion and a decrease in Δ. Thus, like the greater polarizability of ammonia relative to water this factor favors the observed sequence OH$^-$ < H$_2$O < NH$_3$ for ligand-field strengths, because the pairs of nonbonding electrons that can interact in this way increase from 0 to NH$_3$ to 2 on OH$^-$.

The falling off in the series (H$_2$O >) F$^-$ > Cl$^-$ > Br$^-$ > I$^-$ results from the increasing radius of the anion more than offsetting the increase in polarizability of the halides from F$^-$ to I$^-$.

Little is known about LFSE values for systems containing P, S, and higher atoms. It has been suggested[11] that for lower valencies of transition metal ions the increased back-double-bonding will raise ligand-field strengths for P and S compounds relative to N and O. At higher valencies there will be a relative lowering. In general, the effect will also be P > As; S > Se > Te; and Cl > Br > I.

Representative values of Δ for some of the ligands given in the spectrochemical series are listed in Table 4.2. They show similar trends—

TABLE 4.2

Values of Ligand-Field Splitting, Δ, for Some Octahedral Complexes[a]

Ion		Δ, kcal						
		Cl$^-$	F$^-$	H$_2$O	Ox^{2-}	NH$_3$	en	CN$^-$
Cr^{3+}	($3d^3$)	39.3	43.3	49.5	49.8	61.5	62.3	76.0
Mn^{3+}	($3d^4$)							85.0
Fe^{2+}	($3d^6$)			29.6				93.9
Co^{3+}	($3d^6$)			52.6	51.5	65.4	66.0	95.3
Ni^{2+}	($3d^8$)	20.5	20.8	24.2		30.7	32.7	
Rh^{3+}	($4d^6$)	58.0		76.8	75.1	97.1	98.5	
Ir^{3+}	($5d^6$)	71.1					117.9	
Pt^{4+}	($5d^6$)	82.5	93.9					

[a] Jørgensen, C. K., quoted in J. S. Griffith, *The Theory of Transition-Metal Ions*, Cambridge University Press, Cambridge, 1961, p. 310.

increasing with charge and with the row in the periodic table—that were noted for the aquo complexes, and provide useful material for the semiquantitative discussion of some oxidation-reduction potentials. Some of the biggest effects are observed among the cyanide complexes, examples of which are listed in Table 4.3.

TABLE 4.3

Oxidation-Reduction Potentials of Some Transition Metal
Aquo and Cyanide Complexes, in Volts

Metal		E^0 for M^{3+} aq + $e \rightleftharpoons M^{2+}$ aq	E^0 for $M(CN)_6{}^{3-}$ + $e \rightleftharpoons M(CN)_6{}^{4-}$
Cr	$d^3 \rightleftharpoons d^4$	-0.41	-1.28
Mn	$d^4 \rightleftharpoons d^5$	$+1.51$	-0.22
Fe	$d^5 \rightleftharpoons d^6$	$+0.77$	$+0.36$
Co	$d^6 \rightleftharpoons d^7$	$+1.84$	-0.83

Because Δ is a complex quantity (involving contributions from purely electrostatic perturbations and the effects of σ lone pairs from the ligands, of metal-to-ligand $d_\pi - p_\pi$ bonding, and of ligand-to-metal $p_\pi - d_\pi$ bonding) it has been found convenient to construct the *nephelauxetic series* to express the covalent tendencies of ligands in bond formation.[12] It has been constructed from detailed analyses of particular spectroscopic bands in transition metal ions and their complexes in terms of a parameter B, introduced by Racah to describe electrostatic interaction. It measures electron-electron repulsion. Jørgensen argues that the decrease in B when a complex is formed is a quantitative measure of the covalency of bonds in the complex. The shifts of absorption bands in different environments are interpreted as due to the spreading out of the charge cloud of the d electrons, resulting from covalent interactions and leading to reduced separations between absorption bands. The series is

$$F^- > H_2O > \text{urea} > NH_3 > \text{oxalate}^{2-} \approx \text{en} > SCN^- > Cl^-$$
$$\approx CN^- > Br^-$$

That is, covalent character is highest in bond formation of complexes with bromide ion, and least for fluoride ion. Cotton, Goodgame, and Goodgame[13] give the similar series

$$OH^- \sim (C_6H_5)_3PO > -NCS^- \sim Br^- \sim Cl^-$$

$$\sim NCO^- > N_3{}^- \sim I^- \sim \begin{matrix} CH_2-NH \\ | \quad\quad | \\ CH_2 \quad C{=\!=}S \\ \diagdown \diagup \\ NH \end{matrix}$$

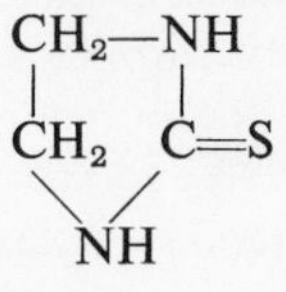

With only minor exceptions, these sequences appear to be the same for all metal ions so far examined, although some dependence on the electronic arrangements in metal ion and ligand may be expected. The orders roughly parallel the polarizabilities of the donor atoms.

4.4 Potentials of Some Transition-Metal Cyanide Complexes

The high ligand-field strength of cyanide ion leads to low-spin states for the d electrons of the metal ions in octahedral complexes because the separation Δ between the t_{2g} and the e_g orbitals is great enough to lead to pairing up of these electrons. If Π is the average energy needed to pair the d electrons of the metal ion, the gains in stability for these (low-spin) complexes of metal ions of transition metals, due to ligand-field effects, are as summarized in Table 4.4. This table also gives values of Π, calcu-

TABLE 4.4

Ligand-Field Stabilization for Low-Spin States of Metal Ions and Some Estimates of the Mean Pairing Energy Π for d Electrons in Gaseous Ions

Number of d Electrons	Gain in Stability	Ion	Number of d Electrons	Π, in kcal*
1	0.4Δ	Cr^{2+}	4	67
2	0.8Δ	Mn^{3+}	4	80
3	1.2Δ	Mn^{2+}	5	73
4	$1.6\Delta-\Pi$	Fe^{3+}	5	85
5	$2.0\Delta-2\Pi$	Fe^{2+}	6	50
6	$2.4\Delta-2\Pi$	Co^{3+}	6	60
7	$1.8\Delta-\Pi$	Co^{2+}	7	64
8	1.2Δ	Ni^{3+}	7	77
9	0.6Δ			

* Griffith, J. S., and L. E. Orgel, *Quart. Revs.*, **11**, 381 (1957).

lated for some gas ions. In the corresponding cyanide complexes the increased delocalization of the d electrons would reduce these values somewhat.

Assuming that the differences in LFSE are the main factors governing differences in the stabilities of the complexes, these facts provide a ready explanation of the potentials in Table 4.3. Thus in the $Co(CN)_6$ complexes, the LFSE is $1.8\Delta - \Pi$ and $2.4\Delta - \Pi$ for $Co^{2+}(d^7)$ and $Co^{3+}(d^6)$, respectively. From Table 4.2, the similarity of Δ for Cr^{3+}, Co^{3+}, and

Fe^{2+} suggests that the increased back-double-bonding expected in the lower-valent state approximately offsets the decrease to be expected, on purely electrostatic grounds, in Δ in going from M^{3+} to M^{2+}. Taking $\Delta = 90$ kcal for $Co(CN)_6^{4-}$, and using the gas ion values for Π, leads to a conservative estimate of 11 kcal for the preferential stabilization of $Co(CN)_6^{3-}$ relative to $Co(CN)_6^{4-}$; that is, to a drop of at least 0.5 v in the standard oxidation-reduction potential relative to the aquo ions.

The corresponding differences for $Cr(CN)_6^{4-}(d^4)$ and $Cr(CN)_6^{3-}(d^3)$ are $1.6\Delta - \Pi$ and 1.2Δ, respectively. Taking Δ to be roughly the same for both valence states gives a maximum stabilization of $Cr(CN)_6^{3-}$ relative to $Cr(CN)_6^{4-}$ of about 36 kcal, or 1.5 v. (1 ev = 23.06 kcal.)

For the Mn^{2+} and Mn^{3+} complexes both values of Δ are taken to be 85 kcal, and the relevant LFSE terms are $2\Delta - 2\Pi$, and $1.6\Delta - \Pi$ respectively. Values of Π taken from Table 4.4 lead to the conclusion that in this case, also, the trivalent cyanide complex is favored, by about 32 kcal, corresponding to a lowering of E^0 by 1.4 v.

In $Fe^{2+}(d^6)$ and $Fe^{3+}(d^5)$ the gains in stability are $2.4\Delta - 2\Pi$ and $2\Delta - 2\Pi$, respectively. The special stability of half-filled d shells so greatly increases the value of Π for ferric ion that, assuming values of Δ for the cyanide complexes of Fe^{2+} and Fe^{3+} to be roughly the same, the LFSE difference should stabilize the lower-valent state.

In spite of the rather tenuous nature of the above arguments, it is clear that the treatment correctly predicts the trends in oxidation-reduction potentials consequent on complex formation.

In the series Fe, Ru, Os, the ionic potential falls with increasing ionic radius. This leads to progressively smaller coulombic effects on the overall stability of their complexes and to an increasing tendency to covalent-bond formation. For M^{2+}/M^{3+} complex systems this would give greater stability to the divalent state relative to the aquo ions, whereas entropy changes favor greater complex formation for M^{3+} the larger the cation. Similarly, because the entropy of a complex ion depends on its size and charge, the decrease from, say, $Fe(CN)_6^{4-}$ to $Fe(CN)_6^{3-} + e$ results in an increased disorder of the solvent shell surrounding the ion, and hence in an increase in entropy. Thus the entropy change again favors the higher-valent state. The LFSE changes, which increase from Fe to Os, favor the divalent cations, while cyanide ion not only provides a strong ligand field in its complexes but also makes strong back-double-bonding possible, especially in the lower-valence state. These combined effects make divalent $Ru(CN)_6^{4-}$ and $Os(CN)_6^{4-}$ more stable than the corresponding trivalent ions, even though for anions such as the halides (where these contributions are less important) Ru(III) and Os(III) complexes are the more stable. Similar considerations apply to Co, Rh, and

Ir, but here the large LFSE for the trivalent ions results in the $M(CN)_6{}^{3-}$ complexes being the stable ones.

Cyanide complexes find limited application in oxidation-reduction titration. For example, in ammoniacal solution, cobalt(II) can be titrated potentiometrically against ferricyanide ion. A bigger difference between the Co(II)-Co(III), Fe(II)-Fe(III) systems and hence a better endpoint is obtained if ethylenediamine is used instead of ammonia to form cobalt complexes.[14]   Alternatively, the more powerful oxidizing agent, potassium molybdicyanide, $K_3Mo(CN)_8$, can be used instead of $K_3Fe(CN)_6$.[15]

4.5   Potentials of Some Copper Complexes

The ease of dismutation of hydrated Cu(I) ion into Cu(II) ion and free copper limits the range of oxidation-reduction potentials that can be obtained in copper complex systems.[16]   The reason for this can be clearly seen from oxidation state–free-energy diagrams of the type suggested by Frost.[17]   In these diagrams standard free energy is plotted against the oxidation state of the metal so that the standard oxidation potential for any two states forming a couple is the slope of the line joining them. The further ΔG^0 for the Cu(I) state lies above the line joining ΔG^0 for Cu and Cu(II), the greater the free-energy difference in favor of the disproportionation reaction.   Similarly, reduction of Cu(II) leads in such a case directly to the free metal, whereas, if the Cu(I) state lies below the line, Cu(II) can be reduced to Cu(I).   It is not necessarily true either that disproportionation will be prevented if the stability constants of Cu(I) complexes are greater than those of the Cu(II) complexes, or that it will occur if the Cu(II) complexes are the more stable.   Thus, the lowest points in Fig. 4.2 represent an example where the Cu(II) complex is (slightly) more stable than the Cu(I) complex (measured by differences in ΔG^0 from the solvated metal ions) but where disproportionation of Cu(I) will not occur.   On the other hand, it can readily be shown from Fig. 4.2 that complex formation does not prevent disproportionation in a system for which, say, $\log K = 4$ for the Cu(I) complex and $\log K = 2$ for the Cu(II) complex.

Over the range accessible to study, the stereochemistry of the metal ions appears to be the major factor in determining the relative stabilities of their complexes and hence the values of the potentials.   This is well illustrated by considering the 1:2 copper complexes of 2,9-dimethyl-1,10-phenanthroline and of ethylenediamine, which have the highest and lowest oxidation-reduction potentials so far recorded for corresponding pairs of copper (I) and copper (II) complexes ($E^0 = 0.624$ v at $20°$,[18] and -0.38 v,[19] respectively.)   For the aquo ions $E^0 = 0.164$ v at $20°$.

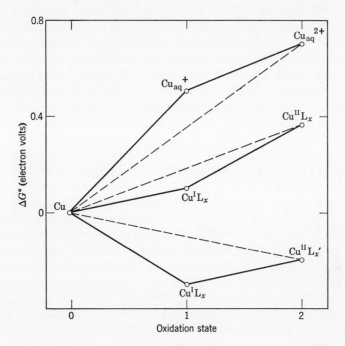

Fig. 4.2.   Oxidation state–free-energy diagram for copper complexes.

When 1,10-phenanthroline or 2,2′-bipyridine is the ligand, E^0 for the 1:2 copper complexes is not very different from the potential for the aquo ions.[20]   This suggests that the increased back donation of π electrons by Cu(I) is largely offset by the LFSE, which helps Cu(II).   However, in 2,9-dimethyl-1,10-phenanthroline, the methyl atoms on pairs of ligands prevent them from lying in a plane round the Cu(II) ion; instead, they are forced into a distorted, energetically less favored, tetrahedral configuration. This does not affect the Cu(I) complex, where a regular tetrahedral arrangement is preferred and possible.

Ethylenediamine behaves towards Cu(II) as a powerful bidentate ligand. With Cu(I), on the other hand, its high basic strength results in a strong preference for linear complexes in which ethylenediamine can act only as a monodentate ligand.

Monodentate amines preferentially stabilize Cu(I) in 1:1 and 1:2 complexes, but the effect is not very great; the maximum increase in E^0 (for the 1:2 benzimidazole complexes) over the value for the aquo ions does not exceed 0.2 v.   Sulfur-containing ligands such as thiourea should favor Cu(I) (raising the oxidation-reduction potential) because the lower-valent state should be able to back-double-bond strongly into the vacant $3d$ orbitals on the sulfur atom. In general, decreasing electrostatic and increasing covalent contributions should increase the relative stability of the Cu(I) state. However, if as with cyanide, thiocyanate, and iodide ions the ligand is too strongly polarized by its proximity to cupric ion, an electron may be transferred (irreversibly) from the ligand ion to the metal, so that the ligand decomposes.

4.6   Potentials of Iron Complexes

Because of the special stability of half-filled d orbitals, the pairing-up energy for electrons in Fe^{3+} is high (Table 4.4). Also, the ligand-field strengths of anions derived from organic acids and phenols are comparable with water, so that, in complexes with such ligands, only high-spin states are to be expected. Under these conditions there is no ligand-field stabilization of Fe^{3+} and, in octahedral complexes, the LFSE values for Fe^{2+} (0.4Δ) are only about 10 kcal, the value for the aquo ion. This leads to the expectation that in iron complexes derived from organic anions of these types the potential-determining factors will be the electrostatic and entropy effects, leading to preferential stabilization of the Fe(III) state. A collection of representative potentials of Fe(III)-Fe(II) couples[1] confirms this. For univalent anions the potentials are about 0.2–0.4 v less for the 1:1 complexes than for the aquo ions (0.771 v) and are lower still for 1:2 and higher complexes. Di- and higher-valent anions give greater depressions. Bidentate ligands involving one oxygen- and one nitrogen-binding group also slightly favor Fe(III).

An analytical application of this effect is the addition of phosphate ion to lower the Fe(II)-Fe(III) potential in the titration of potassium dichromate using diphenylamine or diphenylbenzidine as indicator. Here, again, the ferric complex is more stable than the ferrous complex because the ligand is an anion and π bonding is unlikely. Fluoride ion can also be added to lower the Fe(II)-Fe(III) potential, for the same reason. Conversely, in the presence of a large excess of ferrous ion this potential is such that ferric ion is no longer able to oxidize iodide ion to iodine. Thus, by using such a mixture of ferrous and ferric ions, thiocyanate ion can be determined colorimetrically in the presence of iodide ion. In mixtures of ferrous and ferric ions, aerial oxidation of ferrous to ferric ions is facilitated in the presence of ligands, such as fluoride ion, that stabilize the higher-valent state, whereas it is greatly diminished if species such as α,α'-bipyridine or o-phenanthroline are present.

With neutral ligands, electrostatic effects in stabilizing higher-valent states become less important because the energy involved in ion-dipole interactions is always less than that between ions. In unsaturated amines such as 2,2'-bipyridine and 1,10-phenanthroline the π-electrons are able to occupy molecular orbitals which extend over the entire molecule. The resulting strong electron delocalization ("aromatic character") increases the ligand polarizability and facilitates π bonding with vacant d orbitals in metals. However, in the low-spin complexes, Fe(bipy)$_3$ and Fe(phen)$_3$, formed by Fe(II) and Fe(III), the lowest vacant levels are the antibonding molecular orbitals formed between the ligands and the metal e_g orbitals. This means that forward bonding of this type is less important than the back-double-bonding of the electrons in the t_{2g} orbitals into vacant orbitals on the ligands. This process favors Fe(II) in complex formation. So, also, does the difference in LFSE, and the observed potentials are higher than for the aquo ions:[21]

$$Fe(phen)_3^{3+} + e \rightleftharpoons Fe(phen)_3^{2+}, \quad E^0 \text{ in } 1M \text{ } H_2SO_4 = +1.06 \text{ v}$$
$$Fe(bipy)_3^{3+} + e \rightleftharpoons Fe(bipy)_3^{2+}, \quad E^0 \text{ in } 1M \text{ } H_2SO_4 = +1.06 \text{ v}$$

Among related ligands, such as 5-substituted-1,10-phenanthrolines, the potentials of the iron complexes vary with the pK values of the ligands.[22] As the basic strength of the ligand is increased, Fe(II) complexes gain in relative stability. In the 1:1 iron-aminoacid complexes, $dE^0/d(pK)$ is about -0.075 v.[23] In the 1:1 iron complexes of 8-hydroxyquinolines and polyaza-1-naphthols it is about -0.045 v.[24] For 1:3 iron complexes of substituted 8-hydroxyquinolines in 50% dioxan-water the slope is -0.080 v, and for some 1:3 iron complexes of 5-substituted-1,10-phenanthrolines in $1M$ sulfuric acid the slope is -0.120 v.

This effect of substituents has been used in analytical chemistry to provide a series of oxidation-reduction indicators of graded potential. Some examples from the ferroin (tris(1,10-phenanthroline) ferrous ion) series are given in Table 4.5.

4.7   Some General Observations

In the metals Hg, Tl, Sn, and Pb the outermost pair of s electrons is not very readily ionized or used as bonding electrons. It is the behavior of this "inert pair" of electrons that is responsible for the two valence states of those metals in their ions. Unfortunately, nothing seems to be known concerning the effects of complex-forming species on the oxidation-reduction potentials of the couples Hg^{2+}/Hg_2^{2+} and Sn^{4+}/Sn^{2+}. The potential of the EDTA complexes of Hg^{2+} and Hg_2^{2+} must be low; the very much greater stability of HgEDTA (log $K_1 = 22$) leads to the rapid dismutation, $Hg_2^{2+} \rightarrow Hg^{2+} + Hg$, when EDTA is added to a solution containing mercurous ion.

TABLE 4.5

Potentials of Some Redox Indicators in the Ferroin
Series (in $1M$ Sulfuric Acid)

Indicator	E_0' in Volts
5-Nitroferroin	1.25
5-Sulfoferroin	1.20
Ferroin (1,10-phenanthroline)$_3$Fe(II)	1.06
5-Methylferroin	1.02
5,6-Dimethylferroin	0.97
4,7-Dimethylferroin	0.88
3,4,7,8-Tetramethylferroin	0.81

The high charges of Ce(IV) and Ce(III) ions make electrostatic effects the main contributors to the stabilities of their complexes, so that, in general complex formation will lead to a lowering of the potential. For example, E_0 in $0.5M$ sulfuric acid is 1.44 v, whereas in $1M$ perchloric acid (where complex formation is negligible) $E_0 = 1.70$ v.[25]

A special stability associated with "inner complex" formation, when the charge on the ligand balances the charge on the metal ion, has been suggested[26] as the reason why Co(III) is stabilized in the tris(o-hydroxy-azobenzene) complex (XVIII), whereas Co(II) is more stable in the bis(o-hydroxy-o'-aminoazobenzene) complex (XIX).

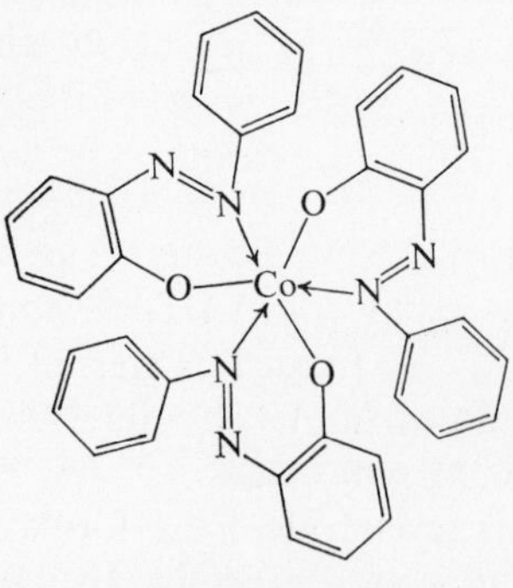

XVIII* 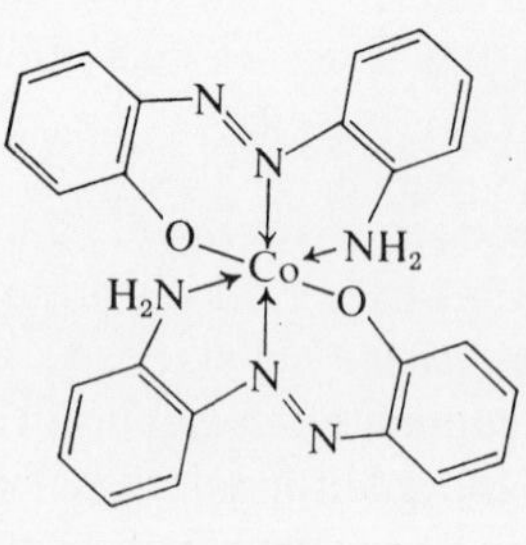   XIX

Among the transition metal ions, LFSE differences provide a useful guide in assessing the effect of nitrogen-containing ligands, such as am-

* In this and subsequent formulas of metal complexes no attempt is made to represent the stereochemistry of the complex. (In this example the ligands are disposed octahedrally about the central metal ion.)

monia and ethylenediamine, on oxidation-reduction potentials. Thus, for the same reasons as discussed for cyanide ion, differences in LFSE values for Co(II) and Co(III) lead to the expectation of preferential stabilization by ammonia and ethylenediamine of Co(III), relative to the aquo ions, to a lesser extent than in the cyanide complexes, but to a greater extent than in the EDTA complexes.   This is what is found:

$$Co(H_2O)_6^{3+} \quad + e \rightleftharpoons Co(H_2O)_6^{2+} \quad E_0 = +1.84 \text{ v}$$
$$Co(dipy)_3^{3+} \quad + e \rightleftharpoons Co(dipy)_3^{2+} \quad E_0 = 0.31 \text{ v}$$
$$Co(NH_3)_6^{3+} \quad + e \rightleftharpoons Co(NH_3)_6^{2+} \quad E_0 = +0.14 \text{ v}$$
$$Co(en)_3^{3+} \quad + e \rightleftharpoons Co(en)_3^{2+} \quad E_0 = -0.22 \text{ v}$$
$$Co(CN)_6^{3-} \quad + e \rightleftharpoons Co(CN)_6^{4-} \quad E_0 = -0.83 \text{ v}$$
$$Co(III)\text{-}EDTA + e \rightleftharpoons Co(II)\text{-}EDTA \quad E_0 = +0.60 \text{ v}$$

Precipitation of one of the pairs of an oxidation-reduction couple as a means of changing the potential serves as the basis of a method for determining zinc.[27]   In a mixture of ferro- and ferricyanide ions at pH 5, 3,3'-dimethylnaphthidine (XX) is almost colorless.   If zinc is added to the system zinc ferrocyanide is precipitated, the oxidation-reduction potential rises, and the indicator is oxidized to the red-violet species (XXI).

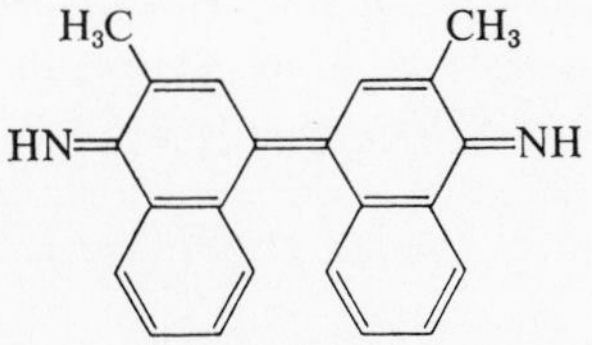

XX 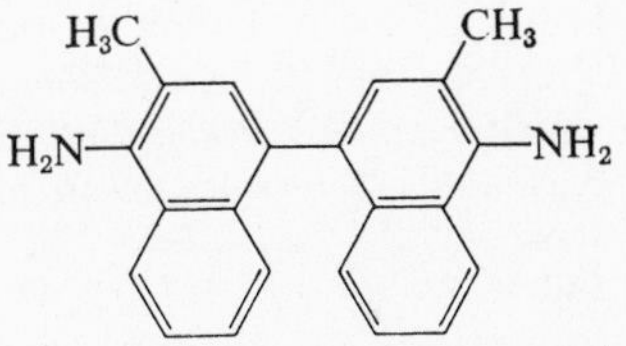   XXI

The reaction is reversible, and can be used as an indicator for either the forward- or the back-titration of a zinc solution with EDTA.   Similarly, metals such as Cu, Ni, Fe, Al, Cd, and Ga can be titrated if excess of EDTA is added and, after adding pH 5 buffer, ferro- and ferricyanide, and indicator, the solution is titrated with a standard zinc solution.[28]

From consideration of thermodynamic cycles involving formation of gas ions, followed by complexation and solvation, it can be predicted that if a solvent of lower dielectric constant than water is used, the oxidation-reduction potential of a complex couple will rise.   That is, the lower-valent state will gain in stability.

A factor capable of considerably modifying oxidation-reduction potentials of metal ions with related ligands is the spin state ("high" or "low") in the pairs of complexes.   Taking ferrous and ferric ions as examples, it is known that the high stability of the tris(1,10-phenanthroline) ferrous complex is due to the low-spin state of the $3d$ electrons, which are thereby favorably placed for π bonding with vacant orbitals on the ligands. The bis(1,10-phenanthroline) complex is paramagnetic ("high-spin" state) and bonding is much weaker. Similarly, the stabilities of ferric complexes will vary, depending on whether they are "high" or "low" spin, but, because of the special stability of half-filled shells, higher ligand fields will be needed to force d-electron pairing in ferric than in ferrous ions. Thus, if ligand-field strengths are progressively increased, these three types of behavior should result:

1. Low fields. High-spin Fe(II), high-spin Fe(III).
2. Higher fields. Low-spin Fe(II), high-spin Fe(III).
3. Very high fields. Low-spin Fe(II), low-spin Fe(III).

In general, E_0 for ligands in (2) should be greater than for (1) or (3), but within each group potentials should vary (roughly linearly) with the pK of the ligand.

References

1. Perrin, D. D., *Rev. Pure Appl. Chem.*, **9**, 257 (1959).
2. Belcher, R., D. Gibbons, and T. S. West, *Anal. Chim. Acta*, **12**, 107 (1955).
3. Erdey, L., and A. Bodor, *Z. Anal. Chem.*, **137**, 410 (1953).
4. Vydra, F., and R. Pribil, *Talanta*, **8**, 824 (1961).
5. Vydra, F., and R. Pribil, *Coll. Czech. Chem. Comm.*, **26**, 3081 (1961).
6. Fajans, K., *Naturwissenschaften*, **11**, 165 (1922).
7. Tsuchida, R., *Bull. Chem. Soc. Japan*, **13**, 388, 436, 471 (1938); Tsuchida, R., and M. Kobayashi, *ibid.*, **13**, 47 (1938).
8. Jørgensen, C. K., *Energy Levels of Complexes and Gaseous Ions*, Gjellerups, Copenhagen, 1957. Jørgensen, C. K., Technical Report to the U.S. Army, "Absorption Spectra of Complexes of Heavy Metals," September 1958.
9. Jørgensen, C. K., *Absorption Spectra and Chemical Bonding in Complexes*, Pergamon Press, Oxford, 1962, p. 109.
10. Sutton, L. E., *J. Chem. Ed.*, **37**, 498 (1960).
11. Chatt, J., G. A. Gamlen, and L. E. Orgel, *J. Chem. Soc.*, **1959**, 1047.
12. Schaffer, C. E., and C. J. Jørgensen, *J. Inorg. Nuclear Chem.*, **8**, 143 (1958).
13. Cotton, F. A., D. M. L. Goodgame, and M. Goodgame, *J. Am. Chem. Soc.*, **83**, 4690 (1961); Goodgame, D. M. L., M. Goodgame, and F. A. Cotton, *ibid.*, **83**, 4161 (1961).
14. Diehl, H., and J. P. Butler, *Anal. Chem.*, **27**, 777 (1955).
15. Kratochvil, B., and H. Diehl, *Talanta*, **3**, 346 (1960).
16. See Perrin, D. D., and C. J. Hawkins, *Proc. 1st Australian Electrochem. Conf.*, Pergamon Press, Oxford, 1964.
17. Frost, A. A., *J. Am. Chem. Soc.*, **73**, 2680 (1951).
18. Hawkins, C. J., and D. D. Perrin, *J. Chem. Soc.*, **1963**, 2996.
19. Estimated from literature, reference 1.
20. James, B. R., and R. J. P. Williams, *J. Chem. Soc.*, **1961**, 2007.

21. Hume, D. N., and I. M. Kolthoff, *J. Am. Chem. Soc.*, **65**, 1897 (1943).
22. Brandt, W. W., and D. K. Gullstrom, *J. Am. Chem. Soc.*, **74**, 3532 (1952).
23. Perrin, D. D., *J. Chem. Soc.*, **1958**, 3120, 3125.
24. Albert, A., and A. Hampton, *J. Chem. Soc.*, **1954**, 505; A. Albert, *Biochem. J.*, **54**, 646 (1953).
25. Smith, G. F., and C. A. Getz, *Ind. Eng. Chem. (Anal. Ed.)*, **10**, 191 (1938).
26. Bailar, J. C., and C. F. Callis, Paper 20, Division of Physical and Inorganic Chemistry, 115th Meeting of the American Chemical Society, San Francisco, Calif., 1949.
27. Brown, E. G., and T. J. Hayes, *Anal. Chim. Acta*, **9**, 6 (1953).
28. Flashka, H., and W. Franschitz, *Z. Anal. Chem.*, **144**, 421 (1953); Flashka, H., and H. Abdine, *Mikrochim. Acta*, **1955**, 37.

CHAPTER 5

Factors Governing the Rates of Formation and Dissociation of Complexes, and Also Their Rates of Oxidation and Reduction

Although theories of organic reactions have been well established for some years and are supported by extensive kinetic data, corresponding treatments of reactions involving inorganic species are much less well developed.[1] For present purposes, reactions can be classified as "rapid" if they are effectively complete within several minutes, and "slow" if an appreciably longer time is required. Our concern is mainly with the latter.

5.1 Reaction Mechanisms

Following the terminology of Ingold[2] it is convenient to divide substitution reactions into *nucleophilic* (S_N) and *electrophilic* (S_E) depending on whether the incoming reagent gives electrons to, or takes electrons from, the species with which it reacts. Depending on the reaction mechanism involved, these two classes are further subdivided into *dissociation* (S_N1 and S_E1) and *displacement* (S_N2, S_E2) types. In S_N1 and S_E1 reactions, the complex undergoes a slow dissociation, followed by a rapid reaction of one of the products with either a nucleophilic or an electrophilic reagent. On the other hand, S_N2 or S_E2 reactions involve the formation of activated complexes between the metal complex and the reagent, followed by dissociation into products. This means that in the transition state for S_N1 and S_E1 reactions involving metal complexes, the number of groups coordinated round the metal ion is one less (because of the loss of the ligand to be replaced), whereas for S_N2 and S_E2 reactions it is one more, than in the stable complexes. Thus for an S_N1 reaction involving an octahedral complex the relatively slow and hence rate-determining step is the formation of a five-coordinated intermediate, whereas for an S_N2

reaction an extra ligand is added directly to give a seven-coordinated activated complex. In practice, the reaction mechanism often lies between these extremes. "Concerted" mechanisms are sometimes involved, in which the entering ligand begins to bond to the metal ion before the outgoing ligand has been completely lost from the complex. Only in a small number of cases, so far, has it been possible to decide unambiguously from experimental evidence the mechanism of any particular reaction.

Reactions by predominantly S_N1 mechanisms include the acid hydrolysis of trans[$Co(en)_2(OH)Cl$]$^+$ and [$Co(en)_2Cl_2$]$^+$, and the base hydrolysis of Co(III) ammines. Most Co(III) and Cr(III) complexes appear to react by S_N1 mechanisms, provided the ligands are electron-donating. If they are electron-attracting, the reactions tend to be predominantly S_N2; examples include the acid hydrolysis of trans[$Co(en)_2NO_2Cl$]$^{2+}$ and $Co(en)_2NH_3Cl$]$^{2+}$. The reaction between $PtCl_6^{2-}$ and I^- probably has an S_N2 mechanism. This is probably true also for many reactions involving square planar complexes. The labile Rh(III) and Ir(III) anionic complexes may dissociate by a rapid S_E1 reaction. Their kinetically inert cationic and neutral complexes (all of which are low-spin d^6 systems) probably undergo slow bimolecular substitution.

As a useful generalization, tetrahedral complexes reacting by an S_N2 displacement mechanism do so more rapidly than octahedral complexes, where an S_N1 dissociation process is usually involved.

The major rate-determining step in a reaction is the energy required to form the *activated complex* from the reactant molecules. (For present purposes factors such as the entropy of activation are ignored.) By its nature such a complex is less energetically stable than either the species from which it is formed or the products into which it dissociates. If the potential energy of the reactants could be plotted as a function of the stage of a reaction, curves such as those in Fig. 5.1 would be obtained. Where several alternative transition states appear possible, the one with the lowest energy will be the preferred one.

5.2 "Inert" Complexes

Whereas most metal ions form "labile" complexes that react rapidly in aqueous solution, complexes of others, notably some transition metal ions, may persist almost unchanged for hours or days even when they are thermodynamically unstable. Labile complexes dissociate rapidly if the ligand concentration is reduced, so that substances quite different from those existing in solutions may be obtained on precipitation or extraction into another solvent. "Inert" complexes, under the same conditions, persist unchanged.

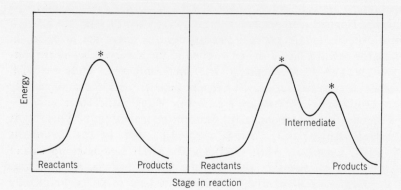

Fig. 5.1.   Energy diagrams for chemical reactions.   In the first example, the reactants pass through an activated complex to products.   In the second example, reaction is shown as proceeding through an activated complex to an intermediate which then forms a second activated complex prior to dissociation into the final products.   Asterisks denote *transition state* regions.

Table 5.1 lists some transition metal ions that give rise to inert complexes. If the d-electron configurations in these complexes are examined, an interesting fact emerges.   Almost without exception, the systems are d^3 or low-spin d^4, d^5, and d^6.   The exceptions come mainly from the second or third row of the periodic table.   The dividing line is sharp.   Thus complexes of V(III), a d^2 system, are labile, whereas spin-paired CN^- and 1,10-phenanthroline complexes are inert.   Complexes of Co(II) (d^7) are labile, while low-spin Co(III) complexes (which are d^6) are inert. On the other hand, the high-spin Co(III) fluoride complex is labile.

Qualitatively, a good guide to whether a complex will be inert or labile is to consider whether or not the formation of the transition state involves the loss of much ligand-field stabilization energy.   Orgel[3] explained the much greater reactivity of d^0, d^1, and d^2 systems compared to d^3 (and, by the same reasoning, low-spin d^4, d^5, and d^6) on the grounds that, in an S_N2 reaction, the entering group could approach the complex in the direction of a vacant, low-energy d orbital (t_{2g}) only in the d^0, d^1, and d^2 cases.   For this reason formation of an activated complex would not lead to so great a loss of LFSE as would be involved if, as in the group of inert complexes, a higher-energy d orbital (e_g) had to be used.   Basolo and Pearson[4] approached the problem by taking the five-coordinate square pyramidal and the seven coordinate pentagonal bipyramidal complexes as approximations to the activated complexes formed from an octahedral complex in an S_N1 and an S_N2 reaction, respectively.   They then calculated the changes in LFSE that would result for the different d-electron configurations.   In this way they predicted that, in strong fields, reactions by either S_N1 or S_N2 mechanisms would be fast for d^0, d^1, and d^2, and slow for d^3, d^4, d^5, and d^6, the rates being $d^6 < d^3 < d^4 < d^5$.   In the weak-

TABLE 5.1

Some Hexacoordinated Ions Giving Rise to "Inert" Complexes

Ligand	d Electrons	Ions
CN^-	d^1	Mo(V), W(V)
	d^2	Mo(IV), W(IV)
	d^3	V(II), Cr(III)
	Low-spin d^4	Mn(III)
	Low-spin d^5	Mn(II), Fe(III)
	Low-spin d^6	Fe(II), Ru(II), Os(II)(?), Co(III), Rh(III), Ir(III)
	Low-spin d^7	Co(II)(?)
CNS^-	d^3	Cr(III), Mo(III)
	d^6	Pt(IV)
Br^-	d^3	Mo(III), Re(IV)
	d^5	Ru(III)
Cl^-	d^3	Cr(III), Mo(III), W(III), Re(IV)
	d^4	Cr(II), Re(III), Ru(IV), Os(IV)
	d^5	Ru(III), Os(III), Ir(IV)
	d^6	Ru(II), Os(II), Rh(III), Ir(III), Pt(IV)
	d^8	Pt(II), Au(III)
Oxalate	d^3	Mn(IV)
	d^5	Ru(III)
	d^6	Co(III), Ir(III)
NH_3	d^3	Cr(III), Mo(III)
	d^4	Re(III)(?)
	d^5	Ru(III)
	d^6	Co(III), Ru(II), Rh(III), Ir(III), Pt(IV)
	d^8	Au(III)
2,2'-Bipyridine	Low-spin d^4	Cr(II)
	Low-spin d^6	Fe(II)
	d^8	Ni(II)
1,10-Phen- anthroline	Low-spin d^5	Fe(III)
	Low-spin d^6	Fe(II)
	d^8	Ni(II)

field case for systems from d^4 to d^7, and also for d^8, d^9, and d^{10}, only d^8 would be predicted to be slow.   Table 5.1 includes known inert complexes formed by the d^8 ions, Pt(II), Au(III), and Ni(II).

Not much is at present known concerning nonoctahedral inert complexes, which occur, for example, in the low-spin, eight-coordinate $Mo(CN)_8^{4-}$, $Mo(CN)_8^{3-}$, $W(CN)_8^{4-}$, and $W(CN)_8^{3-}$, and in the square planar Pt(II) complexes.

Both the valence bond and the ligand-field theories predict that non-transition elements, the rare earths, and d^{10} systems will react very rapidly. In fact, outside the transition elements, it is only among complexes such as PF_6^-, AsF_6^-, $SbCl_6^-$, SF_6, SeF_6, and TeF_6, where the central ion carries a high formal charge, that slow reactions are commonly observed.

A different class of inert complex is found when the ligand is poly-dentate, as in EDTA and the porphyrins.   In such complexes, a high activation energy is required if all the ligand-to-metal bonds are to be broken at the same time.   The d configuration and spin state of the metal ion are unimportant.   For example, Fe(II) in hemoglobin is high-spin, and Mg (which occurs in chlorophyll) has no d electrons.

Table 5.2 lists some representative rates of exchange of inert complexes obtained using isotopic tracers.   It emphasizes the fact that such complexes, once formed, may persist for quite a long time under conditions when they would be expected, from stability constant data, to dissociate completely. This is true, for example, of $Cr(en)_3^{3+}$ added to $1M$ nitric acid.   Con-versely, complexes that cannot be prepared directly may sometimes be obtained by exploiting this inertness.   Thus in weakly acid solutions attempts to make $Fe(phen)_3^{3+}$ and $Fe(bipy)_3^{3+}$ by direct combination of Fe^{3+} with the ligands lead only to the formation of binuclear complexes. The tris ferric complexes can, however, be prepared without difficulty by oxidation of $Fe(phen)_3^{2+}$ and $Fe(bipy)_3^{2+}$ under the same conditions. Most of the exchange reactions of these octahedral complexes have prop-erties consistent with an S_N1 mechanism,[5] so that the charge and size of the entering group have little effect.   Similarly, whereas increasing the positive charge on the central atom decreases the rate, increasing the size of the central atom increases the rate.   So, too, do the increasing negative charge and size of other ligands on the complex.   However, in complexes containing electron-attracting groups such as $—NO_2$ an S_N2 mechanism would be favored, partly by increasing the positive charge on the central metal ion and also partly by removing the d electrons from positions where they would hinder the approach of an incoming reagent.   Hydroxide ion reacts very rapidly with many complexes, especially in cases where one of the coordinated groups has an ionizable proton (for example, H_2O or NH_3); this may be an S_N2 reaction but S_N1 seems more likely.[6]   This mechanism is further distinguished as S_N1CB because it involves the (rapid) rate-determining dissociation of the conjugate base of the metal complex.

In substitution reactions in mixed square planar Pt(II) complexes such as $Pt(NH_3)_3Br^+$, *cis* or *trans* substitution can be distinguished, depending

TABLE 5.2

Some Typical Rates of Exchange on Inert Complexes at Room Temperature

Complex	Exchanging Species	Medium	$t_{1/2}$
$Cr(H_2O)_6^{3+}$	H_2O	$0.01-1M$ $HClO_4$	1–3 days
$Cr(CN)_6^{3-}$	$Cr(H_2O)_6^{3+}$	pH 3–4	36 hr
	CN^-	pH 10	~24 days
$Cr(SCN)_6^{3-}$	$Cr(H_2O)_6^{3+}$	$0.05-2.0M$ acid	> 3 days
$Cr(oxalate)_3^{3-}$	$Cr(H_2O)_6^{3+}$	$0.02M$ $HClO_4$	> 3 days
$Cr(en)_3^{3+}$	en	$1M$ HNO_3	> 3 days (40°)
$Mo(CN)_8^{4-}$	CN^-	pH 11	~500 days (dark)
	CN^-	pH 11	11 days (light)
$Mn(CN)_6^{3-}$	CN^-	pH 9–11	35–80 min (0°)
$Fe(CN)_6^{4-}$	CN^-	pH 3.5	2 days
$Fe(CN)_6^{3-}$	CN^-	pH 10	> 5 days
$Fe(bipy)_3^{2+}$	$Fe(OH_2)_6^{2+}$	pH 1.5	~5 hr
$Fe(phen)_3^{2+}$	$Fe(OH_2)_6^{2+}$	pH 1.5	~97 min
$OsCl_6^{2-}$	Cl^-	$0.1-2.0M$ acid	> 63 days (50°)
$Co(CN)_6^{3-}$	$Co(H_2O)_6^{2+}$		> 2.5 days
	CN^-	pH 11	> 8 days
$Co(NH_3)_6^{3+}$	H_2O	pH 4.7	15–60 min
$Co(en)_3^{3+}$	H_2O	pH 4.7	30–60 min
	en	pH 7.0	> 65 hr (100°)
cis-$Co(en)_2Cl_2^+$	Cl^-	Methanol	100 min (36°)
$Co(oxalate)_3^{3-}$	Oxalate^{2-}		> 25 min (50°)
$Ni(bipy)_3^{2+}$	Ni^{2+}		5 min
$Pd(NH_3)_4^{2+}$	H_2O	pH 6.6–7.6	13 min–2 hr (0°)
$Pt(CN)_4^{2-}$	CN^-		~1 min
$PtCl_4^{2-}$	Cl^-		~14 hr
$PtBr_4^{2-}$	Br^-		~6 min
PtI_6^{2-}	I^-		30 min
$Pt(NH_3)_4^{2+}$	H_2O	pH 5.5	35 min

(From the extensive collection of Stranks, D. R. and R. G. Wilkins, *Chem. Rev. (London)*, **57**, 743 (1957).) Some of the ligand-exchange reactions, for example of $Cr(CN)_6^{3-}$, $Mo(CN)_8^{4-}$, and $Fe(CN)_6^{4-}$, are photocatalyzed.

on whether the NH_3 group that is replaced is alongside the bromide ion in the complex (*cis*) or diagonally opposite to it (*trans*). Groups in such complexes may be described as *cis* or *trans* directing, and the approximate order of increasing *trans* effect, as measured by the efficacy of a substituent in labilizing a group *trans* to it, is:[7]

$$CN^- > C_2H_4 > CO \sim NO > I^- \sim NO_2 \sim HSO_3^- \sim PR_3 \sim$$
$$R_2S \sim SC(NH_2)_2 \sim NCS^- > Br^- > Cl^- > py > RNH_2 \sim$$
$$NH_3 > OH^- > H_2O$$

In non-π-bonding ligands, the *trans* effect is due mainly to electrostatic forces; in the other cases, π bonding is the dominant factor. The order of *trans* effect for ligands appears to be the same as the observed rate of exchange in the complexes PtX_4^{2-}. Also, the stronger the bond the incoming ligand can form with Pt, the faster the exchange reaction becomes. Reaction may proceed through a square pyramidal activated complex in which the rate-determining step is the formation of the bond with the incoming ligand, provided it is high in the *trans* series; that is, by an S_N2 mechanism.

A different kind of "inertness" in chemical reaction has been found in square planar or distorted octahedral complexes of Cu(II), Ni(II), Co(II), and Zn formed from bi- or quadridentate ligands of the Schiff base type. Metal ion exchange with metal chelates of this type appears to involve a progressive unwrapping of the ligand from around one metal ion, with simultaneous wrapping around of the other metal ion. Studies, mainly in pyridine solution, indicate that the rate of exchange increases in the sequence Zn > Co(II) > Cu(II) > Ni(II). The Ni complexes of N,N'-ethylene-bis(salicylaldimine) and N,N'-*o*-phenylene-bis(salicylaldimine) showed no exchange in 48 hr at room temperature.[8] Similarly, at pH 6.8 and 25°, $t_{1/2}$ for Ni exchange in the bis complex of 1,1,2,2-tetramethyl-ethylenediamine was 67 min,[9] while for Cu(II) it was only 3 min. (The unsubstituted ethylenediamine complexes exchange much more rapidly.) Similarly, loss of optical activity of neutral solutions of metal complexes of 1,2-propylenediaminetetraacetic acid proceeds very slowly for Ni^{2+}, Co^{2+}, and Fe^{3+} (measured in days), less slowly for $Cu^{2+} > Zn^{2+} > Cd^{2+}$ (hours), and rapidly for Ca^{2+} and Mn^{2+}.[10]

The slow step in the stepwise displacement of EDTA in the Ni(II)-EDTA complex by cyanide ion has been identified with the conversion of the octahedral, high-spin complex into a planar, low-spin complex.[11]

A factor that is sometimes important in determining the rate of exchange in a complex is catalysis by oxidizing and reducing agents, including ions of the same metal but differing by ± 1 in their electronic charge. This is readily understandable because the "inertness" of complexes of the same metal in different valence states will not, in general, be the same. The photocatalysis observed in some cases may have a similar explanation (see discussion on charge-transfer spectra). This is also true of the catalyzed racemization of complex ions, e.g. $Co(en)_3^{2+}$ by Co^{3+}.

As discussed above, the making and breaking of covalent bonds can be a slow process. Conversion of molybdate anion to Mo^{6+} as a preliminary to the formation of, say, the tris(toluene-3,4-dithiol) complex involves just such processes. In the absence of iron, which acts as a catalyst, conversion to the cation is incomplete after 100 min at room temperature. Heating at 75° for 15–20 min is required.[12]

The high ligand-field strength to be expected in the dithizone molecule should lead to Ni(II) forming a low-spin complex as in 2,2'-bipyridine and 1,10-phenanthroline, and hence to "inertness" towards dissociation. This is also true of the Co(III) complex, which should be a low-spin d^6 system. This slowness of formation and dissociation has been observed experimentally.

5.3   Oxidation and Reduction of Metal Complexes

Because they involve displacements of electrons relative to the atomic nuclei, all chemical reactions may be looked on as oxidation-reduction processes. It is convenient, however, to restrict discussion to those reactions where there is more or less complete transfer of one or more electrons from one ion or molecule to another.

The definitions of oxidation as a process resulting in the loss of electrons and of reduction as a process in which electrons are gained tell us nothing about the mechanisms involved in the reactions. In fact, this field, considering its importance, has been little explored. Qualitatively, the bigger the difference between the oxidation-reduction potentials of the couples involved in a reaction the faster the reaction usually goes. Final equilibrium conditions can be calculated from these potential differences, but not the rate at which this equilibrium will be approached. In fact, the lack of a suitable reaction mechanism can prevent a reaction from proceeding at a detectable rate although apparently favorable thermodynamic conditions exist. The usual "balance" equations, such as $MnO_4^- + 8H^+ + 5Fe^{2+} = Mn^{2+} + 5Fe^{3+} + 4H_2O$, give no indication of the steps by which the reactions proceed. The effect of complex formation on oxidation-reduction potentials was examined in Chapter 4. The present discussion is concerned with rates and mechanisms of oxidation-reduction reactions in (mainly aqueous) solution.

Large, symmetrical complex ions such as $Fe(CN)_6^{3-}$ and $Fe(CN)_6^{4-}$ can transfer an electron from the reduced to the oxidized form of the complex much more rapidly than is possible in the corresponding aquo ions, Fe_{aq}^{3+} and Fe_{aq}^{2+}. Other couples that undergo very rapid oxidation-reduction, probably because electron transfer does not require rearrangement of the coordination sphere, include MnO_4^{2-}, MnO_4^-; $IrCl_6^{3-}$, $IrCl_6^{2-}$; $Fe(phen)_3^{2+}$, $Fe(phen)_3^{3+}$; $Fe(bipy)_3^{2+}$, $Fe(bipy)_3^{3+}$; $Os(bipy)_3^{2+}$, $Os(bipy)_3^{3+}$; and $Co(bipy)_3^{2+}$, $Co(bipy)_3^{3+}$. In all these cases, electron transfer takes place much more rapidly than substitution reactions do. In general, irrespective of whether the complexes are labile or inert, metal ions surrounded by unsaturated or large, polarizable ligands exchange electrons rapidly and usually much faster than the corresponding aquo ions or ammine complexes. Libby[13] explained this more rapid electron exchange on the basis of the Frank-Condon principle, according to which the motions of atomic nuclei are so slow relative to those of electrons that an electron transfer must occur without any appreciable movement of the nuclei. With small ions considerable re-orientation of solvent around them must occur before the transition can be a stable one, and this large energy barrier opposes the transfer. With large, complex ions this difficulty is greatly reduced, especially if the ligands are unsaturated and π bonding occurs between the metal and the ligand. The latter helps to reduce the radius of the lower-valent complex to a value more nearly comparable with that of the higher-valent complex. Such ligands also facilitate electron conduction more than species like water and ammonia, which contain saturated single bonds. Subsequently it was suggested[14] that electron transfer proceeds in two steps—a rearrangement of the coordination spheres around the metal ions, followed by a quantum-mechanical electron tunneling from one reactant to another through a solvent barrier. At present there is no obvious way of deciding between these two theories; they differ essentially only in that in one case the electron has to surmount an energy barrier whereas in the other case it tunnels through it. Often, especially with organic ligands, it is convenient to picture the situation as one in which there is sufficient overlap of orbitals of matching energy on the oxidant and the reductant for reasonable probability of electron transfer.

In the extreme case, this leads to a "bridged" activated complex in which an atom or group is part of the coordination sphere of both the oxidant and the reductant. An example is the reaction of Cr^{2+} with $(NH_3)_5CoCl^{2+}$ (in which the Cl is not readily removed from the Co). On mixing, a rapid reaction takes place to give $CrCl^{2+}$, Co^{2+}, and NH_4^+. $CrCl^{2+}$ is an "inert" complex and could not be formed from $Cr^{3+} + Cl^-$ during the course of the experiment.[15] Similar transfer to Cr^{2+} has been found for the ligand L in the inert complexes $(NH_3)_5Co^{III}L$, where $L = F^-$, Br^-, I^-, SO_4^{2-}, N_3^-, CNS^-, $RCOO^-$, $P_2O_7^{4-}$, PO_4^{3-}, and

OH^-.[16] In all cases, formation of a bridged intermediate $[(NH_3)_5Co^{III}$ —L—$Cr^{II}(H_2O)_5]$ appears likely. Comparable mechanisms have been found for electron transfer between Cr^{2+} and some complexes of the types $(NH_3)_5Cr^{III}X$ and $(H_2O)_5Cr^{III}X$,[17] and between $Pt(en)_2^{2+}$ and $Pt(en)_2$ Cl_2^{2+}.[18] The isolation of the intermediate $[(CN)_5Co^{III}NCFe^{II}(CN)_5]^{6-}$ in the oxidation of $Co(CN)_5^{3-}$ by $Fe(CN)_6^{3-}$ has been claimed.[19] Similarly, in strongly acid perchlorate solutions Fe^{3+} and Sn^{2+} do not react perceptibly,[20] but the reaction proceeds if Cl^-, Br^-, and I^- are added, or if the pH is raised to produce —OH^-, all of which act as bridging ligands.[21]

The fact that Cl is a better "bridging group" than H_2O explains why electron transfer between $Cr(H_2O)_6^{2+}$ and $Cr(H_2O)_5Cl^{2+}$ is much more rapid than that between $Cr(H_2O)_6^{2+}$ and $Cr(H_2O)_6^{3+}$. The importance of H_2O as a bridging group is clearly shown in a comparison of the rates of reaction of Cr^{2+} with $[Co(NH_3)_6]^{3+}$ and $[Co(NH_3)_5H_2O]^{3+}$; the former is slower by a factor of at least 100. This is ascribed to the absence of any electron pair on a coordinated NH_3, and to the presence of such a pair on the coordinated H_2O so that bridging can occur. Taube[22] has reported examples of the bridging of oxidizing and reducing groups by dibasic acids such as maleic, oxalic, and p-phthalic acid to form complexes like (XXII), in which the oxidation-reduction proceeds much more rapidly because of the conduction of an electron along the bridging group.

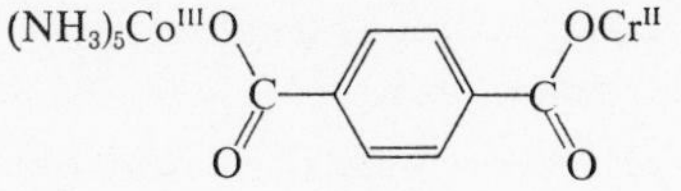

XXII

Oxygen atom transfer has been shown with the use of oxygen O^{18} labeling, to occur in the following oxidations: SO_3^{2-} with ClO^-; SO_3^{2-} with ClO_2^-; SO_3^{2-} with BrO_3^-; and NO_2^- with $HClO$.[23]

5.4 Slow Reactions and Catalysts

Most oxidation-reduction reactions involving pairs of metal ions or their complexes proceed rapidly at room temperature, especially if free-energy changes are favorable. Some exceptions, mainly studied by isotope exchange, are given in Table 5.3. The slowness of reactions involving Co(II) and Co(III) is due partly to the fact that conversion of Co(III) to Co(II) requires the placing of one or two d electrons in antibonding

e_g orbitals (depending on whether the Co(II) complex is low- or high-spin), and partly to the fact that in a pair of complexes such as $[Co(NH_3)_6]^{2+}$ and $[Co(NH_3)_6]^{3+}$ the cobalt-nitrogen bond distances are quite different.[24] Systems involving Tl(I) and Tl(III) probably owe their slow rate of reaction to the instability of Tl(II) intermediates.

In some cases, small negative ions such as F^- and Cl^- speed up oxidation-reduction reactions, including the catalysis of Eu(II)-Eu(III)

TABLE 5.3

Some Oxidation-Reduction Reactions
That Are Slow at 25°

$Fe(phen)_3^{2+}$ with $TlOH^{2+}$

Tl_{aq}^+ with Tl_{aq}^{3+}

Tl_{aq}^+ with $TlOH^{2+}$

Cr_{aq}^{2+} with Cr_{aq}^{3+}

Tl_{aq}^+ with Co_{aq}^{3+}

$Co(en)_3^{2+}$ with $Co(en)_3^{3+}$

$Co(EDTA)^{2-}$ with $Co(EDTA)^-$

$Co(NH_3)_6^{2+}$ with $Co(NH_3)_6^{3+}$

$Co(oxalate)_3^{4-}$ with $Co(oxalate)_3^{3-}$

$Co(oxalate)_3^{4-}$ with Ce^{4+}

$Fe(CN)_6^{4-}$ with H_2O_2

Co_{aq}^{2+} with $Co(NH_3)_6^{3+}$

$Co(NH_3)_6^{2+}$ with $Co(en)_3^{3+}$

Eu_{aq}^{2+} with Eu_{aq}^{3+}

Ce^{3+} with Ce^{4+}

Cr_{aq}^{2+} with $Co(NH_3)_6^{3+}$

Cr_{aq}^{2+} with CrF^{2+}

Cr_{aq}^{2+} with $CrNCS^{2+}$

Cr_{aq}^+ with $Cr(NH_3)_5X^{2+}$,   X = F, Cl

V_{aq}^{2+} with $Co(NH_3)_6^{3+}$

V_{aq}^{3+} with Fe_{aq}^{3+}

by Cl^-, of Ce(III)-Ce(IV) by F^-, and of Co(III) + Tl(I) by sulfate ion. Hydroxo complexes also exchange more rapidly than aquo complexes. In these examples the increased rates can probably be explained by the improved bridging possible between oxidant and reductant, although it is possible that, in some of the hydroxo complexes and aquo ions, the mechanism of electron transfer is through the transfer of a hydrogen atom between the hydration shells of the metal ions.[25] It is also suggested[26] that the electron exchange between Sb(III)-Sb(V), Sn(II)-Sn(IV) and Tl(I)-Tl(III) in the presence of excess chloride ions proceeds through a transition state in which the two metal ions are linked by two bridging chloride ions in a structure analogous to that of Al_2Cl_6.

Transition metal ions can sometimes greatly accelerate reactions between oxidizing and reducing agents by providing an easier reaction path. Two examples are the catalytic action of Mn(III) on the oxidation of oxalate ion by chlorine, and the decomposition of hydrogen peroxide by iron salts. Both of these reactions involve free-radical mechanisms, Other examples include the Cu(II)-catalyzed aerial oxidation of Fe(II), V(III), and U(IV), and the "mediation" by ceric salts of the reduction of arsenate to arsenite in alkaline solution.

In acid solutions, the catalysis of the reaction $2Ce^{4+} + As^{3+} \rightarrow 2Ce^{3+} + As^{5+}$ by traces of iodide ion (and, to a smaller extent, by chloride, bromide, and osmium) has been suggested as a method for determining iodide ion.[27] Catalysis of the same reaction by ruthenium and osmium has also been proposed[28] as a means of determining sub-microgram quantities of these elements. Ions such as Cu^{2+} and Ag^+ frequently catalyze reactions involving pairs of metal ion couples. Thus V(III) + Fe(III) → V(IV) + Fe(II) is catalyzed by Cu(II), and Tl(I) + 2Ce(IV) → Tl(III) + 2Ce(III) is catalyzed by Ag(I). In these reactions, catalysis probably proceeds through the transient formation of Cu(I) and Ag(II). Similarly, in the mixed Ag(I) Mn(II) catalyst for the slow reactions between ceric(IV) sulfate and mercurous ion, metal 8-hydroxy-quinolinates, hypophosphite, phosphite, and tellurite ions, Ag(II) and Mn(III) oxidation states are probably involved.[29] It is likely that Ag(II) is the active species in the silver-catalyzed reactions between Mn(III) and Ce(IV) and $2.5M$ hydrochloric acid, with the liberation of chlorine, and between manganous and persulfate ions in weakly acid solutions to give permanganate ion. The first of these reactions can be used as a test for silver.[30]

The ability of Hg(II) salts to catalyze the reduction of Sn(IV) to Sn(II) by acid hypophosphite solutions is probably due to the ability of Hg(II) to undergo reduction to Hg(I) and to Hg(metal), so that transfers involving either one or two electrons become possible. In general, mechanisms for catalytic oxidations or reductions involving anions or neutral molecules are still largely speculative. Examples include the catalysis by Cu(II) of reaction between ferric and thiosulfate ions to give ferrous and tetra-thionate ions, in which the rate-determining step is probably the oxidation of the anion, $Fe(S_2O_3)_2{}^-$, with Fe^{3+} (or Cu^{2+}). Addition of thiocyanate ion to mask Fe^{3+} reduces the rate. Reduction of methylene blue to methylene white, using hydrazine in acid solution, is catalyzed by Mo(VI). The reaction may involve reduction of Mo(VI) to Mo(V) by the hydrazine, the Mo(V) then reducing the methylene blue. Similarly, W(VI) (and less effectively Mo(VI)) catalyzes the reduction by Ti(III) of malachite green to its leuco compound.

Direct oxidation or reduction of an organic reagent by an inorganic species sometimes finds analytical application. The methods are non-specific, and the products are often unstable. Oxidation of leuco-crystal violet,[31] leuco-malachite green, o-anisidine,[32] and benzidine[33] by Ir(IV), and of o-toluidine,[34] leuco-malachite green,[35] and o-dianisidine[36] by Au(III), and of tetramethyldiaminodiphenylmethane in acetic acid solution by anodically deposited lead dioxide[37] are examples. Conversely, a qualitative test for tin consists in the reduction of cacotheline (a nitro derivative of brucine) by Sn(II) and other strong reducing agents to a soluble violet-colored form.[38]

The "robustness" of the tris(1,10-phenanthroline) complexes of Fe(II) and Fe(III) coupled with their rapid rates of oxidation and reduction explain their use as oxidation-reduction indicators. The intense red color of the ferrous complex is due to a charge-transfer process (see Chapter 8). This is probably also true of the tris(2,2'-bipyridine) complex.

The following semiempirical rules governing inorganic oxidation-reduction reactions have been suggested.[39]

1. Species derived from transition elements react with one another by a series of univalent changes.

2. Otherwise, species will react with one another in a series of bivalent changes, unless at least one of the reactants is a free radical, in which case a univalent change will occur.

3. Reactions involving a transition element and a nontransition element will usually involve univalent changes, but bivalent changes can also occur.

Where there is a net transfer of more than two electrons (e.g. Mn(II)–Mn(VII), or Cr(III)–Cr(VI)), multistep mechanisms are almost certainly operative.

References

1. For an up-to-date and comprehensive discussion of Mechanisms of Inorganic Reactions, see the book of this title by Basolo, F., and R. G. Pearson, John Wiley and Sons, New York, 1958.
2. Ingold, C. K., Structure and Mechanism in Organic Chemistry, Cornell University Press, Ithaca, New York, 1953.
3. Orgel, L. E., J. Chem. Soc., 1952, 4756.
4. Ref. 1, p. 108.
5. Ref. 1, p. 163.

6. Pearson, R. G., H. H. Schmidtke, and F. Basolo, *J. Am. Chem. Soc.*, **82**, 4434 (1960).
7. Chatt, J., L. A. Duncanson, and L. M. Venanzi, *J. Chem. Soc.* **1955**, 4456.
8. Hall, N. F., and B. R. Willeford, *J. Am. Chem. Soc.*, **73**, 5419 (1951).
9. Wilkins, R. G., *J. Chem. Soc.*, **1957**, 4521.
10. Bosnich, B., F. P. Dwyer, and A. M. Sargeson, *Nature*, **186**, 966 (1960).
11. Margerum, D. W., T. J. Bydalek, and J. J. Bishop, *J. Am. Chem. Soc.*, **83**, 1791, (1961).
12. Gilbert, T. W., Ph.D. thesis, University of Minnesota, 1956.
13. Libby, W. F., *J. Phys. Chem.*, **56**, 863 (1952).
14. Marcus, R. J., B. Zwolinski, and H. Eyring, *J. Phys. Chem.*, **58**, 432 (1954).
15. Taube, H., H. Myers, and R. L. Rich, *J. Am. Chem. Soc.*, **75**, 4118 (1953).
16. Murmann, R. K., H. Taube, and F. A. Posey, *J. Am. Chem. Soc.*, **79**, 262 (1957); Taube, H., *ibid.*, **77**, 4481 (1955); Taube, H., and H. Myers, *ibid.*, **76**, 2103 (1954).
17. Chia, Y. T., and E. L. King, *Discussions Faraday Soc.*, **29**, 109 (1960); Ogard, A. E., and H. Taube, *J. Am. Chem. Soc.*, **80**, 1084 (1958).
18. Basolo, F., M. L. Morris, and R. G. Pearson, *Discussions Faraday Soc.*, **29**, 80 (1960).
19. Haim, A., and W. K. Wilmarth, *J. Am. Chem. Soc.*, **83**, 509 (1961).
20. Gorin, M. H., *J. Am. Chem. Soc.*, **58**, 1687 (1936).
21. Duke, F. R., and R. C. Pinkerton, *J. Am. Chem. Soc.*, **73**, 3045 (1951).
22. Taube, H., *Advan. Inorg. Chem. Radiochem.*, **1**, 1 (1959).
23. Taube, H. *Record Chem. Progr.* (*Kresge-Hooker Sci. Lib.*), **17**, 25 (1956).
24. Biltz, W., *Z. Anorg. Allgem. Chem.*, **164**, 246 (1927).
25. Dodson, R. W., and N. Davidson, *J. Phys. Chem.*, **56**, 866 (1952).
26. Ref. 1, p. 327.
27. Sandell, E. B., and I. M. Kolthoff, *Mikrochim. Acta*, **1951**, 9; Lambert, J. L., P. Arthur, and T. E. Moore, *Anal. Chem.*, **23**, 1101 (1951).
28. Surasiti, C., and E. B. Sandell, *Anal. Chim. Acta*, **22**, 261 (1960); Sauerbrunn, R. D., and E. B. Sandell, *Mikrochim. Acta*, **1953**, 22.
29. McCurdy, W. H., and G. G. Guilbault, *Anal. Chem.*, **32**, 647 (1960).
30. Feigl, F., and E. Fränkel, *Ber.*, **65**, 544 (1932).
31. Ayres, G. H., and W. T. Bolleter, *Anal. Chem.*, **29**, 72 (1957).
32. Berman, S. S., F. E. Beamish, and W. A. E. McBryde, *Anal. Chim. Acta*, **15**, 363 (1956).
33. Khlopin, V. G., *Ann. Inst. Platine*, **1**, 324 (1926).
34. Schreiner, H., H. Branter and F. Hecht, *Mikrochem. Mikrochim. Acta*, **36/37**, 1056 (1951).
35. Kul'berg, L. M., *Zavodsk. Lab.*, **5**, 170 (1936).
36. Jamieson, A. R., and R. W. Watson, *Analyst*, **63**, 702 (1938).
37. Miller, H., *Z. Anal. Chem.*, **113**, 161 (1938).
38. Rosenthaler, L., *Mikrochim. Acta*, **3**, 190 (1938).
39. Higginson, W. C. E., and J. W. Marshall, *J. Chem. Soc.*, **1957**, 447.

CHAPTER 6

Effects of Complex-Forming Species
on Cation Concentrations

Complex formation as a means of reducing the concentrations of free metal ions in solution finds many familiar applications in analytical chemistry, particularly in "masking" and "demasking" reactions, in the precipitation of metal hydroxides, sulfides, and metal-organic complexes, and in the quantitative treatment of solvent extraction. The properties of metal complexes are important, also, in ion exchange and chromatography, as well as in ultimate determinations by physical methods such as spectrophotometry, potentiometry, polarography, chronopotentiometry, and conductometry. Electrodeposition, as a means of separating or isolating different metals, depends on complex formation to secure the low metal ion concentrations necessary for smooth and adherent deposits and also to ensure that only certain metals will be plated out from the solutions: Fig. 6.1 shows how the relative composition of a common electroplating mixture varies with the ligand concentration. Recently complexometric titrations, especially with ethylenediaminetetraacetic acid (EDTA) and its derivatives, have enabled direct volumetric titrations to be carried out on metal ions in solution.

Chapter 3 discussed qualitatively the factors governing the stabilities of metal complexes and also stability sequences for metal ions with given ligands. These factors can be summarized briefly as follows.

Where a ligand is an oxygen donor or a fluoride ion complex formation is essentially an electrostatic process; the important factors governing bond strength in a complex are the charge on the metal ion and the reciprocal of its radius. Among related ligands, bond strength also increases regularly with the basic strength of the ligand, as measured by proton addition. Such ligands are general complexing agents, with rather poor discrimination between metal ions of similar charge.

By contrast, cyanide ion, sulfur donors, the halides other than fluoride, and to some extent nitrogen donors coordinate much more strongly to the cations having 18 outer electrons than they do to cations having an inert-gas electronic structure. Charge and cation radius are not dominant factors in this group. Covalent-bond character becomes important, especially for cations of low charge, such as Cu^+, Ag^+, and Au^+, and (contrary to electrostatic predictions) stabilities of halide complexes fall in the sequence $I^- > Br^- > Cl^- \gg F^-$. Bond strengths increase as the ionization potential of the metal increases (i.e. with increasing electronegativity of the metal ion) and as the electronegativity of the ligand atom decreases. Qualitatively, this can be pictured in terms of increased ease of acceptance of electrons by the metal ion and of electron donation by the ligand atom, both effects leading to increased covalent-bond strength. The greater the charge on the cation, however, the smaller becomes the covalent (and the greater becomes the electrostatic) contribution to bond character.

The transition metal ions are intermediate in properties between these two groups, with the important difference that ligand-field stabilization effects can now operate, often modifying decisively the nature and extent of complex formation. It is not surprising that the Irving-Williams stability series for complexes of divalent transition metal ions follows the sequence that would be predicted from variations in ionic radii and ionization potentials.

6.1 Some Quantitative Aspects

Equilibria in solution between metal ions and complex-forming species are similar to those for protonation reactions. This is to be expected from the Lewis definitions of metal ions and protons as acids, and of all ligands (because they are proton acceptors) as bases. In the same way, just as acetate-acetic acid and ammonia-ammonium ion are hydrogen ion buffers, systems containing metal ions and ligands act as metal ion buffers. Comparison of typical equations brings out this similarity.

$$M^{2+} + L^{2-} \rightleftharpoons ML \qquad H^+ + L^{2-} \rightleftharpoons HL^-$$
$$M^{2+} + L^- \rightleftharpoons ML^+, \qquad H^+ + L^- \rightleftharpoons HL$$
$$M^{2+} + L \rightleftharpoons ML^{2+}, \qquad H^+ + L \rightleftharpoons HL^+$$

In all cases, omitting charges:

$$\frac{1}{K_{ML}} = \frac{[M][L]}{[ML]}, \qquad K_a = \frac{[H^+][L]}{[HL]}$$

where K_{ML} is the stability constant of ML, so that, just as one can write

$$pH = pK_a + \log \frac{[L]}{[HL]}$$

the negative logarithm of the free metal ion concentration is given by $pM = -pK_{ML} + \log [L]/[ML]$, where $[L]$ is the free-ligand concentration. The equations become more complicated, but no new principle is involved, in cases where a series of metal complexes, such as ML, ML_2, ML_3, ML_4, is formed.

From the definition of the stepwise formation constant K_n of the complex ML_n from ML_{n-1} and L, it can readily be deduced that

$$pM = p(M)_{total} + \log (1 + K_1[L] + K_1K_2[L]^2 + K_1K_2K_3[L]^3 + \cdots)$$

This equation indicates that the more ligand molecules there are attached to the metal the greater will be the difference produced in pM by a small change in ligand concentration. For this reason, use of polydentate complexes such as triethylenetetramine (which forms only a 1:1 complex with Cu^{2+}) permits better control of analytical conditions than, say, ammonia (which in quite dilute solutions can form a series of complexes up to $Cu(NH_3)_4{}^{2+}$). The composition of a system comprising a metal ion in equilibrium with a series of complexes, ML, ML_2, ML_3, ..., and free ligand, can be represented conveniently by a plot of percentage composition against pL $(= -\log [L])$.[1] Such a plot is shown in Fig. 6.1 for the system $Cd^{2+} - CN^-$ at 25° in $3M$ sodium perchlorate.[2] At any value of pL the vertical intercepts give the concentrations of the species represented by the areas in which the intercepts lie. In constructing such figures it is helpful to remember that, when only mononuclear complexes are formed, the ratios of concentrations of different complex species are independent of the metal ion concentrations. Of the total metal species in a solution, the fraction x_i that is present as any complex ML_i is given by

$$x_i = \frac{[ML_i]}{[M]_{total}} = \frac{\beta_i[A]^i}{1 + \sum\limits_{i=1}^{i=n} (\beta_n[A]^n)}$$

where β_i is the overall stability constant of the complex. The quantity x_i depends only on the ligand concentration. Bjerrum's *formation function* $\bar{n}$ at any value of pL, is readily obtained. It is simply

$$\bar{n} = \sum_{i=1}^{i=n} (i \cdot x_i)$$

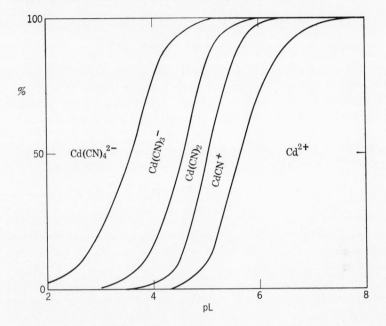

Fig. 6.1.   Complex formation in the $Cd^{2+}-CN^-$ system in $3M$ sodium perchlorate at $25°$.

It is important to remember that all these equations relate to the ligand, that is, to the form which adds directly to the metal ion.   Under any given experimental conditions the ligand may already be protonated to a greater or less degree, so that metal complex formation involves competition between metal ions and protons for the ligands.   Some examples will make this point clearer.   Acetic acid has $pK_a = 4.76$, so that above pH 6.7 the concentration of the ligand, acetate ion, approximates to the total concentration of acetic acid (i.e. free acetic acid + acetate ion). At pH 3.81, on the other hand, the ligand concentration is only one-tenth of the total.   Similarly, in a solution of ammonia ($pK_a = 9.26$) at pH 5.26 only 0.01% of the total $[NH_3] + [NH_4^+]$ is ligand, whereas at pH 9.26 it is 50%.   With tiron (pyrocatechol-3,5-disulfonic acid) the phenolic groups responsible for its complex-forming ability have pK_a values of 7.66 and 12.6, so that at pH 5 the diphenolate ligand makes up only $\frac{1}{2} \times 10^{-10}$ of the total concentration of the tiron present.   For a ligand that can add either one or two protons, the general expressions become, respectively.

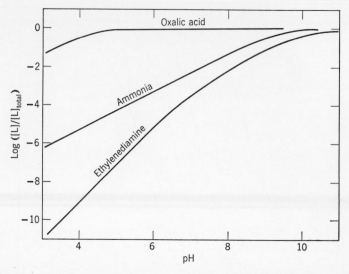

Fig. 6.2.   The effect of pH on the concentration ratio of free ligand to total ligand species, for oxalic acid, ammonia, and ethylenediamine.

$$\frac{[L]}{[L] + [HL]} = \frac{1}{1 + 10^{(pK_1 - pH)}}$$

$$\frac{[L]}{[L] + [HL] + [H_2L]} = \frac{10^{(2pH - pK_1 - pK_2)}}{1 + 10^{(pH - pK_2)} + 10^{(2pH - pK_1 - pK_2)}}$$

where $pK_1 > pK_2$, and the charges on the ligand and protonated species are omitted.   The kind of pH dependence to which these relations lead is shown in Fig. 6.2 for oxalic acid, ammonia, and ethylenediamine. Now, in a system containing oxalic acid, ethylenediamine, and metal ion let concentrations be chosen so that at, say, pH 7 the 1:2 metal ion-oxalic acid and -ethylenediamine complexes are present in equal concentrations. Increasing the pH to 9.0 will lead to a 50,000-fold increase in the bis(ethylenediamine) complex relative to the bis(oxalate) complex.   Conversely, decreasing the pH to 5.0 will favor the bis(oxalate) complex by a factor of 30 million.   When it is recalled that the differences in stability constants for a series of metals with one ligand are not usually the same as those for a different type of ligand, analytical possibilities become apparent. Table 6.1 provides a good example.   The figures for the oxalate complexes reflect the relatively nonselective character of oxygen-type ligands.

The very high stability constant of $Cu(en)_2^{2+}$ is due mainly to LFSE, to the polarizability of amines, and to the covalent character of their bonding.   In such a case it may well be possible to estimate Cu(II) in the presence of Mn(II) at pH 5.0, and yet, at pH 9, Mn(II) might be estimated in the presence of Cu(II).   Even greater differences between

TABLE 6.1

Stability Constants of Some Bis Complexes

	Oxalic Acid	Ethylenediamine
Mn^{2+}	$10^{5.3}$	$10^{4.8}$
Cu^{2+}	$10^{8.4}$	$10^{20.1}$

inert-gas-type cations and cations with filled, or nearly filled, d shells are found with ligands such as thiourea, 2,3-dimercaptopropanol, and dithiotartrate ion where bonding is through sulfur atoms.

6.2   "Apparent" Constants

Where the pH of a solution is maintained constant, it is sometimes convenient to replace stability constants by "apparent" (or "effective," or "conditional") constants.   Such constants, which apply only under the specified experimental conditions, replace the free metal ion concentration by the total concentration of the metal in solution that is not actually complexed with the particular ligand of interest.   Similarly, the ligand concentration is replaced by the total concentration of all ligand species (including protonated forms) that are not complexed with the metal. These "apparent constants" provide quantitative information about the concentrations of the complex that is formed, of the unreacted metal, and of the unreacted ligand.   Schwarzenbach[3] introduced coefficients α_M and α_L to relate such "apparent constants" to true stability constants, β, so that

$$(K_{M_m L_n})_{apparent} = \frac{\beta_{M_m L_n}}{\alpha_M{}^m \alpha_L{}^n}$$

Where the ligand forms complexes with only protons or the particular metal ion, α_L is given by:

$$\alpha_L = 1 + \frac{[H^+]}{K_{a_1}} + \frac{[H^+]^2}{K_{a_1} K_{a_2}} + \cdots$$

If metals other than M are present in the system, additional terms of the form $y \cdot \beta_{xy}[M']^x[L]^{y-1}$ have to be added to α_L, which, if y is greater than 1, can then only be obtained by successive approximations.   Similarly, if the metal ion under study reacts only with the ligand L, $\alpha_M = 1$. Otherwise, if interfering ligands are present, or if hydrolysis occurs (which corresponds formally to complex formation with hydroxyl ion), extra terms must be added.

To analyze a system in detail (knowing the values of β for all the complexes, the pK_a values of the ligands, and the pH of the solution), it is usually simplest to begin by assuming the concentration of the species present in excess to be unchanged by complex formation. If, say, this is $L + HL + H_2L + \cdots$, the concentrations of ML, ML_2, etc., that are obtained can be used to refine the estimate of uncomplexed ligand species and also α_L. Several cycles of such calculations usually lead rapidly to the correct constant values. These calculations are often much simplified in systems involving multidentate ligands because, usually, only 1:1 metal-ligand complexes are formed.

Where a solution containing two metal ions M_I and M_{II} is titrated with a multidentate ligand L and the complex M_IL is much more stable than $M_{II}L$, the following approximation applies:[4]

$$\log (K_{M_IL})_{\text{apparent}} \approx \log K_{M_IL} - \log K_{M_{II}L} + pM_{II}$$

That is, the logarithm of the apparent stability constant of M_IL is equal to the difference between the logarithms of the stability constants of the two complexes, plus pM_{II}. A consequence of this relation is that the more dilute the solution the less, relatively, will M_{II} interfere, so that the selectivity of the titration is improved. For visual titrations, $\log K_{M_IL}$ should exceed $\log K_{M_{II}L}$ by about 4 to 5 units. Ringbom[4] has examined in some detail the mathematics of simultaneous titrations of two metal ions.

6.3 Some Examples Based on Differences in Stability Constants or Solubilities

Differences in complex-forming ability or in the solubility of the complexes find many applications. Most complexometric titrations depend on the former, and an example of the latter is Volhard's method in which titration of Ag^+ in nitric acid with potassium thiocyanate yields insoluble silver thiocyanate. If ferric ion is present in solution, the complex $FeSCN^{2+}$ will be detectable only when precipitation of AgSCN is effectively complete. Relevant quantitative details are:

$$[Ag^+][SCN^-] \sim 7 \times 10^{-13} \text{ (solubility product)}$$
$$\frac{[FeSCN^{2+}]}{[Fe^{3+}][SCN^-]} \sim 100$$
$$\log \epsilon_{\text{max}} \text{ for } FeSCN^{2+} \sim 4$$

A detectable red color (D $\geqslant$ 0.1) should be produced in an $0.01M$ solution of ferric ion when [SCN$^-$] reaches $10^{-5}M$, but this will only be possible when the free Ag$^+$ concentration has fallen below $7 \times 10^{-8}M$. The sparing solubility of AgBr and AgI enables the method to be applied to the determination of bromides and iodides in acid solution by the addition of excess silver nitrate, followed by back-titration with thiocyanate ion. (Except that the ferric ion indicator must not be added until after pre-cipitation of the silver iodide because of its ability to oxidize iodide ion to iodine.)   For chloride estimations, the silver chloride precipitate must be removed from the system before the titration: This is because AgCl is about 200 times more soluble than AgSCN, so that an appreciable con-version, AgCl + SCN$^-$ $\to$ AgSCN(solid) + Cl$^-$, takes place if AgCl is present, leading to considerable error.

Mercuric nitrate titrations of chloride ion in the presence of diphenyl-carbazone depend on the fact that HgCl$_2$ is a stable complex (log $\beta_2 \simeq$ 14) so that the appreciable concentration of Hg^{2+} needed to form the blue-violet diphenylcarbazone complex (XXIII) is not reached until almost all the chloride ion has combined with Hg^{2+}.

$$
\begin{array}{ccccc}
 & \overset{\displaystyle C_6H_5}{\diagup} & \overset{\displaystyle C_6H_5}{\diagdown} & & \\
\text{HN--N} & & & \text{N=N} & \\
\diagup & & & & \diagdown \\
\text{O=C} & & \text{Hg} & & \text{C=O} \\
\diagdown & & & & \diagup \\
\text{N=N} & & & \text{N--NH} & \\
 & \underset{\displaystyle C_6H_5}{\diagdown} & \underset{\displaystyle C_6H_5}{\diagup} & &
\end{array}
$$

XXIII

In the same way, sulfate ion has been titrated with barium ion, using tetrahydroxy-*p*-benzoquinone (disodium salt) as indicator.   The red color of the barium complex of this reagent is not produced until sulfate precipi-tation as insoluble barium sulfate is complete.   This particular method is not very accurate, and the back-titration (of barium solutions with a standard sulfate solution) using the sodium salt of rhodizonic acid as indicator is preferable.   The endpoint is given by the change from red to colorless or yellow.   It indicates the removal of barium from the soluble organic complex (XXIV) and its complete precipitation as the sulfate. The stability constant of this complex is not high, so that rather strong solutions of reagents must be used.

The thiocyanate method for determining ferric ion provides a good example of the effects of competitive complex formation by cations and anions.   Because $\log K_1$ for the $FeSCN^{2+}$ complex is not very high, for quantitative work a high concentration of thiocyanate ion is required and ligands which would compete for Fe^{3+} should be absent.   These include arsenates, fluorides, oxalates, phosphates, tartrates, and sulfuric acid.

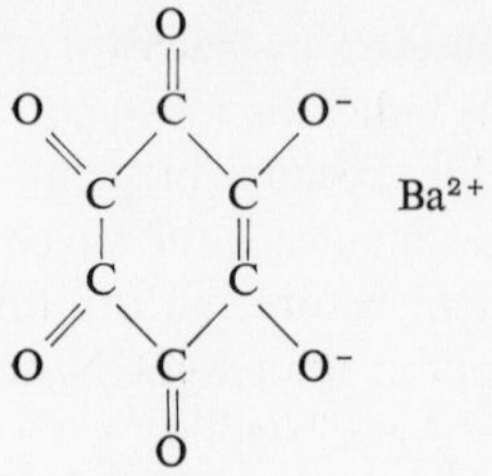

XXIV

Similarly, because this method is a spectrophotometric one, cations interfering by forming either an insoluble or a colored thiocyanate complex must also be absent.   These include Ag, Cu, Ni, Co, Ti, Mo, U, Zn, Hg, and Bi.   In this particular method, the effects of these interfering species can be diminished by extracting the colored ferric complex into suitable hydroxylic solvents.

The foregoing discussion is an oversimplification in so far as it takes no account of mixed ligand complexes, so that the conclusions only apply strictly to those systems where, effectively, only one complexing species is present.   It is known, for example, that in mixtures of bismuth, chloride, and bromide ions all species in the series $BiCl_5^{2-}$, $BiBrCl_4^{2-}$, ..., $BiBr_5^{2-}$ are present in solution.[5]   So, too, zirconium (IV), once it has chelated with 1 mole of EDTA, readily adds 1 mole of tiron, chromotropic acid, 8-hydroxyquinoline,   or   acetylacetone to complete   its   coordination requirements.

6.4   Effects of Hydrolysis

Almost all cations tend to lose one or more protons from their bound water molecules, e.g.

$$Fe(H_2O)_6^{3+} + H_2O \rightleftharpoons Fe(H_2O)_5OH^{2+} + H_3O^+$$

This is particularly true of higher-valent cations and metal complexes with high positive charges.

Hydrogen ions are lost from water molecules bound in this way more readily than they are from free solvent molecules.   This is because the charge on the metal ion, by drawing the lone-pair electrons of a solvated water molecule towards it, weakens the electron density of the O—H bonds and facilitates bond breaking.   In general, the tendency to hydrolyze in this way increases with the charge on the cation.

Hydrolysis of this type, leading in most cases to polynuclear complex formation and finally to precipitation, plays an important part in the quantitative interpretation of metal complex equilibria. Because these metal aquo ions can lose protons in this way, they must be considered to be acids, and some representative dissociation constants determined by potentiometric titration are given in Table 6.2. However, in many

TABLE 6.2

Some pK_a Values of Metal Ions at $20-25°$[a]

	pK_a		pK_a
Mn^{2+}	10.7	In^{3+}	4.4[c]
Fe^{2+}	9.5[b]	Tl^{3+}	1.1[c]
Co^{2+}	10.0	Bi^{3+}	1.6[c]
Ni^{2+}	10.0	U^{4+}	2.0[c]
Zn^{2+}	9.1	Hg_2^{2+}	5.0[d]
Cd^{2+}	9.0[c]	Sc^{3+}	5.1[b]
Hg^{2+}	3.7[d]	Sn^{2+}	3.9[c]
Fe^{3+}	3.1	Pb^{2+}	7.8

[a] These values are obtained by potentiometric titrations. The older technique of measuring the pH of a solution of a "pure salt" is quite unreliable (see example discussed by Sillén, L. G., in *Quart. Rev. (London)*, **13**, 146 (1959)).
[b] In $1M$ $NaClO_4$.
[c] In $3M$ $NaClO_4$.
[d] In $0.5M$ $NaClO_4$.

cases complexes of the form $M_m(OH)_n$ (omitting charges and water molecules) are present, having equilibrium constants

$$*\beta_{mn} = \frac{[M_m(OH)_n][H^+]^n}{[M]^m}$$

Sillén[6] has suggested that these complexes are built up on a "core" by adding "links." For example a Cu^{2+} "core" adds $Cu(OH)_2$ "links" to give the series of complexes

$$Cu^{2+}, Cu_2(OH)_2^{2+}, Cu_3(OH)_4^{2+}, Cu_4(OH)_6^{2+}, \ldots, Cu_n(OH)_{2n-2}^{2+}$$

in which the hydroxyl ions act as bridges between the metal ions. The process leading to the formation of such polynuclear complexes is known as "olation."[7] Where metal ions can give rise to both mono- and polynuclear complexes, the contributions made by the latter increase with metal ion concentration. Conversely, in sufficiently dilute solutions of the metal ion (which may also be brought about by addition of other complex-forming species) or in sufficiently acid solutions, only mononuclear hydroxocomplexes need be considered. Equilibria in such systems have been discussed by Ringbom.[4] Under limiting conditions, the ratio of hydrolyzed species to total metal concentration is independent of the metal ion concentration.

TABLE 6.3

Approximate Maximum Possible
Concentrations of Free Metal Ions
at Different pH Values, at 25°

Metal Ion	Log Max. Concn.
Th^{4+}	$11.1 - 4\,pH$
Fe^{3+}	$4.0 - 3\,pH$
Cr^{3+}	$11.8 - 3\,pH$
Mn^{2+}	$15.2 - 2\,pH$
Fe^{2+}	$12.8 - 2\,pH$
Co^{2+}	$\sim 13 \quad - 2\,pH$
Zn^{2+}	$11.2 - 2\,pH$
Cd^{2+}	$13.8 - 2\,pH$
Hg^{2+}	$2.6 - 2\,pH$
Ag^{+}	$6.4 - 1\,pH$

The sparing solubilities of the uncharged metal hydroxides, which are the endproducts of these hydrolysis reactions, severely limit the attainable free metal ion concentrations in a solution as its pH is increased. The solubility product of a metal hydroxide, $M(OH)_n$, is given by

$$K_s = [M^{n+}][OH^-]^n$$
$$= \frac{[M^{n+}] \cdot K_w^{\,n}}{[H^+]^n}$$

Taking logarithms, we obtain the maximum possible concentration of free metal ion, under equilibrium conditions, as:

$$\log [M^{n+}]_{max} = n \cdot pK_w - pK_s - n \cdot pH$$

Some examples are given in Table 6.3. In some cases (the amphoteric hydroxides, such as $Zn(OH)_2$ and $Al(OH)_3$) anion formation occurs in the presence of high concentrations of hydroxide solution and the precipitates redissolve.

A metal ion that has been fully or partially coordinated with a ligand undergoes hydrolysis less readily than the corresponding hydrated metal ion because electron donation from the ligand to the metal ion decreases its electrostatic interaction with the remaining water molecules coordinated to it.

Nevertheless, where ionization of protons from metal complexes can occur, important effects are often produced.   In such cases, the metal complex can be considered as an entity in which one or more protons may be lost from water coordinated to the central metal ion or from some group or groups in the ligand.   For example, the bis(dimethylglyoxime) complex of Pd(II) dissolves in alkali because of ionization of protons from the two $=N—OH$ groups in the complex.

In some cases, protonation of metal complexes can occur.   This is possible, for example, in some metal-EDTA complexes because, over a suitable pH region, hydrogen ions are able to compete successfully with the metal ion for the last carboxylate ion in the ligand.   A similar situation is found in complex formation between Mg^{2+} and adenosinetriphosphate (ATP).

6.5   Complexometric Titrations

The stepwise nature of complex formation between metal ions and monodentate ligands and the fact that the successive formation constants K_1, K_2, ... of the complexes are usually not greatly different from one another militate against the general use of such ligands as the basis of volumetric procedures.   Some of the few cases where good endpoints can be obtained include Hg^{2+} with Cl^- and CN^-, and Ag^+ with Br^-, Cl^-, and CN^-.   Better titration curves are to be expected in cases where each molecule of ligand displaces two or more of the molecules of water co-ordinated around the metal ion, so that fewer complexes are formed.   Also, the complexes gain in stability because of the operation of the "chelate effect."

These advantages are greatest when the ligand is polydentate, so that only a 1:1 complex is formed with metal ions.   The most familiar of the complex-forming species of this type is ethylenediaminetetraacetic acid (EDTA) (XXV), the tetra-anion of which can act as a quinque- or sexidentate ligand by coordination to a metal ion through its two nitrogen

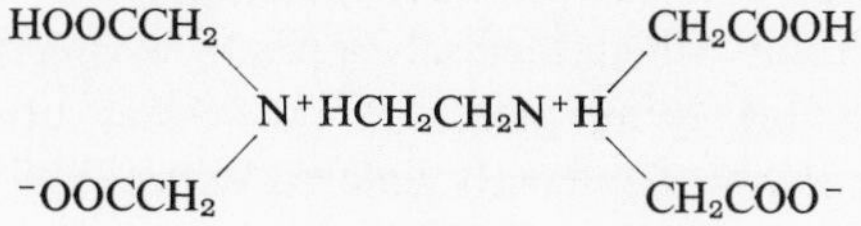

$$HOOCCH_2 \diagdown \qquad\qquad CH_2COOH \diagup$$
$$N^+HCH_2CH_2N^+H$$
$$^-OOCCH_2 \diagup \qquad\qquad CH_2COO^- \diagdown$$

XXV

atoms and three or four of the carboxylic acid groups, to form an octahedral complex which is greatly stabilized by the number of five-membered chelate rings it contains. This structure is also favored because it corresponds to the preferred stereochemistry of most of the common metal ions.

The introduction of EDTA as an analytical reagent for complexometric titrations[3] has marked a major advance in quantitative inorganic analysis. It is possible, by using EDTA, to carry out rapid and usually reliable titrations of a large number of different metal ions, selectivity being achieved by suitable pH control or by using appropriate masking agents.

TABLE 6.4

Stability Constants of Some 1:1 Metal-EDTA Complexes
(At $20°$, in $0.1M$ KNO_3)

Metal Ion	Log K_1	Metal Ion	Log K_1
Li^+	2.8	Mn^{2+}	13.6
Na^+	1.7	Fe^{2+}	14.3
Ag^+	7.3	Co^{2+}	16.2
Mg^{2+}	8.7	Ni^{2+}	18.6
Ca^{2+}	10.7	Cu^{2+}	18.8
Sr^{2+}	8.6	Pd^{2+}	18.5
Ba^{2+}	7.8	Al^{3+}	16.1
Zn^{2+}	16.4	Sc^{3+}	23.1
Cd^{2+}	16.5	Rare earths^{3+}	~16–18
Hg^{2+}	22	Fe^{3+}	25.1
Pb^{2+}	17.7	Ga^{3+}	20.3
VO^{2+}	18.4	In^{3+}	25.0
		V^{3+}	25.9
V^{2+}	12.7	Th^{4+}	23.2
Cr^{2+}	13.0	Co^{3+}	36
		Cr^{3+}	24.0

These titrations fall into three analytically convenient groups—direct, back, and replacement—and endpoints are usually detected by employing suitable colored indicators. Increased sensitivity can be obtained by using physical techniques such as amperometric titration at the dropping mercury electrode[8] and square wave polarography.[9] Sometimes it is possible to use titrants which themselves produce a photometric endpoint without an indicator being present.[10] In visual titrations difficulties such as the formation of intensely colored complexes with the titrating agent (e.g. Fe, Cu, Cr with EDTA), slowness of complex formation (e.g., Al with EDTA), and the reduction in sensitivity because of high salt concentrations can sometimes be encountered. Moreover, unless suitable masking agents are added, interfering metal ions (notably of Fe(III), Cr(III) Cu(II), Co(II), and Ni(II)) may form complexes with the added indicator that are so stable that the indicator is "blocked" and the endpoint of the titration cannot be detected. These few difficulties summarize the main limitations to the use of complexometric titrations.

The stability constants of metal-EDTA complexes in Table 6.4 show the trends expected if the bonding in the complexes is mainly electrostatic: Complexes are least stable for monovalent cations, and stability usually increases with the increasing cationic charge and decreasing ionic radius, so that $\log K_1$ lies in the sequence $Ca^{2+} > Sr^{2+} > Ba^{2+} \gg Li^+ > Na^+$. The relatively small increase in $\log K_1$ from 13.6 for Mn^{2+} to 18.8 for Cu^{2+} is due to the weak ligand field of the carboxyl groups of EDTA. As may be seen from the table, all metal ions except those of the alkali metals form complexes with EDTA having sufficiently high stability constants to allow their estimation by complexometric titration. It can readily be calculated that there is a very big drop in free metal

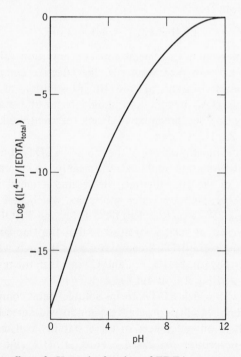

Fig. 6.3. The effect of pH on the fraction of EDTA present as its tetra-anion.

ion concentration near the endpoint for the formation of a 1:1 complex: A fall by a factor of a millionfold is not unusual. However, because the pH of the solutions has a marked effect on the fraction of EDTA present as its tetra-anion (Fig. 6.3), it is necessary to control this factor in analytical determinations. For Mg^{2+}, $K_1 = [MgEDTA^{2-}]/[Mg^{2+}][EDTA^{4-}] = 10^{8.7}$, so that at pH 12 (effectively complete ionization of EDTA), less than 0.01% of the total magnesium is present as Mg^{2+} when the free EDTA concentration reaches $3 \times 10^{-5}M$. At pH 6, on the other hand, 10% is still uncomplexed when the EDTA concentration is $0.001M$. By contrast, even at pH 3 ferric complex formation is complete within one part in one thousand million when the free EDTA concentration is $2 \times 10^{-6}M$. According to Ringbom[11] the optimum pH for complex formation using EDTA is the one at which the metal complex has an apparent stability constant of 10^8. This is readily obtained by taking the values of $\log K_1$ given in Table 6.4 and finding, in Fig. 6.3, the pH for which the ordinate is $8 - \log K_1$.

Hydrolytic equilibria must also be considered in metal-EDTA systems. For example, although $\log K_1 = 25.1$ for the Fe^{3+}-EDTA complex, ferric hydroxide is precipitated if the solution is made too alkaline. This can readily be seen from

$$\log [Fe^{3+}]_{max} = 4.0 - 3\,pH$$

in which the maximum free metal ion concentration falls off rapidly with pH, whereas, with increasing pH, the effective complexing ability of EDTA becomes constant. For a $10^{-3}M$ solution of Fe^{3+}-EDTA, $10^{-3}M$ in free EDTA, precipitation should begin above about pH 9.5. Other metal hydroxides precipitated from sufficiently alkaline solution include Bi, Th, Zr, Hf, U, and Ti.

The last one, or sometimes two, of the groups in EDTA that are involved in metal complex formation bind relatively weakly. This makes it possible for one or two of the coordination sites round a metal ion in such a complex to be occupied by water molecules which can lose protons, giving rise to complexes such as Fe(OH)-EDTA and Fe(OH)$_2$-EDTA.

The overall result of such hydrolysis is that the "apparent" stability constants of many metal-EDTA complexes pass through well-defined pH maxima.[12] For Ni, Cu, Fe(II), Zn, and Cd this is in the region pH 9–10; for Al, Fe(III), and Hg it is about pH 4–5.

The rapidity with which EDTA forms soluble metal complexes and the high values of their stability constants explain its widespread use in chemical analysis. It is on differences in these stability constants that most of the titration procedures are based. Thus, at pH 4, zinc or copper can be titrated in the presence of the alkaline earth metals, but at pH 10 the alkaline earths can themselves be titrated. Endpoints in such titrations are usually detected by adding, as an indicator, a small quantity of a less strongly complexing ligand that gives a distinctly colored metal complex. The endpoint is given by the disappearance of this color, the metal indicator becoming completely dissociated in the presence of free EDTA. (If the stability constant of the metal indicator complex is too high— that is, if it is comparable with or greater than that of the EDTA–metal complex under the same conditions—no satisfactory endpoint can be obtained and the indicator is said to be "blocked.") Conversely, excess EDTA may be added to convert a metal complex to its EDTA complex, the unused EDTA being determined by titration with a standard solution of any suitable metal ion. In this case the endpoint is detected by formation of a colored complex with a less strongly complexing ligand once all the EDTA is in the form of metal complexes.

6.6 Indicators for Complexometric Titrations

The principles of complexometric titration and acid-base titrimetry are very similar. This similarity is further emphasized by the use of pM ($= -\log [M]$), analogous to pH. A pM indicator is normally a very weak complexing agent which exhibits a color change on complex formation (and hence is comparable with the weak acids or bases, used as pH indicators, which change color on proton addition or removal).

Most of the usual colorimetric reagents for metal ions are unsuitable for use in complexometric titrations because their metal complexes are too stable. Some exceptions are salicyclic acid,[13] 5-sulfosalicylic acid,[14] tiron (pyrocatechol-3,5-disulfonic acid),[15] and thiocyanate ion,[16] all of which have been used as indicators in the EDTA titration of ferric iron in acid solution. In all cases the indicator is colorless while the iron complex is colored, so that a high indicator concentration can be used to sharpen the endpoint. Similarly, the yellow complex formed between bismuth and thiourea has served to detect the endpoint in the titration of bismuth with EDTA,[17] and dithizone in acetone-water and alcohol-water mixtures has been used in EDTA titrations of zinc and aluminium.[18] Special chelating agents for use as metal indicators have been developed; some of the more common examples are given in Table 6.5.

In an endeavor to achieve the color intensity necessary for indicator sensitivity, use has often been made of derivatives of organic dyes, such as the azo dyes, as well as phenols, and the phthaleins and sulfonephthaleins. Of these the best known are probably the eriochrome series which are o,o'-dihydroxydinaphthylazo dyes. Initially the search for substances to use as metal indicators was quite empirical. Murexide, the first substance

TABLE 6.5

Some Common Metal Indicators for Complexometric (EDTA) Titrations

Indicator	Experimental Conditions	Metal Ions Titrated	Endpoint
Murexide[a] (pK_a 9.20, 10.50) (XXVI)	pH ~ 12 Alkaline solution	Ca Cu^{2+}, Co^{2+}, Ni^{2+}, Ce^{3+}	Pink to violet-blue Yellow to violet-blue
	Neutral solution	Zn, Cd	Yellow to red-violet
Eriochrome black T[b] (pK_a 6.3, 11.5) (XXVII)	pH range 7–11 Ammonia or tartrate buffers	Mg, Cd, Zn, Mn^{2+}, Pb^{2+} In, La, Hg^{2+}, Ca	Red to blue
	Back-titration with Mg^{2+}	Ba, Sr	
	pH 6.8	Cd in presence of Mg	Purple to grey-blue
Catechol violet[c] (pK_a 1, 7, > 10, > 10) (XXVIII)	Ammoniacal solution, pH 10	Ni, Co, Mn, Zn, Cd, Ca, Mg	Green-blue to red-violet
	Acid solution, pH 2–3	Bi, Th	Blue to yellow, red to yellow
	Acetate buffer, pH 5.5–6.5	Cu^{2+} in presence of Ag, Mg, Ca, Sr, Ba	Blue to yellow
PAN[4 d] (XXIX)	Acetate buffer, pH 5–7	Zn	Pink to yellow
	Acetate buffer, pH ⩾ 6	Cd	Pink to yellow
	Acetic acid	Cu	Red to yellowish-green
	pH 2.3–2.5	In	
Metalphthalein[e] (pK_a 7, 7.8, 11.4, 12.0) (XXX)	20–50% Ethanol, pH 10–11	Ca, Sr, Ba	Red to colorless

(*Continued*)

[a] Schwarzenbach, G., and H. Gysling, *Helv. Chim. Acta*, **32**, 1314 (1949).

[b] Schwarzenbach, G., and W. Biedermann, *Helv. Chim. Acta*, **31**, 678 (1948).

[c] Suk, V., and M. Malat, *Chemist-Analyst*, **45**, 30 (1956).

[d] Cheng, K. L., and R. H. Bray, *Anal. Chem.*, **27**, 782 (1955).

[e] Anderegg, G., H. Flaschka, R. Sallmann, and G. Schwarzenbach, *Helv. Chim. Acta*, **37**, 113 (1954).

TABLE 6.5 (Continued)

Some Common Metal Indicators for Complexometric (EDTA) Titrations

Indicator	Experimental Conditions	Metal Ions Titrated	Endpoint
Xylenol orange[f]	pH 2.5–3.5	Th	Red to lemon-yellow
	pH 3–5	Sc	
	pH 5	Pb, Zn	
	Hexamethylenetetra-mine buffer pH 6	Cd, Hg(II)	
Omega chrome red B[g,h]	pH 4.6	Ni	Red to yellow
(XXXI)	pH 4.5	Cu	
	pH 6.5–10	Zn	
	pH 10	Pb	
Alizarin complex-one (XXXII, R = H)	pH 4.3	Pb, Zn, Co, Cu, In	Red to yellow

[f] Korbl, J., R. Pribil, and E. Emr, *Coll. Czech. Chem. Comm.*, **22**, 961 (1957); Korbl, J., and R. Pribil, *Chemist-Analyst*, **45**, 102 (1956).
[g] Belcher, R., R. A. Close, and T. S. West, *Chemist-Analyst*, **46**, 86 (1957).
[h] Wehber, P., *Z. Anal. Chem.*, **153**, 253 (1956); **154**, 122 (1957).

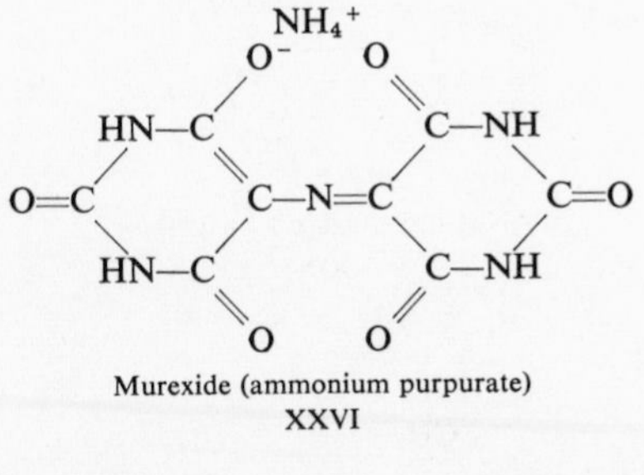

Murexide (ammonium purpurate)
XXVI

used in this way, was found by chance: It was formed as a decomposition product during the synthesis of uramildiacetic acid, and its color change with calcium ion was observed.[3]   The eriochrome dyestuffs themselves were examined because they were commercial dyestuffs known to react with metals.   These substances can react with metal ions and with hydrogen ions, undergoing marked color changes in both instances, so that they may be thought of as being both pH and pM indicators.

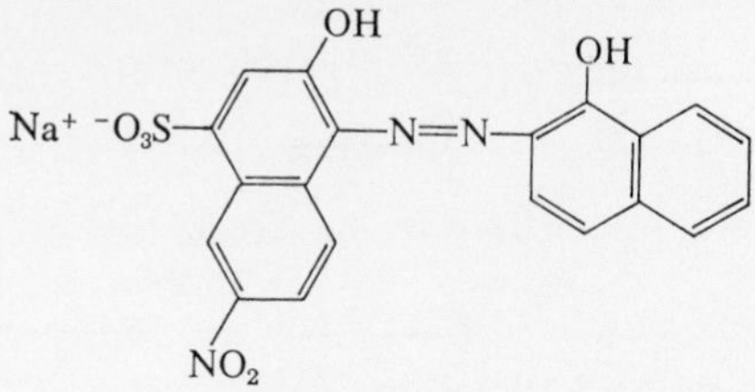

Eriochrome black T (solochrome black T)
XXVII

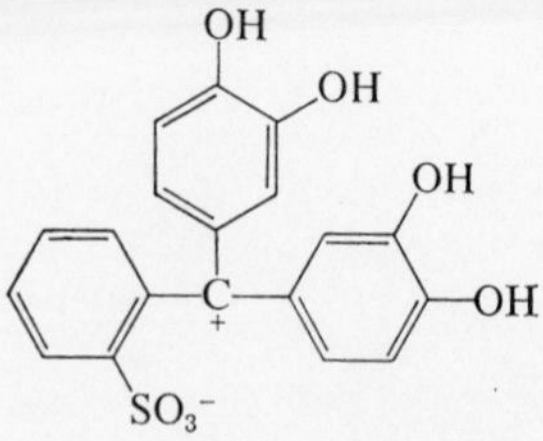

Catechol violet (pyrocatechin violet)
XXVIII

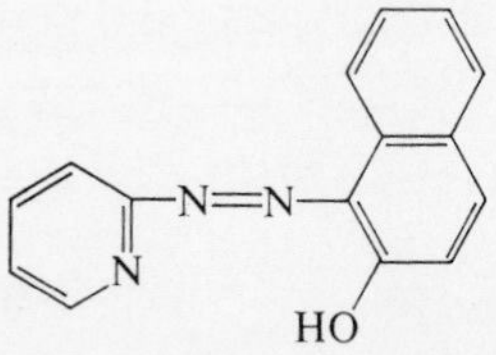

PAN (1-(2-Pyridylazo)-2-naphthol)
XXIX

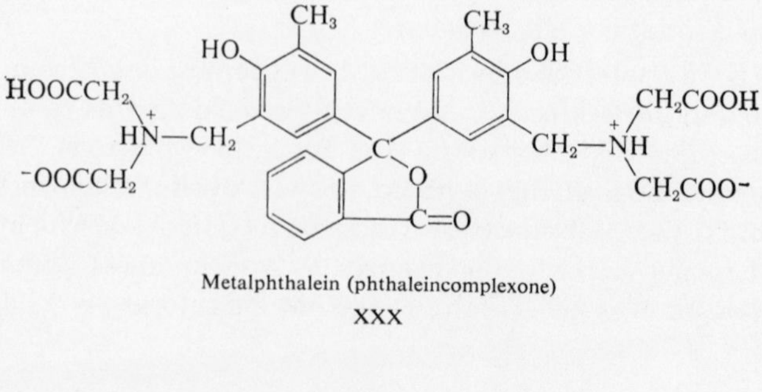

Metalphthalein (phthaleincomplexone)
XXX

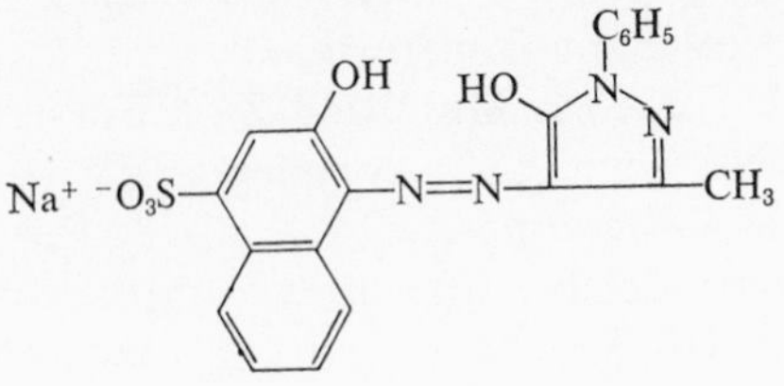

Omega chrome red B
XXXI

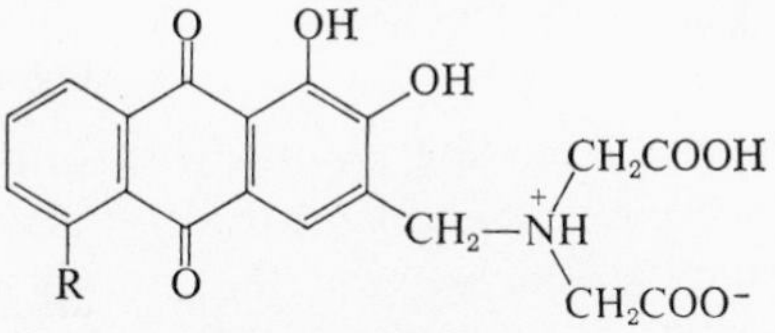

R = H, Alizarin complexone
R = OH, Alizarin-bordeaux complexone
XXXII

The intense color of these metal indicator complexes explains why there is also a voluminous literature describing their applications to the determination of metal ions by direct spectrophotometry.

In the same way that a pH indicator exists, at equivalence point, in equal concentrations of two forms (anion and neutral molecule, or neutral molecule and cation), so, too, at the endpoint of a complexometric titration using a "metallochromic" indicator, there is an equilibrium between metal complex and uncomplexed species. At such an endpoint, pM is equal to the logarithm of the "apparent" stability constant of the metal indicator under the experimental conditions. The mathematical analysis of the equilibria involved in complexometric titrations using such indicators follows closely the principles outlined earlier in this chapter; it is handicapped, however, by the limited stability constant data available for metal indicators. (For a useful compilation of known constants, see reference 4.) With a good visual indicator, a precision of about ± 0.5 pM unit is possible, leading to a titration error of about $\pm 230/([M]_T K_{ML})^{1/2}\%$.[4] Thus, an error of $\pm 1\%$ would be expected for $[M]_T = 10^{-3}M$ and $K_{ML} = 10^8$, for $[M]_T = 10^{-5}M$ and $K_{ML} = 10^{10}$, etc. Use of physicochemical methods of endpoint detection can often increase the precision at least fivefold.

The relative metal-binding abilities of EDTA and other ligands vary, depending on their constitution, so that substances that may be suitable indicators for complexometric titrations with some metal ions may be quite unsuitable with others. Thus, over the series of divalent ions from manganese to copper, $\log K_1$ for the eriochrome black T complexes would be expected to increase much more rapidly than for those of EDTA, and it is found that whereas Mn^{2+} and Zn^{2+} can be titrated using this indicator, Co^{2+}, Ni^{2+}, and Cu^{2+} complexes with eriochrome black T are too stable. So also are those of Al^{3+}, Cr^{3+}, Fe^{3+}, Ag^+, Ti^{4+}, and some of the platinum metals. This leads to the "blocking" of the eriochrome black T unless a sufficiently strong complexing agent such as o-phenanthroline is added to "tie up" the interfering metal ions. (Alternatively, the rate of reaction of the Cu, Co, Ni, and Al complexes of EDTA with this indicator is slow enough for these metals to be determined by back-titration, the excess EDTA being titrated with standard zinc or magnesium solutions.)

The nature of the metal-binding groups in the indicators also varies. In murexide-metal complexes, bonding is through two of the four central oxygens (one of which is ionized) and the central nitrogen atom. In the eriochrome black T and eriochrome blue-black complexes the two phenolate ions and the azo nitrogens are involved. This is true also for chelates of fast sulfon black F (XXXIII), which appears to be a specific indicator for copper and nickel[19] in the presence of ammonium ions. (Only one of the azo groups is involved.) Fast sulfon black F is also a

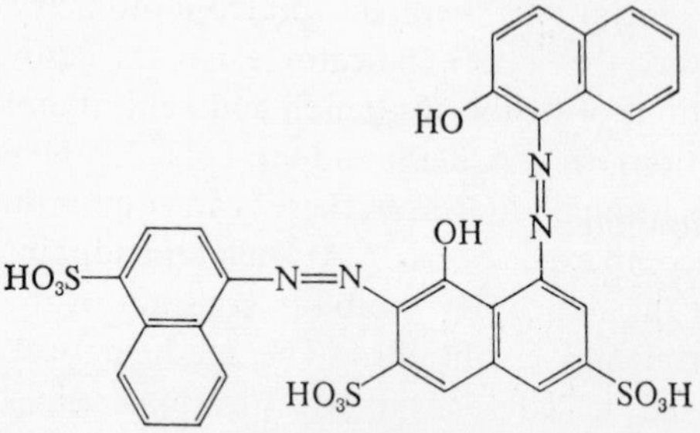

Fast sulfon black F
XXXIII

highly sensitive spectrophotometric reagent for beryllium,[20] forming a 1:1 complex at pH 11. Catechol violet, like tiron, binds metals through a pair of phenolate ions, whereas in PAN the pyridine nitrogen, the azo nitrogens, and the phenolate ion are concerned. Similarly, in 2-(o-arsenophenylazo)-1,8-dihydroxynaphthalene-3,6-disulfonic acid (XXXIV), chelation of metals could occur through the azo nitrogen and the proximal hydroxyl oxygen atoms, but in this case the arseno group is also favorably placed to contribute to the bonding. In metalphthalein, on the other hand, the metal is held by two carboxyl groups and an imino nitrogen

and one of the phenolic OH groups.   It is this OH group which is responsible for the metal complex having a color similar to the alkaline quinonoid form.   The fact that the Ca, Ba, and Mg complexes are intensely

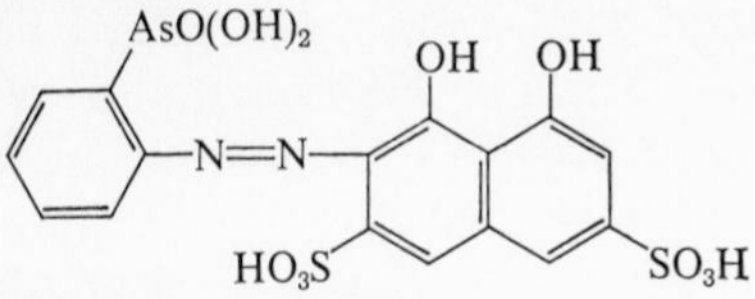

XXXIV

colored, but the Zn complex is not, suggests that in the latter the binding
to the phenolic oxygen is covalent rather than ionic.   These structures are
not mandatory for indicator activity.   For example, omission of the nitro
group in eriochrome black T gives eriochrome blue-black B (solochrome
black 6B), which is also used as a metal indicator: It is actually more
stable and gives sharper endpoints with Mg^{2+} and some other metal ions.
The isomer, eriochrome blue-black R (solochrome dark blue, or calcon)
(XXXV, R = H), is also used in this way.[21]

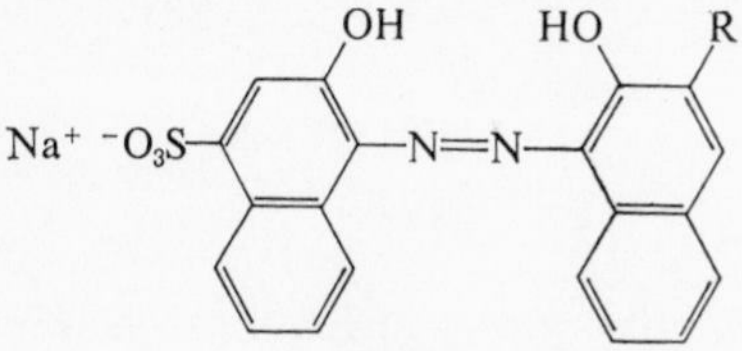

XXXV

The structural relation of omega chrome red B (XXXI) to the
eriochromes is readily seen.   Further modifications give the indicators, 2-hydroxy-1-(2-hydroxy-4-sulfo-1-naphthylazo)-3-naphthoic acid
(HHSNNA),[22] and calmagite (XXXVI), which behave similarly.[23]

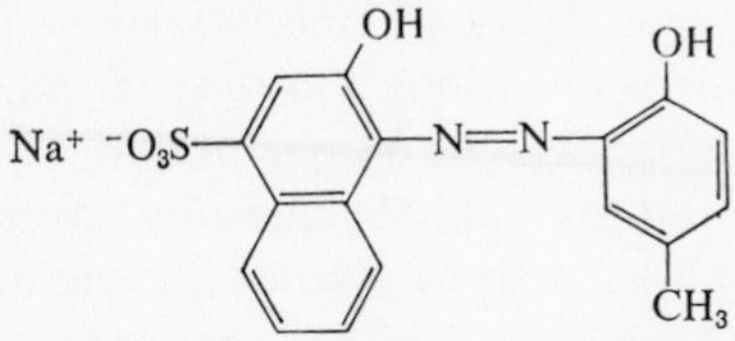

XXXVI

Calmagite has the same color change with calcium and magnesium as
eriochrome black T but the change is clearer and sharper, and aqueous
solutions are stable indefinitely.   The same chelating sequence occurs
twice in acid alizarin black SN (XXXVII), which has been suggested as an

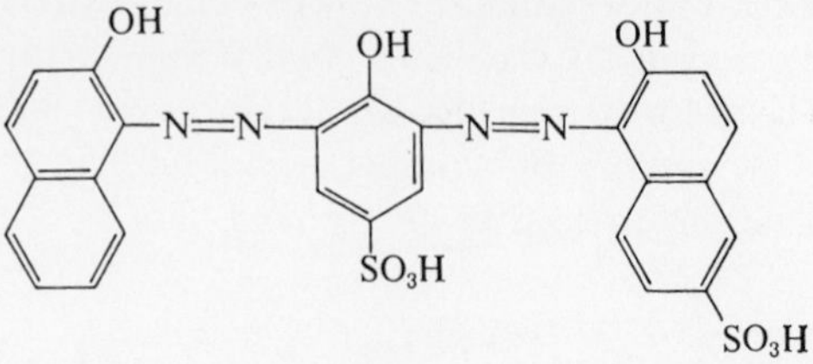

XXXVII

indicator for use at high pH in titrating calcium in the presence of magnesium.[24]　It is also repeated in calcichrome.

The resemblance of pyrogallol red[25] (XXXVIII) and its dibromo derivative, bromopyrogallol red, to catechol violet is obvious, and all three indicators can be used for the same titrations.

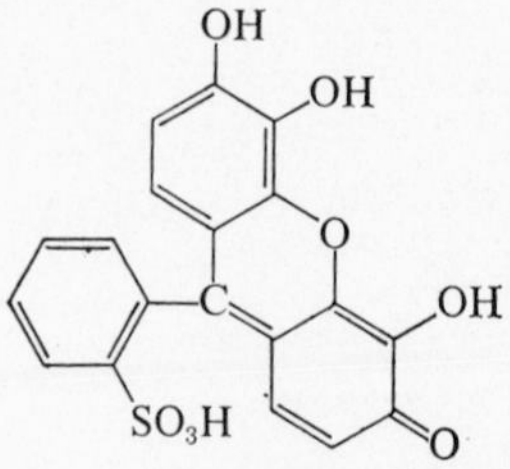

XXXVIII

Similarly, the 2-naphthol group in PAN can be replaced by resorcinol to give 4-(2-pyridyl-azo)-resorcinol, which has been used as a metal indicator in EDTA titrations[26] and in the titration of indium with nitrilotriacetic acid.[27]　It has also been suggested as a water-soluble reagent for the direct colorimetric determination of Co, Pb, and U.[28]　PAN has also been proposed as a colorimetric reagent for uranium.[29]

The main effects of such structure modifications are to produce changes in ligand pK_a values (and hence to modify their useful working range), in the absorption spectra of ligands and their complexes, in solubilities, and in chemical stabilities (against decomposition).

The similarity between pH and pM indicators is further brought out in complexometric indicators such as xylenol orange, methyl thymol blue, and metalphthalein, which contain an NN-di(carboxymethyl)aminomethyl group, as in complexone (EDTA), joined to a pH indicator in such a way that complex formation by the former will modify the degree of ionization of the latter.　Analogous complexometric indicators, such as alizarin complexone and alizarin-bordeaux complexone, have been synthesized from anthraquinones.[30]

In complexes with these ligands, the carboxylate ions, the nitrogen atom, and the phenolic oxygen proximal to the di(carboxymethyl)aminomethyl group are probably directly bonded to the metal ion to form a multi-dentate chelated structure.   By contrast, metal binding to alizarin red S (XXXIX) or (better) 2-quinizarinsulfonic acid and 2-phenoxyquinizarin-

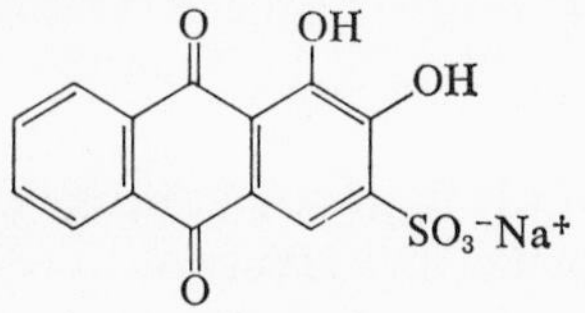

XXXIX

3,4-disulfonic acid (which have been proposed[31] as indicators in the titra-tion of thorium with EDTA) involves only adjacent pairs of oxygen atoms: The sulfonic acid groups are there to confer water solubility.

Calcein[32] is related to fluorescein, and thymolphthalexone[33] to thymol-phthalein in the same way that metalphthalein is a derivative of o-cresol-phthalein.   All three substances are used as indicators in the EDTA titrations of Ca, Sr, and Ba.   However, replacement of the (phthalic acid)carboxyl residue in metalphthalein by a sulfonic acid group gives xylenol orange,[34] which is a useful indicator at much lower pH values.

Calcein and calcein blue (XL) (from 4-methylumbelliferone) have been

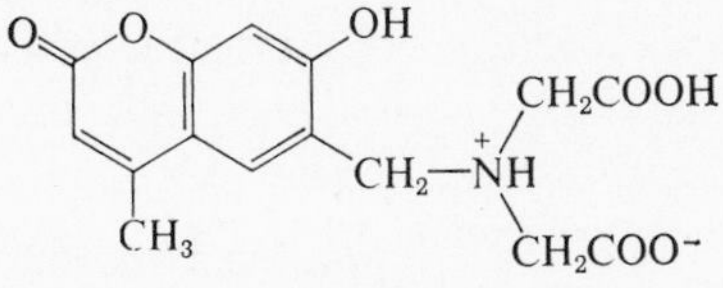

XL

suggested[35] as fluorescent indicators for the complexometric titration of iron, copper, cobalt, chromium, nickel, and zinc at pH 5 with EDTA using back-titration with a standard copper solution.   The endpoints are marked by a quenching of fluorescence resulting from the participation of the phenolic oxygen in the metal binding.   Conversely, above pH 12 the free indicators do not fluoresce but the complexes with calcium, strontium, and barium do.

The same binding groups are involved in 3,5-dihydroxybenzidine-N,N,N',N'-tetraacetic acid (XLI) which, like other di-ortho substituted members of this group,[36] can be used as a metallofluorescent indicator (for Cu and Pb) in EDTA titrations.[37]   The indicator, but not its com-plexes, is blue-fluorescent.   The hydroxyl groups in the 3,3'-positions are undoubtedly involved in the metal bonding, but the suggestion[37] that insertion of hydroxyls in the 5,5′-positions would give much stronger complexes seems unlikely on stereochemical grounds. The 4,4′-diamino-

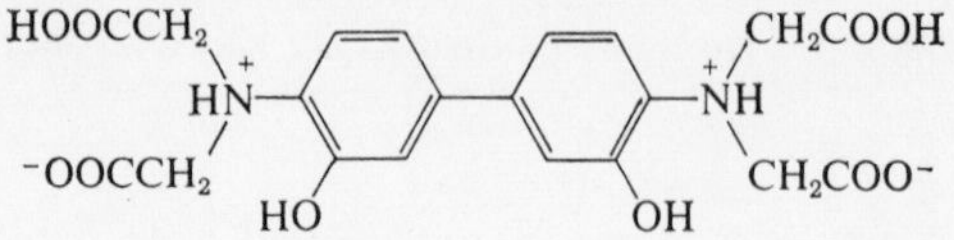

XLI

stilbene analogs of these indicators are much more sensitive and have also been used as fluorescent indicators in Cu(II)-EDTA titrations.[38]

Morin has been used as a fluorescent indicator in complexometric titrations of gallium and indium.[39]

The changes from chrome azurol S ((XLII), $R_2 = R_3 = Cl$, $R_1 = SO_3H$), to eriochrome cyanine RC ((XLII), $R_1 = R_3 = H$, $R_2 = SO_3H$), were made in an endeavor to obtain a better indicator for the complexo-

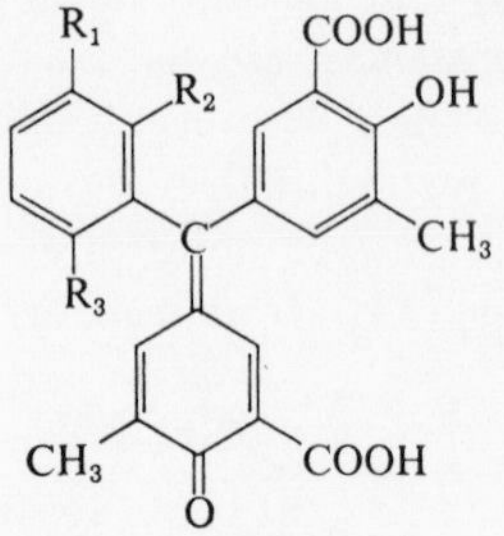

XLII

metric titration of zirconium.[40] However, indicators of quite different structures may sometimes be used for the same metal ion. For example, SPADNS ((XLIII),$R = SO_3H$) has also been proposed as an indicator for zirconium,[41] and for thorium,[42] for which chromotrope 10B (XLIII, $R =$

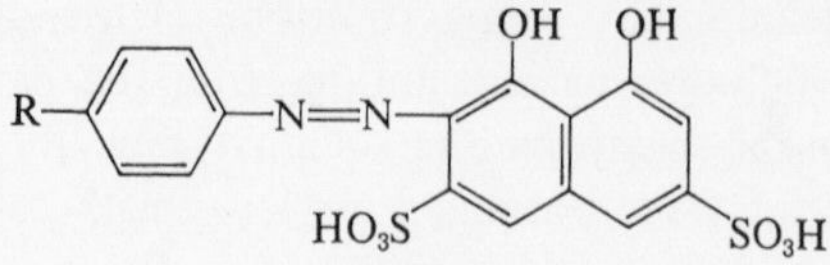

XLIII

OH), has also been used. Both of these dyes, in common with a number of others which have at least one phenolic group *ortho* to an azo linkage, have been suggested for use in spectrophotometric methods for Zr, Ta, Th, U, Be, and Np. It is probable that the azo nitrogen and the phenolic oxygen atoms are involved in bonding to the metal. Other indicators for thorium have included catechol violet and alizarin red S.[43]

Diazotization and self-coupling of three molecules of H-acid (1,7-diamino-8-hydroxynaphthalene-3,6-disulfonic acid) gives calcichrome[44] (XLIV), in which the azo and phenol groups are arranged in a "chelate

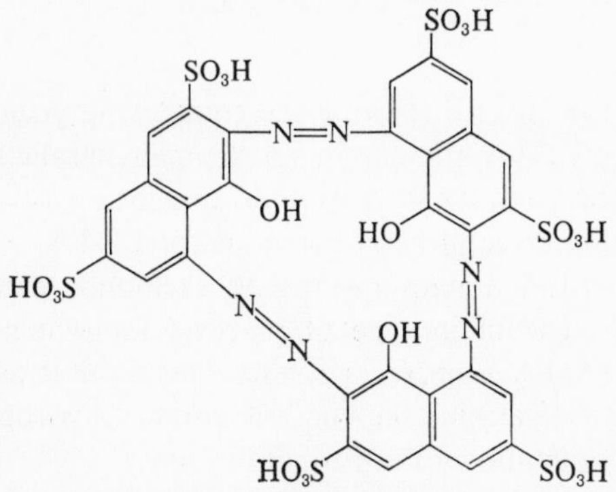

XLIV

cage." This "cage" is of such dimensions that, of the alkaline earth metals, only calcium can enter. Thus at pH 12–13 calcium changes the color of the solution from blue to red, and barium, strontium, and magnesium do not interfere, so that calcichrome can be used as indicator in the specific complexometric titration of calcium in the presence of barium, with 1,2–diaminocyclohexane-N,N,N′,N′-tetraacetic acid.[44] It also forms the basis of a specific spot test.

For further examples of metallochromic indicators, and for practical details of their applications in complexometric titrations, see references 3 and 45.

Under any given experimental conditions, the "apparent" stability constants for complexes with a series of metals vary in a way that depends on the nature of the ligand. Thus, EDTA forms a more stable complex with Ca^{2+} than with Mg^{2+}, whereas with eriochrome black T the order is reversed, and the constant for Ca^{2+} is too small to permit satisfactory titration. Addition of a little Mg-EDTA complex to the solution leads to a sharp endpoint. So long as any Ca^{2+} remains uncomplexed with EDTA, free Mg^{2+} will be present in the solution and will form a colored complex with the indicator. The Mg-EDTA complex is sufficiently stable, however, that when it is finally re-formed the color is discharged. This is an example of an *indirect metal indicator*. The principle has potential applications in analysis.

6.7 Other Reagents Used in Complexometric Titrations

Nitrilotriacetic acid as its trisodium salt (XLV) is also widely used in

$$
N
\begin{cases}
CH_2COO^- & Na^+ \\
CH_2COO^- & Na^+ \\
CH_2COO^- & Na^+
\end{cases}
$$

XLV

complexometric titrations. Because the complexing groups involved are similar to those of EDTA, there is an approximate parallelism between the logarithms of metal complex stability constants for the two ligands (log K_1 for NTA is roughly three-fifths of the value for EDTA, so that NTA can be used satisfactorily for many metal ions, excluding manganese and the alkaline earths). The main type of reaction for which NTA is more convenient than EDTA is where its di-alkali metal salt is used, followed by a back-titration to determine the concentration of hydrogen ion that has been liberated by metal complex formation.

Uramildiacetic acid (H_3Ur) (XLVI) forms complexes with Li^+ and Na^+

$$
\begin{array}{c}
O \\
\parallel \\
HN-C \\
\diagdown \\
O=C \qquad CH-N^+H \\
\diagup \qquad\qquad\qquad \diagdown \\
HN-C \qquad\qquad CH_2COO^- \\
\parallel \\
O
\end{array}
\qquad
\begin{array}{l}
CH_2COOH \\
\\
\end{array}
$$

XLVI

of quite exceptional stability.[46]. Thus log K_{ML} = 5.61 for Li^+, 3.33 for Na^+, 1.94 for K^+, and 6.70 for Tl^+, at 20°.[47] The stable salt $H_3UrNaH_2UrH_2O$ can readily be recrystallized from dilute perchloric acid and used to remove sodium ion from solution. The anion of uramildiacetic acid probably acts as a tri- or quadridentate chelate, giving tetrahedral structures as preferred forms. This would explain why its complexes with Li, Na, and Be (log K_{ML} = 10.36) are stronger than with EDTA, whereas the complexes with most bivalent metals are weaker. Consistent with this is the observation that the formation by NTA of more stable complexes than imino-diacetic acid is due mainly to the change from tri- to quadridentate character. Also, 1- or 3-methyl substitution in H_3Ur produces very little effect on the stability constants for Li, Na, K, or Tl, and it is suggested[47] that the ligand forms a sterically favored conformation with a cagelike structure to accommodate small ions and favor a tetrahedral environment.

Attempts to modify complexing ability by making ligands derived from EDTA have not been very fruitful.   These have included homologs of EDTA in which $-(CH_2)_2-$ was changed to $-(CH_2)_n-$, where $8 > n > 2$,[48] and others in which the chain length of the carboxylic acids was increased.[49]   Oxygen and thioethers of EDTA have been prepared,[3] and rotation about the carbon-carbon bond of the ethylenediamine bridge has been restricted.[50]   Replacement of carboxylate groups in EDTA by ortho-linked phenolic groups[51] and by phosphonic acid groups[52] has also been tried, but the complexes are less stable.   Di-(2-aminoethyl)ether-N,N,N',N'-tetraacetic   acid   and   di-(2-aminoethyl)ethyleneglycol-N,N,N',N'-tetraacetic acid show better selectivity for Ca^{2+} and larger cations in the presence of Mg^{2+} than does EDTA,[53] and *trans*-1,2-diamino-cyclohexane-N,N,N',N'-tetraacetic acid (CDTA) has higher stability constants with metal ions than EDTA has,[54] but this is partly offset by its higher pK_a value.   The higher stability constants can probably be ascribed to a steric factor—removal of the free rotation about the C-C linkage that is possible in the ethylenediamine bridge of EDTA.

Replacement of the cyclohexane ring of CDTA with cyclopentane and cycloheptane to give CPDTA and CHDTA, respectively, gives the stability constant sequence for their metal complexes:[55]

$$CHDTA > CDTA > CPDTA \geqslant EDTA$$

Some restriction of rotation about the ethylene bridge of EDTA results from the replacement of a hydrogen atom on either or both of the carbon atoms by a methyl group to give 1,2-diaminopropane-N,N,N',N'-tetra-acetic acid and 2,3-diaminobutane-N,N,N',N'-tetraacetic acid.   These reagents are much more soluble than EDTA, and the stability constants of their metal complexes are somewhat greater.[55]

The penta-anion of diethylenetriaminepentaacetic acid (DTPA) (XLVII) can form octadentate chelates, and its higher negative charge

$$
\begin{array}{ccc}
HOOCCH_2 & & CH_2COOH \\
& N-CH_2CH_2-N-CH_2CH_2-N & \\
HOOCCH_2 & CH_2COOH & CH_2COOH \\
\end{array}
$$

XLVII

also helps to make its metal complexes generally more stable than those of EDTA.   It is a better complexometric reagent,[56] especially for the heavy alkaline earths, the first members of the lanthanide cations, and Th^{4+}. It also forms binuclear complexes.

Picolinic acid (which forms complexes as strong as iminodiacetic acid) and 2,6-pyridinedicarboxylic acid (which is comparable with nitrilotriacetic acid in complexing ability) have possibilities for complexometric titrations, especially in low-pH regions.

Relative values for stability constants of metal ions with polydentate amines would be expected to show much wider variation than with ligands such as EDTA. This consequence of the difference in the nature of the complexing groups is supported by the values of some complexes with EDTA, triaminotriethylamine (TREN), and triethylenetetramine (TRIEN), given in Table 6.6. Also, complex formation with alkaline earth cations

TABLE 6.6

Stability Constants of Some 1:1 Metal Complexes
(At 20° and an Ionic Strength of 0.1)

| | Ligand | | |
Metal	EDTA	TREN	TRIEN
Fe^{2+}	14.3	8.8	—
Ni^{2+}	18.6	14.8	14.1
Cu^{2+}	18.8	18.8	20.5
Zn^{2+}	16.4	14.6	11.8
Cd^{2+}	16.5	12.3	10.0
Hg^{2+}	22.1	—	25.0
Pb^{2+}	17.9	—	10.4

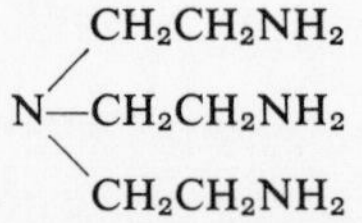

$$
\begin{array}{c}
\quad\quad CH_2CH_2NH_2 \\
\quad\quad \diagup \\
N{-}CH_2CH_2NH_2 \\
\quad\quad \diagdown \\
\quad\quad CH_2CH_2NH_2
\end{array}
$$

TREN
(pK_a 8.6, 9.6, 10.3)

$$
\begin{array}{c}
\quad\quad CH_2CH_2NH_2 \\
\quad\quad \diagup \\
NH \\
\mid \\
CH_2 \\
\mid \\
CH_2 \\
\mid \\
NH \\
\quad\quad \diagdown \\
\quad\quad CH_2CH_2NH_2
\end{array}
$$

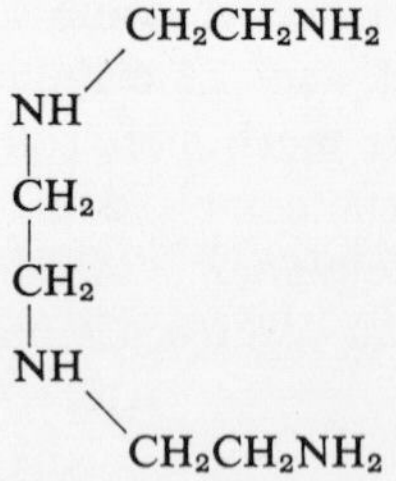

TRIEN
(pK_a 3.3, 6.7, 9.2, 9.9)

is important for EDTA but is negligible for TRIEN. Metals coordinating more readily with nitrogen than with oxygen, such as Cu, Ni, Co, Zn, Cd, and Hg, form the most stable complexes, but differences are much greater because of the greater ligand-field strengths of amines than of carboxylic acids. Similarly, the fact that two of the four coordinating groups in the indicator zincon (XLVIII) are nitrogen atoms probably explains its preferential complex formation with Cu, Zn, Ni, and Co.

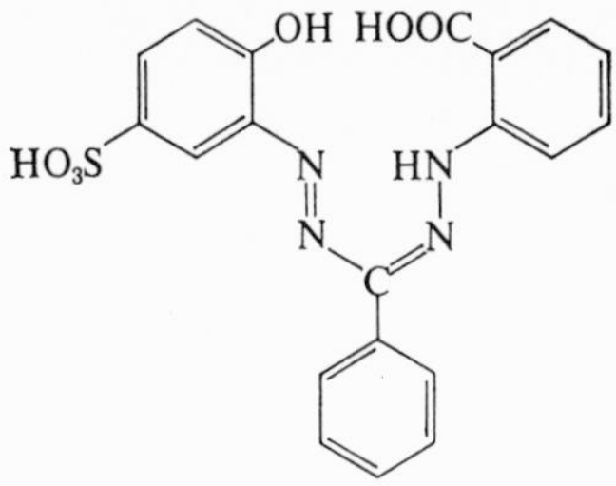

XLVIII

The differences in log K_1 for the Cu, Ni, and Fe complexes with TREN are sufficiently great that successive titration of these metals in the same solution should be possible. Mainly because of the difficulty of obtaining pure materials, very few titrations using polyamines have so far been described.[57] Also, because of the unfavorable pK_a values of the ligands, titrations must be carried out in weakly alkaline solutions to give sufficiently high apparent stability constants.

Nevertheless, TRIEN has been used in titrating Cd, Cu, Zn, Pb, Ni, and Hg, the endpoints being detected by metallochromic indicators[58] and by potentiometry.[59] More recently, tetraethylenepentamine has been introduced, using potentiometric[60] and amperometric[61] titrations.

The disadvantages associated with the high and multiple pK_a values of aliphatic polyamines are avoided in a complexometric agent such as tris(acetonyltrioxime)amine,

$$N(CH-C-CH_3)_3$$
$$\overset{\|}{N}OH$$

although chelation through nitrogens is retained. However, this group of reagents hydrolyzes fairly readily.

6.8 "Masking" of Chemical Reactions

In an acidic cyanide medium cuprous sulfide is not precipitated when hydrogen sulfide is bubbled through copper solutions. Similarly, in the presence of excess EDTA, ferric ion does not form the colored $FeSCN^{2+}$ complex with thiocyanate ion. Because the normal course of a chemical change has been prevented in both cases, the reactions are said to be "masked." They are "masked" because substances in the solutions are able to form sufficiently stable complexes with one or more of the reactants for the usual changes to be undetectable. For example, in the presence of excess EDTA free metal ion concentrations become pH-dependent, so that, by suitable pH control, they can be brought down to sufficiently low levels to prevent many of the usual inorganic reactions. On the other hand, if the reaction involves the formation of a sufficiently stable or insoluble complex with some other ligand, EDTA is unable to affect it. This is particularly true of ions such as Ag^+ for which the stereochemistry is such that reaction with EDTA does not lead to a very stable complex.

Thallium (I) can be separated from lead (II) by using EDTA to mask the lead (log K_{ML} = 18.3 for Pb, 6.47 for Tl) while thallium is precipitated as the very sparingly soluble TlI.[62]   Similarly, in the presence of EDTA and an ammonium acetate-acetic acid buffer, only tungsten, molybdenum, and vanadium are precipitated quantitatively by 8-hydroxyquinoline, whereas 25 other cations that are normally precipitated remain in solution.[63]   By judicious pH control some of the other oxinates can also be precipitated.   Lead can be separated from Cu, Zn, Cd, Co, and Ni by "masking" these metals with cyanide ion, adding sodium diethyldithiocarbamate, and extracting the lead complex into chloroform.

A weak masking agent can be used to lower the concentration of a species to a level at which it can be used as a reagent.   Thus Fehling's solution consists of an alkaline solution of copper (II) that is masked against precipitation of copper hydroxide by the addition of tartrate ion which does not, however, lower the level of free Cu^{2+} below that at which it can be reduced by certain reducing agents, such as aldose sugars, to insoluble cuprous oxide.   Other masking agents, such as triphosphate ion, can be used for this purpose, and Cu(II) can be replaced by bismuth.

The examples so far quoted have all involved masking of cations, but anions can be treated in the same way.   Thus, cyanide ion is masked by addition of mercuric ion to give undissociated $Hg(CN)_2$, and sulfite ion is prevented from showing many of its properties if formaldehyde is added to form the formaldehyde-bisulfite addition compound.

As would be expected from the nature of its metal binding, which is through anionic oxygens, one of the most general masking agents. is sodium triphosphate, $Na_5P_3O_{10} \cdot 6H_2O$, which, in neutral or alkaline solutions, forms soluble complexes with many cations, including those of Li, Be, Mg, Ca, Sr, Ba, Zn, Cd, Fe(II), Fe(III), Co, Ni, Mn, Cu, Pb, VO, Al, Y, In, La, Ce(III), Pr, Nd, Ag, Hg(I), TiO, Zr, Bi, Sn(II), Sn(IV), Th, and UO_2. In all cases precipitation with alkali hydroxide, ammonia, or phosphate, carbonate, or borate ions is prevented. Similarly, it masks calcium against precipitation by fluoride, oxalate, citrate, tartrate, and mesotartrate ions, prevents the formation of colored ferric complexes with salicylate and sulfosalicylate solutions, and masks lead against precipitation by fluoride, chromate, sulfate, and aliphatic anions.   However, it is unable to mask sulfide precipitation of cations such as those of

Zn, Hg, Pb, and Cu, where binding to sulfur is much stronger than to oxygen. This masking agent is of biochemical interest because it is directly related to adenosine triphosphate, which plays a vital role in muscular contraction and other physiological processes.

In masking reactions the important properties are the relative concentrations and complex-forming abilities of reagent and masking agent for the species concerned, and the solubility product of any insoluble complex that may be formed. For example, the less soluble a precipitate is, the more difficult it becomes to find a masking agent able to prevent its formation. Tartrate ion will mask Fe(III) against precipitation as $Fe(OH)_3$ but not as Fe_2S_3. Ammonia, by giving with silver ions the complex $Ag(NH_3)_2{}^+$, is able to mask Ag^+ against precipitation with chloride ion: It is unable, however, to prevent precipitation of the less soluble AgBr and AgI, and hence can be used as a reagent for detecting bromide and iodide in the presence of chloride. The use of masking agents makes it possible for such solutions to function as reservoirs of ions or species that would otherwise be insoluble.

Quantitatively, a "masking" reagent can be thought of as reducing the concentration of free metal ion or free ligand, and hence of decreasing the apparent stability of a complex under the particular experimental conditions. The simplest case, prevention of precipitation, for example by addition of excess ammonia to Ni^{2+}, Cu^{2+}, Zn^{2+}, and Cd^{2+}, or of tartrate or citrate to Mn^{2+}, Pb^{2+}, and In^{3+}, is discussed in Chapter 9. In the presence of excess ammonia, EDTA can be used to titrate calcium ahead of copper, whereas, normally, the reverse is true. In spectrophotometric determinations, the concentration of an interfering metal ion must often be made very low if complex formation with the color-forming ligand is not to be detected: In such cases a high masking effect is called for. This also requires that the masking agent does not, itself, form complexes having similar colors or absorbing appreciably in the spectral region in which measurements are made. No such restriction applies in precipitation reactions, so that, for example, α,α'-bipyridine, o-phenanthroline, or thioglycollic acid can be used as a masking reagent for ferrous ion (although all form strongly colored complexes) in the precipitation of magnesium and beryllium by phosphate ion. In the complexometric titrations using a metal indicator masking conditions are usually much less stringent than in spectrophotometric measurements. The relation, given in Section 6.2, that

$$\log (K_{M_I L})_{\text{apparent}} \approx \log K_{M_I L} - \log K_{M_{II} L} + pM_{II}$$

can be combined with the experimental requirement that, for visual titrations, the minimum value of $\log K_{M_I L}$ must be about 10^7 if the

TABLE 6.7

Some Examples of Masking of Cations in EDTA Titrations

Conditions	Masking Reaction
1. Alkaline solutions	Cyanide ion with Ag^+, Cu^+, Hg^{2+}, Fe^{2+}, Zn^{2+}, Cd^{2+}, Co^{2+}, Ni^{2+} (Enables titration of Pb, Mn, In, Mg, Ca, Sr, Ba without interference)
2. pH 10	Fluoride ion with Al^{3+}, Ca^{2+}, Mg^{2+}, Ti^{4+}, (Nb and Ta), rare earth ions (Zinc, cadmium, nickel or cobalt, can then be titrated)
3. Alkaline solutions	Triethanolamine with Fe^{3+}, Al^{3+}, Mn^{3+} (Calcium and nickel can then be titrated using murexide as indicator)
4.	2,3-Dimercaptopropanol with Hg^{2+}, Cd^{2+}, Zn^{2+}, As^{3+}, Sb^{3+}, Sn^{2+}, Pb^{2+}, Bi^{3+} (Calcium, magnesium, manganese, and nickel can then be titrated)
5.	Tiron with Al^{3+}, Ti^{4+}, Fe^{3+} (Alkaline earths or rare earths can then be titrated using eriochrome black T)
6.	Sulfosalicylic acid with Al and U(VI)
7.	Acetylacetone with Fe^{3+}, Al^{3+}, Be^{2+}, Pd^{2+}, and UO_2^{2+} (Zinc and lead can then be titrated, using xylenol orange as indicator)
8. pH 5-6	1,10-Phenanthroline with Cd^{2+}, Co^{2+}, Cu^{2+}, Ni^{2+}, Mn^{2+}, and Zn^{2+} (Lead and aluminium can then be titrated)
9.	Iodide ion with Hg^{2+}
10.	Ascorbic acid with Fe^{3+}, Cu^{2+}
11. Acid solutions	Thiosemicarbazide with Hg^{2+} (Bismuth, cadmium, zinc, and lead can then be titrated)
12. Strongly alkaline solutions	Hydrogen peroxide with Ti(IV)

determination is to be satisfactory. This leads to the result[4] that the metal M_{II} is masked if

$$(K_{M_{II}L})_{apparent} < 10^{-7} \frac{(K_{M_IL})_{apparent}}{([M_{II}])_{apparent}}$$

Some examples of the use of masking agents to prevent the titrations of particular metal ions by EDTA are given in Table 6.7, while Table 6.8 lists some cases where EDTA itself is used as a masking agent. The advances that have been made in the technique of complexometric titrations stem, very largely, from the development of suitable masking reactions: By its nature, EDTA is very unselective. Surveys have been made of the masking effects of EDTA in qualitative analysis.[64-66]

Table 6.9 (which is based mainly on a table by Cheng[65]) gives a useful summary of many of the common masking agents and the cations for

TABLE 6.8

Some Examples of the Use of EDTA as a Masking Agent

Reaction Masked	Application
Fe, Co, Ni with sodium diethyldithio-carbamate	Determination of Cu (extracted into organic solvents)
Fe^{III}, V^v with Tiron	Determination of Ti(IV)
Fe, Co, Cu, Ni, Cr with 2-nitroso-1-naphthol	Determination of Pd
Pb, Hg, Bi, Cu, Cd, As, Sb, Fe, Al, Cr, Be, U, Mo, W, Ce, Th, Ni, Co, Mn, Zn, Mg with oxalate	Determination of Ca
Ag(I), Pb(II) with chromate	Precipitation of Ba and Tl chromates
Hg(I), Pb(II) with chloride	Precipitation of Ag and Tl chlorides
Bi(III), Pb(II) with iodide (acid solution)	Precipitation of Ag and Tl iodides
Tl(I) with iodide (ammonia)	Precipitation of Ag iodide
Ni(II), Co(II), Mn(II) with sulfide	Precipitation of Zn(II) and Fe(III) sulfides
Hg(II), Bi(III), Fe(III), Cr(III), Al(III), Mn(III) with ammonia	Precipitation of Sb(III), Sn(IV), Be(II), Ti(IV), UO_2(VI) as hydroxides

TABLE 6.9

Common Masking Agents

1	
Elements	Masking Agents for Their Cations
Ag	CN^-, NH_3, $S_2O_3^{2-}$, Br^-, I^-, Cl^-, thioglycollic acid
Al	F^-, $C_2O_4^{2-}$, OAc^-, citrate, tartrate, EDTA, OH^-, BAL, NTE, gluconate, acetylacetone, sulfosalicylate
As	S^{2-}, OH^-, BAL
Au	CN^-, Br^-, $S_2O_3^{2-}$
B	F^-, hydroxy acids, glycols
Ba	EDTA, citrate, tartrate, NTA, DHG, SO_4^{2-}
Be	F^-, citrate, tartrate
Bi	Citrate, tartrate, EDTA, I^-, Cl^-, NTA, DHG, thiourea, NTE, BAL, thioglycollic acid
Ca	EDTA, citrate, tartrate, $P_2O_7^{4-}$, NTA, DHG, F^-
Cd	EDTA, CN^-, $S_2O_3^{2-}$, SCN^-, I^-, citrate, tartrate, NTA, DHG, unithiol, thioglycollic acid
Ce	F^-, NTA, EDTA, DHG, citrate, tartrate, tiron
Co	NH_3, NO_2^-, SCN^-, CN^-, H_2O_2, $S_2O_3^{2-}$, NTA, EDTA, DHG, citrate, tartrate, ethylenediamine, BAL, tren, penten
Cr	EDTA, NTA, citrate, tartrate, NTE, ascorbic acid
Cu	NH_3, I^-, SCN^-, CN^-, $S_2O_3^{2-}$, thiourea, EDTA, S^{2-}, DTC, DHG, BAL, citrate, tartrate, NTA, TG, NTE, tren, penten, thioglycollic acid, cysteine
Fe	F^-, PO_4^{3-}, $P_2O_7^{4-}$, NTA, EDTA, DHG, DTC, citrate, tartrate, BAL, SCN^-, $S_2O_3^{2-}$, $C_2O_4^{2-}$, CN^-, tiron, ACB, thiourea, phen, S^{2-}, TG, NTE, gluconate, sulfosalicylate, α,α'-bipyridine
Ge,	$C_2O_4^{2-}$, F^-
Hf	F^-, H_2O_2, SO_4^{2-}, DHG, citrate, tartrate, NTA, EDTA, $P_2O_7^{4-}$, PO_4^{3-}, $C_2O_4^{2-}$, NTE
Hg	I^-, SO_3^{2-}, CN^-, NTA, EDTA, DHG, Cl^-, citrate, tartrate, NTE, tren, penten, unithiol, thiosemicarbazide, cysteine, thioglycollic acid

(Continued)

TABLE 6.9 (*Continued*)

Common Masking Agents

1	
Elements	Masking Agents for Their Cations
In	Thioglycollic acid
Ir	SCN^-, citrate, tartrate, thiourea
Mg	NTA, DHG, EDTA, $C_2O_4^{2-}$, citrate, tartrate, OH^-, $P_2O_7^{4-}$, glycols, F^-
Mn	F^-, $C_2O_4^{2-}$, $P_2O_7^{4-}$, NTA, EDTA, DHG, citrate, tartrate, BAL, NTE, oxidizing agents, CN^-
Mo	SCN^-, $C_2O_4^{2-}$, H_2O_2, citrate, tartrate, EDTA, NTA, tiron
Nb	F^-, OH^-, citrate, tartrate, $C_2O_4^{2-}$, H_2O_2, tiron
Ni	CN^-, SCN^-, NTA, EDTA, NH_3, citrate, tartrate, tren, penten
Os	CN^-, SCN^-
Pb	I^-, OAc^-, $S_2O_3^{2-}$, citrate, tartrate, NTA, EDTA, DHG, SO_4^{2-}, unithiol, BAL, thioglycollic acid
Pd	CN^-, I^-, NH_3, NO_2^-, SCN^-, $S_2O_3^{2-}$, NTA, EDTA, DHG, citrate, tartrate, NTE, acetylacetone
Pt	NH_3, I^-, CN^-, NO_2^-, SCN^-, $S_2O_3^{2-}$, NTA, EDTA, DHG, citrate, tartrate
Rh	Thiourea, citrate, tartrate
Sb	Citrate, tartrate, BAL, I^-, S^{2-}, OH^-, F^-
Se	Tartrate, citrate, reducing agents, F^-, I^-
Sn	Citrate, tartrate, BAL, F^-, I^-, $C_2O_4^{2-}$, OH^-, NTE, thioglycollic acid, PO_4^{3-}
Sr	SO_4^{2-}, NTA, EDTA, DHG, citrate, tartrate
Ta	F^-, OH^-, citrate, tartrate
Th	F^-, NTA, EDTA, DHG, citrate, tartrate, NTE, OAc^-
Ti	SO_4^{2-}, OH^-, H_2O_2, F^-, NTA, EDTA, citrate, tartrate, tiron, NTE, gluconate, sulfosalicylate
Tl	Cl^-, CN^-, NTA, EDTA, citrate, tartrate, NTE, thioglycollic acid

(*Continued*)

TABLE 6.9　(*Continued*)

Common Masking Agents

1	
Elements	Masking Agents for Their Cations
U	F^-, CO_3^{2-}, $C_2O_4^{2-}$, H_2O_2, citrate, tartrate
V	CN^-, H_2O_2, F^-, EDTA, tiron, NTE
W	tiron, F^-, SCN^-, H_2O_2, tartrate
Zn	CN^-, NTA, EDTA, DHG, citrate, tartrate, SCN^-, BAL, OH^-, NH_3, glycols, tren, penten, unithiol, thioglycollic acid
Zr	F^-, SO_4^{2-}, citrate, tartrate, NTA, EDTA, DHG, H_2O_2, $P_2O_7^{4-}$, PO_4^{3-}, $C_2O_4^{2-}$, NTE

2	
Elements and Anions	Masking Agents
Cl^-	Hg
CN^-	HCHO, transition metals, Hg
F^-	H_3BO_3, Al, Be, Zr, Hg, Ti, Nb, Ta, Fe
I^-	Hg
S	CN^-, S^{2-}, SO_3^{2-}
S^{2-}	S
SO_3^-	Hg^{2+}, HCHO
Se and its anions	S^{2-}, SO_3^{2-}, diaminobenzidine

Abbreviations: BAL = 2,3-dimercapto-1-propanol; DTC = diethyldithio-carbamate; DHG = N,N-di(2-hydroxyethyl)glycine; NTA = nitrilotriace-tate; NTE = 2,2′,2″-nitrilotriethanol = triethanolamine; penten = tetrakis (aminoethyl)ethylenediamine; phen = *o*-phenanthroline; TG = thioglycollic acid; tren = 2,2′,2″-triaminotriethylamine; ACB = ascorbic acid.

which they are used.   Qualitatively, the conditions under which a masking agent can be employed successfully depend on a number of factors.   These include the particular species that is to give the desired analytical reaction (in contradistinction to the masking reaction), and the concentrations of reactants.   Other factors are the pH of the solution, the presence of more than one masking agent in the solution, the nature of the solvent, the temperature, the rates of reactions, and the possibility of producing changes in oxidation states.   A brief theoretical discussion of quantitative aspects of masking and demasking reactions is given in reference 65.

Clearly, masking can often be undesirable, as when the presence of oxalic acid impairs the precipitation of molybdenum sulfide or the formation of phosphomolybdate.   An unexpected type of masking is sometimes encountered in spot testing, when metal ions, including those of copper and gold, absorb strongly to the cellulose of the paper so that the expected reactions are not found when appropriate reagents are added.   On the other hand, by judicious pH control, MoO_3 and MoS_3 can be separated from solutions also containing tungsten if tartaric acid is used as the masking agent.   (Because W(VI) lies below Mo(VI) in the periodic table, it forms more stable complexes with tartrate ion and hence is less readily precipitated.)   Whether or not any such interference is likely can often be predicted by considering the nature of the metal ion, the kinds of ligand atoms for which it shows preferences in complex formation, and the number of metal-ligand bonds that might be formed.   Thus the masking of the reaction between ferric and thiocyanate ions by fluoride, phosphate, tartrate, and citrate ions is in line with expectation, and so, in turn, is the inability of phosphate ion to mask the reaction of ferric with 7-iodo-8-hydroxyquinoline-5-sulfonic acid, with which it forms a soluble tris complex.

An interesting hypothetical application that has been analyzed in detail is the use of 2,2',2"-triaminotriethylamine as a masking agent for the EDTA titration of each of the ions Cu^{2+}, Ni^{2+}, Fe^{2+}, Mn^{2+}, and Ca^{2+}, in a mixture of all of them, by successive adjustment of the pH of the solution.[4]

6.9 "Demasking"

"Demasking" also finds analytical applications.   For example, calcium is masked by fluoride ion, which prevents the extraction of calcium into chloroform as its red complex with glyoxal bis(2-hydroxyanil).   The calcium is "demasked" if aluminium is added, owing to formation of the highly stable $[AlF_6]^{3-}$ complex, so that the calcium complex with glyoxal bis(2-hydroxyanil) is produced.   The reaction has been suggested as a specific test for aluminium.[67]   Stannic tin can be masked against precipitation of SnS_2 by addition of fluoride ion to form SnF_6^{2-}, but it is demasked if boric acid is added to convert fluoride ion to the complex anion

BF_4^-. Similarly, in their color reactions with xylenol orange zirconium and hafnium are masked by fluoride but demasked if excess beryllium or aluminium is added, whereupon the color reaction proceeds. A slight excess of EDTA in alkaline medium masks cobalt (II) so that it does not react with diethyldithiocarbamate. Addition of a large amount of calcium displaces cobalt, which can then react with diethyldithiocarbamate. In this case the use of this masking and demasking leads to a selective method for cobalt.[68] The same principle is inherent in the suggested use of the lead salt of diethyldithiocarbamate as a specific reagent for copper.[69]

A demasking reaction used as a rapid test for silver halides depends on their ability to form complex silver cyanides with potassium nickel cyanide, $K_2Ni(CN)_4$, the liberated nickel cyanide then reacting with dimethylglyoxime in ammoniacal solution to give the insoluble red nickel complex. Pd(II) and Hg(II) react in the same way as Ag.[70] A similar test involves the demasking of ferrous iron in ferrocyanide ion, using an ammoniacal solution of α,α'-bipyridine as indicator.[71]

All these are examples of demasking by a replacement mechanism. Another possible method depends on pH adjustment in those cases where the pK of the ligand lies within a readily accessible pH range. Thus at pH 7 the presence of EDTA masks barium against precipitation by sulfate, but at pH 5 it is unable to do so.

Demasking can frequently result from a change in oxidation state of a metal ion because of the difference in stability constants of the corresponding metal complexes with a given ligand. In slightly acidic medium, copper (I) forms a very stable complex with thiosulfate ion, thereby masking the reaction of copper (as copper (II)) with PAN. On the other hand, in alkaline solution the copper (I) thiosulfate is readily oxidized to the weak copper (II) thiosulfate so that copper (II) can then react with PAN.

In some cases the masking agent can be easily decomposed. For example, precipitation of $Ti(OH)_4$ in alkaline solutions is masked by hydrogen peroxide, but the latter is destroyed, and precipitation proceeds normally, if a reducing agent such as formaldehyde, hexamethylenetetramine, sulfite ion, or nitrite ion is added. Similarly, Mo(VI) and W(VI) in acid solutions containing hydrogen peroxide are demasked by formaldehyde. Also, the cyanide complexes of cadmium and zinc, such as $Zn(CN)_4^{2-}$, can be selectively demasked in acid solutions by aldehydes (commonly formaldehyde) to give free metal ions and cyanhydrins. Peroxides can be decomposed by boiling or by addition of iron (III) as a catalyst. In extreme cases, ligands such as EDTA can be destroyed by digestion with a strong acid or by using a strong oxidizing agent such as permanganate or ceric sulfate in an acidic medium.

Volatilization of fluoride and cyanide in the presence of a strong acid, or of chromium as chromyl chloride, and arsenic, germanium, selenium, and tin as their halides, provides another possible avenue for demasking a reaction or removing interfering species.

References

1. Bjerrum, J., "Metal Ammine Formation in Aqueous Solution," Dissertation, Copenhagen, 1941.
2. Leden, I., *Svensk Kem. Tidskr.*, **56**, 31 (1944).
3. Schwarzenbach, G., *Complexometric Titrations*, Interscience, New York, 1957.
4. Ringbom, A., in *Treatise on Analytical Chemistry*, Kolthoff, I. M., and P. J. Elving, eds., Interscience, New York. 1959, Vol. 1, Part 1, Chapter 14.
5. Newman, L., and D. N. Hume, *J. Am. Chem. Soc.*, **79**, 4571, 4581 (1957).
6. Sillén, L. G., *Acta Chem. Scand.*, **8**, 299, 318 (1954).
7. For a fuller discussion, see Rollinson, C. L., in *Chemistry of the Coordination Compounds*, J. C. Bailar, ed., Reinhold Publishing, New York, 1956, Chapter 13; Pokras, L., *J. Chem. Ed.*, **33**, 152, 223, 282 (1956).
8. Tanaka, N., R. Koizumi, T. Murayama, M. Kodama, and Y. Sakuma, *Anal. Chim. Acta*, **18**, 97 (1958).
9. Hamm, R. E., and C. T. Furse, *Anal. Chem.*, **34**, 219 (1962).
10. Flaschka, H., *Talanta*, **8**, 381 (1961).
11. Ringbom, A., *Svensk Kem. Tidskr.*, **66**, 159 (1954).
12. For quantitative calculations, see reference 4.
13. Milner, G. W. C., and J. L. Woodhead, *Analyst*, **79**, 363 (1954).
14. Flaschka, H., *Mikrochim. Acta*, **39**, 38 (1952).
15. Schwarzenbach, G., and A. Willi, *Helv. Chim. Acta*, **34**, 528 (1951).
16. Lydersen, D., and O. Gjems, *Z. Anal. Chem.*, **138**, 249 (1953).
17. Fritz, J. S., *Anal. Chem.*, **26**, 1978 (1954).
18. Wanninen, E., and A. Ringbom, *Anal. Chim. Acta*, **12**, 308 (1955).
19. Belcher, R., R. A. Close, and T. S. West, *Chem. Ind.*, **1957**, 1647.
20. Cabrera, A. M., and T. S. West, *Anal. Chem.*, **35**, 311 (1963).
21. Belcher, R., R. A. Close, and T. S. West, *Chemist-Analyst*, **46**, 86 (1957); Hildebrand, G. P., and C. N. Reilley, *Anal. Chem.*, **29**, 258 (1957).
22. Patton, J., and W. Reeder, *Anal. Chem.*, **28**, 1026 (1956).
23. Lindstrom, F., and H. Diehl, *Anal. Chem.*, **32**, 1123 (1960).
24. Belcher, R., R. A. Close, and T. S. West, *Chemist-Analyst*, **47**, 2 (1958).
25. Suk, V., M. Malat, and A. Jenickova, *Coll. Czech. Chem. Comm.*, **21**, 418 (1956).
26. Wehber, P., *Z. Anal. Chem.*, **166**, 186 (1959).
27. Busev, A. I., and N. A. Kamaev, *Nauchn. Dokl. Vysshei Shkoly, Khim. i Khim. Tekhnol.*, No. 2, 299 (1959), through *CA*, **53**, 18747c (1959).
28. Pollard, F. H., P. Hanson, and W. J. Geary, *Anal. Chim. Acta*, **20**, 26 (1959).
29. Shibata, H., *Anal. Chim. Acta*, **22**, 479 (1960).
30. Belcher, R., M. A. Leonard, and T. S. West, *J. Chem. Soc.*, **1958**, 2390.
31. Owens, E. G., and J. H. Yoe, *Anal. Chim. Acta*, **23**, 321 (1960).
32. Diehl, H., and J. L. Ellingboe, *Anal. Chem.*, **28**, 882 (1956).
33. Körbl, J., and R. Pribil, *Chem. Listy*, **51**, 1804 (1957).

34. Körbl, J., and R. Pribil, *Chemist-Analyst*, **45**, 102 (1956).
35. Wilkins, D. H., *Talanta*, **2**, 12 (1959); Wilkins, D. H., *Anal. Chim. Acta*, **20**, 324 (1959); Wilkins, D. H., *Talanta*, **4**, 182 (1960).
36. Rees, D. I., and W. I. Stephen, *J. Chem. Soc.*, **1961**, 5101.
37. Kirkbright, G. F., and W. I. Stephen, *Anal. Chim. Acta*, **28**, 327 (1963).
38. Kirkbright, G. F., D. I. Rees, and W. I. Stephen, *Anal. Chim. Acta*, **27**, 558 (1962).
39. Dolezal, J., V. Patrovsky, Z. Sulcek, and J. Svasta, *Chem. Listy*, **49**, 1517 (1955).
40. Fritz, J. S., and M. O. Fulda, *Anal. Chem.*, **26**, 1206 (1954).
41. Banerjee, G., *Z. Anal. Chem.*, **146**, 417; **147**, 105 (1955).
42. Banerjee, G., *Z. Anal. Chem.*, **148**, 349 (1955).
43. ter Haar, K., and J. Bazen, *Anal. Chim. Acta*, **9**, 235 (1953).
44. Close, R. A., and T. S. West, *Talanta*, **5**, 221 (1960).
45. Welcher, F. J., *The Analytical Uses of Ethylenediamine Tetraacetic Acid*, D. Van Nostrand Co., Princeton, 1958. A comprehensive list of published metal titrations is given by Chaberek, S., and A. E. Martell, *Organic Sequestering Agents*, John Wiley and Sons, New York, 1959, pp. 282–292.
46. Schwarzenbach, G., E. Kampitsch, and R. Steiner, *Helv. Chim. Acta*, **29**, 364 (1946); Schwarzenbach, G., and W. Biedermann, *Helv. Chim. Acta*, **31**, 456 (1948).
47. Irving, H., and J. J. R. F. da Silva, *J. Chem. Soc.*, **1963**, 448, 458.
48. Schwarzenbach, G., and H. Ackermann, *Helv. Chim. Acta*, **31**, 1029 (1948).
49. Courtney, R. C., S. Chaberek, and A. E. Martell; see Martell, A. E., and M. Calvin, *Chemistry of the Metal Chelate Compounds*, Prentice-Hall, New York, 1952, pp. 539, 560.
50. Schwarzenbach, G., and H. Ackermann, *Helv. Chim. Acta*, **32**, 1682 (1949); Schwarzenbach, G., R. Gut, and G. Anderegg, *Helv. Chim. Acta*, **37**, 937 (1954).
51. Schwarzenbach, G., G. Anderegg, and R. Sallman, *Helv. Chim. Acta*, **35**, 1785 (1952).
52. Banks, C. V., and R. E. Yerick, *Anal. Chim. Acta*, **20**, 301 (1959).
53. Schwarzenbach, G., H. Senn, and G. Anderegg, *Helv. Chim. Acta*, **40**, 1886 (1957).
54. Pribil, R., Z. Roubal, and E. Svatek, *Coll. Czech. Chem. Comm.*, **18**, 43 (1953).
55. West, T. S., *Recent Developments in Inorganic and Organic Analytical Chemistry*, Royal Inst. of Chem. Lectures, Monographs and Reports, No. 1, 1959, p. 13.
56. Anderegg, G., P. Nägeli, F. Müller, and G. Schwarzenbach, *Helv. Chim. Acta*, **42**, 827 (1959).
57. See, for example, Flaschka, H., and H. Soliman, *Z. Anal. Chem.*, **158**, 254; **159**, 30 (1957).
58. Reilley, C. N., and M. V. Sheldon, *Chemist-Analyst*, **46**, 59 (1957).
59. Reilley, C. N., and M. V. Sheldon, *Talanta*, **1**, 127 (1958).
60. Reilley, C. N., and A. Vavoulis, *Anal. Chem.*, **31**, 243 (1959).
61. Jacobsen, E., and K. Schrøder, *Anal. Chim. Acta*, **27**, 179 (1962).
62. Pribil, R., *Coll. Czech. Chem. Comm.*, **16**, 86 (1951).
63. Pribil, R., and V. Sedlar, *Chem. Listy*, **44**, 200 (1950); *Coll. Czech. Chem. Comm.*, **16**, 69 (1951).
64. Pribil, R., *Coll. Czech. Chem. Comm.*, **16/17**, 542 (1951).
65. Cheng, K. L., *Anal. Chem.*, **33**, 783 (1961).

66. Hoyle, W., I. P. Sanderson, and T. S. West, *Anal. Chim. Acta*, **26**, 290 (1962).
67. Jungreis, E., and A. Lerner, *Anal. Chim. Acta*, **25**, 199 (1961).
68. Pribil, R., and J. Jenik, *Coll. Czech. Chem. Comm.*, **19**, 470 (1954).
69. Adamiec, I., *Rudy Metale Niezalazne*, **5**, 409 (1960).
70. Ubbelohde, A. R., *Analyst*, **59**, 339 (1934).
71. Feigl, F., and A. Caldas, *Anal. Chem. Acta*, **3**, 526 (1955).

CHAPTER 7

Surface Phenomena

Most chemical reactions take place under homogeneous conditions, usually in a liquid phase. Nevertheless, physical and chemical processes involving surfaces are by no means negligible. These include the growth of precipitates, adsorption effects, ion exchange, and chromatographic separations, as well as spot test reactions on filter paper. Rapid growth of crystals during a precipitation can result in the inclusion of a high proportion of lattice defects, facilitating inclusion of contaminants that would not "fit" into the normal crystal structure. So, too, the throwing down of a flocculent precipitate with a large surface-to-volume ratio often provides an opportunity for the entrainment of other species. In both cases, the precipitates develop, with time, a more ordered structure, often resulting in a partial decontamination.

These effects arise because, by its nature, a surface introduces a discontinuity into many measured properties of a system. Whereas a molecule or ion in the interior of a liquid or solid is, on the average, exposed to a spherically symmetrical set of interactions with other species, this is no longer the case at a surface. There is in consequence a surface-energy effect at any interface. This is why in a suspension of crystals of different sizes in a saturated solution the small crystals slowly dissolve and the large crystals grow at their expense. The topography of a surface is also important in relation to wetting by the solvent, in the adsorption of species from solution (including chemical combination), and in providing active sites in chemical reactions. In addition to ionic and covalent bonding, part of the adsorption effects on solid surfaces can be due to Van der Waals forces which arise from interactions between induced dipoles in large molecules when they are placed in juxtaposition.

Detailed discussion of the interplay of these factors lies outside the scope of this chapter, but it is necessary to be aware of their possible contributions.

7.1 Adsorption Indicators

The use of these indicators, which are either acid dyes (such as eosin and fluorescein and its derivatives) or basic dyes (e.g. rhodamine 6G), depends on a rather unusual type of complex formation. A typical example is the gradual addition of a silver nitrate solution to a solution containing chloride ion and a low concentration of fluorescein or some other suitable colored anion. At the endpoint of the titration, when the solution contains a slight excess of silver ions, the fluorescein suddenly adsorbs onto the precipitate and the colloidal suspension, where it undergoes a color change. During the titration, there is some adsorption of chloride ions onto the AgCl precipitate, but once all the chloride ion in the solution is removed, so that silver ion is in excess, there will, instead, be adsorption of silver ion onto the surface of the precipitate. This, in turn, immediately orients fluorescein anions, presumably on the other side of the double layer, the surface behaving as a charged ion lattice.

Alternatively, it is possible that the situation is similar to the mercuric nitrate-diphenylcarbazone example discussed in Chapter 6: The silver fluorescein complex cannot be formed while chloride ion, competing for the silver, predominates in the solution and on the surface of the precipitate. Just past the equivalence point, the silver complex is formed and adsorbs onto the precipitate.[2] Consistent with this interpretation is the requirement that the indicator not be too strongly adsorbed by the precipitate, because if this happens the endpoint is indicated before the equivalence point. (Eosin (tetrabromofluorescein), if used in the titration of chloride ion, would be an example.)

It may be more correct in many cases to picture silver ions built into the surface of the precipitate but still having sites available around them to coordinate further ligands which, so long as halide ions are present in appreciable concentrations, will be these halide ions. The indicator species cannot compete successfully. Further addition of silver ion during the course of titration will, in turn, bond the silver to the halide ions on the surface, so that there is a progressive growth of solid silver halide particles. This process comes to an end only when the supply of halide ions is exhausted, whereupon the silver-indicator complex can form at the surface. Conversely, where silver is titrated with halide or thiocyanate ions the silver-indicator complex can persist only so long as silver ion is present in excess. At the endpoint this complex dissociates and the surface acquires a negative charge, so that if the adsorption indicator can form a cation the latter will now be adsorbed at the surface. p-Ethoxychrysoidine is an example.[3] Similarly, when silver is titrated with bromide ion in the presence of rhodamine 6G the endpoint is indicated

TABLE 7.1

Some Representative Adsorption Indicator Reactions

Indicator	Ion	Titrated With
Alizarin red S[a]	$Fe(CN)_6^{4-}$, MoO_4^{2-}	$Pb(NO_3)_2$
[b]	F^-	$Th(NO_3)_4$
Bromophenol blue[c,d]	SCN^-, Cl^-, Br^-, I^-	$AgNO_3$
[a,e]	Br^-	$Hg_2(NO_3)_2$
[d]	Ag^+ and Tl^+	I^-
[f]	Hg_2^{2+}	CNS^-, Cl^-, or Br^-
Chromotrope F4B[g]	Br^- and I^-	$AgNO_3$
Congo red[h]	SCN^-, Cl^-, Br^-, I^-	$AgNO_3$
Dibromo(R)fluorescein[i]	HPO_4^{2-}	$Pb(OAc)_2$
Dichloro(R)fluo-rescein[h,j-n]	Cl^-, Br^-, I^-	$AgNO_3$
[o]	BO_2^-	$Pb(OAc)_2$
Diphenylcarbazone[o-q]	CN^-, Br^-, SCN^-	$AgNO_3$
Mercurochrome[r]	Cl^- and SCN^-	$AgNO_3$
Phenosafranine[m,s]	Cl^- and Br^-	$AgNO_3$
	Ag^+	Br^-
Rhodamine 6G[t]	Ag^+	Br^-
Solochrome red B[u]	$Mo_7O_{24}^{6-}$ and $Fe(CN)_6^{4-}$	Pb^{2+}
Tartrazine[e,s,t]	Ag^+	SCN^-, halides
Tetrachlorofluorescein	Cl^- and Br^-	Ag^+
Brilliant yellow[v,w]	Br^-, I^-, SCN^-	Ag^+
Bromocresol purple[j]	SCN^-	Ag^+

(*Continued*)

[a] Burstein, R., *Z. Anorg. Chem.*, **164**, 219 (1927); **168**, 327 (1927).

[b] Willard, H. H., and O. B. Winter, *Ind. Eng. Chem. (Anal. Ed.)*, **5**, 7 (1933).

[c] Kolthoff, I. M., *Z. Anal. Chem.*, **70**, 395 (1927); **71**, 235 (1927).

[d] Mehrotra, R. C., *Anal. Chim. Acta*, **3**, 73, 78 (1949).

[e] Zombory, L., von, *Z. Anorg. Chem.*, **184**, 237 (1929); **215**, 235 (1933).

[f] Burrill, F., and S. A. Jimeno, *Anales Real Soc. Espan. Fis. Quim. (Madrid)*, **50B**, 185 (1954).

[g] Belladen, L., and G. Piazza, *Ann. Chim. Applicata*, **22**, 631 (1932).

[h] Mehrotra, R. C., *Anal. Chim. Acta*, **2**, 36 (1948).

[i] Wellings, A. W., *Analyst*, **60**, 316 (1935).

[j] Mehrotra, R. C., *Anal. Chim. Acta*, **4**, 38 (1950).

[k] Kolthoff, I. M., W. M. Lauer, and C. J. Sunde, *J. Am. Chem. Soc.*, **51**, 3273 (1929).

[l] Hölscher, F., *Anal. Chim. Acta*, **3**, 69 (1949).

[m] Sanchez-Pedreno Martinez, D. M. de la C., *Anales Univ. Murcia*, **15**, 41 (1956–57).

TABLE 7.1 *(Continued)*

Some Representative Adsorption Indicator Reactions

Indicator	Ion	Titrated With
Bromothymol blue[x]	SCN^-	Ag^+
Eosin [l,m,y,z]	Br^-, I^-, SCN^-	Ag^+
Fluorescein [z]	halides, SCN^-, and $Fe(CN)_6^{4-}$	Ag^+
[aa]	SO_4^{2-}	$Ba(OH)_2$
[aa,bb]	oxalate	$Pb(OAc)_2$
Di-iodo-(R)-dimethyl-(R)-fluorescein	I^-	Ag^+
Dibromo(R)-fluorescein [j]	SCN^-, Cl^-, Br^-, and I^-	Ag^+
Dimethyl(R)fluorescein	Cl^-	Ag^+
Rose bengal	I^-	Ag^+
Brilliant archil C	Br^-, I^-	$AgNO_3$
	Ag^+	Br^-
Diphenylamine blue [ee]	Cl^-, Br^-	$AgNO_3$
p-Ethoxychrysoidin [cc]	I^-, CNS^-	$AgNO_3$
[dd]	Ag^+	I^-

[n] Duckleiter, L., and K. Ilver, *Dansk Tidsskr. Farm. Suppl.*, **2**, 69 (1956).

[o] Wellings, A. W., *Analyst*, **58**, 331 (1933).

[p] Matsuo, T., *J. Chem. Soc. Japan, Ind. Chem. Sect.*, **56**, 483 (1953).

[q] Gentry, C. H. R., and L. G. Sherrington, *Analyst*, **70**, 460 (1945).

[r] Airan, J. W., N. D. Ghatage, and E. B. Sandell, *Current Sci. (India)*, **16**, 343 (1947).

[s] Berry, A. G., and P. T. Durrant, *Analyst*, **55**, 613 (1930).

[t] Fajans, K., *Die Chem. Anal.*, **33**, 161 (1935).

[u] Holness, H., *Analyst*, **69**, 145 (1944).

[v] Boguer, J., and J. Vereskoi, *Acta Chim. Acad. Sci., Hung.*, **5**, 91 (1954).

[w] Oliveira Meditsch, J. de, *Eng. Quim. (Rio de Janeiro)*, **8**, No. 3, 1 (1956).

[x] Mehrotra, R. C., *Z. Anal. Chem.*, **130**, 390 (1950).

[y] Kolthoff, I. M., and E. B. Sandell, *Quantitative Inorganic Analysis*, Macmillan, London, 1938, pp. 453 and 542.

[z] Kolthoff, I. M., and L. H. van Berk, *Z. Anal. Chem.*, **70**, 369 (1927).

[aa] Wellings, A. W., *Trans. Faraday Soc.*, **28**, 565, 665 (1932).

[bb] Mehrotra, R. C., *Anal. Chim. Acta*, **3**, 69 (1949).

[cc] Schulke, E., and P. Rozsa, *Z. Anal. Chem.*, **115**, 185 (1958).

[dd] Schulke, E., and E. Pungor, *Anal. Chim. Acta*, **4**, 109 (1950).

[ee] Lang, R., and J. Messinger, *Ber.*, **B63**, 1429 (1930).

by strong adsorption of the dye onto the precipitate. Tartrazine can be used in the same way in the titration of silver nitrate with chloride ion.

Other typical examples include the titration of cyanide ion with silver nitrate if diphenylcarbazone is used as adsorption indicator, and the titration of bromide ion with mercurous perchlorate in the presence of bromphenol blue to give a precipitate that changes from yellowish to lilac at the endpoint if the titration is carried out in near-neutral solutions.

In most titrations using adsorption indicators it is necessary to consider the charge on the indicator. Thus if the complex-forming species is an anion, as it generally is, it is important to work at pH values near or above its pK_a value. (For example, with fluorescein, $pK_a \sim 8$, the desirable region is pH 7–10.)

The use of phenosafranine is interesting. During the titration of chloride or bromide ions with silver nitrate, the precipitate (like the bulk of the solution) is red but, at the endpoint, it suddenly changes to lilac

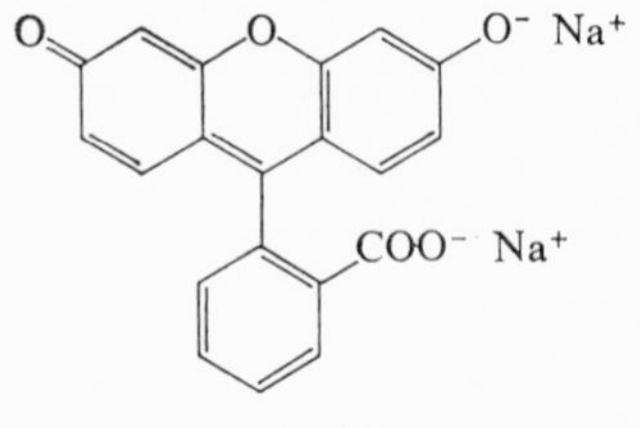

XLIX

(for chloride ion) or blue (for bromide ion). It can also be used for the reverse titrations, in which case the endpoint of the titration is the change from lilac or blue to red.

By carrying out pairs of titrations, mixtures of halides can sometimes be analyzed. Examples include the use of dichlorotetraiodofluorescein and fluorescein for chloride plus iodide, and eosin (or fluorescein) and di-iododimethylfluorescein for bromide plus iodide.

Some adsorption indicators and the reactions for which they are used are listed in Table 7.1. In all cases a sparingly soluble salt is produced during the titration; it is less soluble than the complex formed between the indicator and the precipitating species. Also, the precipitate adsorbs its own cations and anions strongly. To increase the sensitivity of the method the precipitate must be in a near-colloidal condition so as to give a very high surface-to-weight ratio. The ionic strength of the solutions should be kept low to diminish any tendency to coagulate the precipitate: This is particularly important if the "inert" ions are polyvalent.

The use of the pH indicators congo red, bromocresol purple and bromo-thymol blue as adsorption indicators in near-neutral solutions suggests that these dyes continue to act as pH indicators, but their acid dissociation constants are changed by adsorption onto the silver halide precipitates.[4]

The large number of derivatives of fluorescein (XLIX) used as adsorption indicators, especially in argentometric titrations of halides, provides a good example of how the properties of a reagent—in this case its color, pK_a, and the solubility of its silver salt—can be modified to alter its analytical usefulness.   Eight of the more commonly used members of this series are included in Table 7.1.   Insolubility of the silver salt and adsorbability onto precipitates is increased by halogen substitution in the resorcinol nuclei, so that fluorescein, but not its tetraiodo(R) derivative (erythrosin B), can be used in the usual argentometric titrations of Cl^-, Br^-, and I^-.   However, this increased adsorbability of erythrosin B is advantageous if appreciable concentrations of "inert" electrolytes are present.   Thus, erythrosin is a suitable indicator in the titration of iodide ion with silver under these conditions because it compensates for the greater tendency of the AgI sol to coagulate.[5]   Eosin is too strongly adsorbed to be useful in determinations of chloride ion, but it is suitable for estimations of bromide and iodide ions.   Also, because the adsorbing species is the phenate ion, it is desirable to work at pH values near, or above, the pK_a of the indicator.   Substitution of halogen atoms into the resorcinol nuclei increases the acidity of these dyes, so that whereas fluorescein cannot be used satisfactorily below about pH 7, with dibromo-(R)fluorescein pH 4 is practicable, while tetrabromo(R)fluorescein (eosin) can be used down to pH 1.   Solubilities decrease in the order unsubsti-tuted > Cl > Br > I.   On the other hand, halogen substitution increases the sensitivity of endpoint detection, so that tetra-I > di-I > tetra-Br > di-Br > di-Cl > unsubstituted.   These effects are reduced slightly if there is also halogen substitution in the phthalein nucleus.

As would be expected from the nature of titrations using adsorption indicators, there is often a marked change in fluorescence at the endpoint.

7.2   Ion Exchange

An ion-exchange resin comprises particles made up of an elastic hydro-carbon network to which is attached a large number of ionizable groups (which are usually all of the same kind).   The resin is insoluble in water and organic solvents, although it may swell in them, but by virtue of its active groups it can exchange ions present as gegenions at its surface with other ions in the solution.   This process has been familiar for many years; natural and synthetic zeolites have been widely used for water softening because of their ability to remove calcium and magnesium ions from hard water and replace them with sodium ions. The elasticity of these resins is necessary to enable them to withstand the internal forces generated by the osmotic pressure of hydrated ions which result from a type of Gibbs-Donnan equilibrium between the inside of the resin particles and the outside solution. The free energy of the exchange reaction governs the volume change of the resin, so that the amount of cross linking in the resin influences, directly, the efficiency of an ion-exchange resin.[6]

Ion-exchange resins fall into two main groups, namely cation exchangers and anions exchangers. Cation exchangers are further subdivided into strongly acid types, in which the functional group is the anion of a sulfonic acid, and weakly acid types, containing carboxylic acid or possibly phenolic groups. Strongly basic anion exchangers contain quaternary ammonium groups, whereas in weakly basic exchangers the functional group is usually a simple amino group. The resin is generally some form of cross-linked polystyrene matrix.

In dilute solutions the strongly acid cation exchangers show a preference for combining with metal ions of higher valency, in agreement with simple electrostatic expectations. The usual series is

$$Th^{4+}(as\ NO_3) > Fe^{3+} > Al^{3+} > Ba^{2+} > Pb^{2+}$$
$$> Sr^{2+} > Ca^{2+} > Co^{2+} > Ni^{2+}$$
$$\approx Cu^{2+} > Zn^{2+} \approx Mg^{2+} > UO_2^{2+}(as\ NO_3)$$
$$\approx Mn^{2+} > Ag^+ > Tl^+ > Cs^+ > Be^{2+}(as\ SO_4)$$
$$\approx Rb^+ > Cd^{2+} > NH_4^+ \approx K^+ > Na^+ > H^+ > Li^+ > Hg^{2+}$$

Incompleteness of dissociation of their salts explains the low positions of Be, Cd, and Hg. With the alkali and alkaline earth metals, the stronger adsorption for ions of greater radius is probably due to the ions of smaller size being more strongly hydrated, so that the radii of hydrated ions may lie in a sequence different from crystal radii. Decreasing the water content of a solution, e.g. by adding ethanol, brings the affinities of Cs and Na closer together. The rare earth metal ions, on the other hand, follow the expected trend, smaller ions being more strongly held than larger ones. The more dilute the solution is, the more selective the exchanger becomes. Conversely it is relatively easy to displace higher-valent ions from the resin by passing through it a strong solution of a less strongly held species. The weakly acid cation exchangers behave like an insoluble weak acid. When their own pH buffer capacity is utilized, an exchange can be carried out at a controlled pH. These resins have a high affinity for hydrogen ions, so that the order becomes $H^+ > Ca^{2+} > Mg^{2+} > Na^+$.

The following order has been reported for strongly basic anion exchangers:[7] $SO_4^{2-} > CrO_4^{2-} > $ citrate $>$ tartrate $> NO_3^- > AsO_4^{3-} >$

$PO_4^{3-} > MoO_4^{2-} > $ acetate $= I^- = Br^- > Cl^- > F^-$. Weakly basic resins, which have a high affinity for hydroxyl ions, can be used only in neutral or acid solutions.

In the presence of a complex-forming species, the distribution of two metals between an ion-exchange resin and their complexes will be governed only by their exchange ratios (between solution and resin) and their metal-ligand stability constants.[8]

For experimental details of the preparation and use of ion-exchange resins see reference 9.

Three main types of ion exchange (and chromatographic) separation comprise displacement, elution, and selective displacement techniques. The last of these processes consists in using a suitable complexing agent to elute one type of metal ion from a mixture adsorbed on the column. At pH 1, citrate elutes Mo but leaves Fe, Cr, Ni, whereas at pH 5.6 it elutes Pb and leaves Ba. Similarly, at pH 0.6, EDTA elutes Ti and Fe from Zr, but at pH 2.1 it separates Th from the rare earths. In selective displacements of this kind, pH buffering is essential.

Some of the more obvious applications of ion exchange in analytical chemistry include the substitution of particular ions in a solution either by other ions lying further to the right in the exchange series or by hydrogen ions, analysis for trace constituents, and separation of ions having similar properties. Closely related to these uses are the preparation of carbonate-free sodium hydroxide by passing the solution through a column of strongly basic anion exchanger in the free base form, and the standardization of pure salt solutions by passage of an aliquot through a strongly acidic cation exchanger in its free acid form, followed by alkalimetric titration of the eluate.

Complexing agents can be used to enable the separation of transition metal ions from alkali and alkaline earth metals. For example, iron, nickel, and cobalt can be masked by adding excess cyanide ion. Similarly, alkali metals can be separated from alkaline earth metals by adding ethylenediaminetetraacetic acid prior to ion exchange. Anion-exchange resins can adsorb complex ions such as $FeCl_4^-$ and $ZnCl_4^{2-}$ but not cations such as Mg^{2+}, the complexes subsequently being eluted with dilute acid. Using 9M-hydrochloric acid, cobalt as $CoCl_3^-$ can be easily separated from nickel, which is not adsorbed.[10]

Ion-exchange columns can be used for chromatography to separate ions of similar properties. They have been applied to the large-scale separation of the rare earths[11] by using the resin in the Cu(I) and Fe(III) form and passing in the rare earths as their EDTA complexes. The Cu and Fe complexes with EDTA are more stable so there is progressive deposition of rare earth cations, which are subsequently eluted serially with citric acid solution.[12]   Other chelating agents have been used for the same purpose.[13]   Mixtures of transuranic elements have also been separated in this way.[14]   Many examples of inorganic separations on ion-exchange columns are given in reference 15.   Another advantage of ion-exchange resins is the ease with which interfering anions can be removed from solutions for metal determinations, and vice versa.

More recently, attempts have been made to develop ion-exchange resins having more selective properties.   Dowex A-1 Chelating Resin contains iminodiacetate groups that impart a high affinity for heavy metal cations.   A resin with functional groups similar to dipicrylamine (which forms a sparingly soluble potassium salt) has a higher affinity for potassium than have other ion-exchange resins.[16]   A carboxylic acid resin containing hydroxamic groups selectively retains ferric ions,[17] whereas if 8-hydroxyquinoline groups are built onto a polystyrene resin, Cu, Ni, and Co are strongly adsorbed.[18]   With amino acids as complexing groups in a resin, the affinity for bivalent ions follows the Irving-Williams stability sequence.[19]   A limiting factor in these applications is that if weakly acid groupings are used rates of exchange are slow.   Ion-exchange resins can also be used as collectors, especially for spot test reactions, by shaking a large volume of a very dilute solution of the ion to be determined with a small amount of resin in a suitable form.[20]

Anion exchange resins have been used to separate mixtures of ortho-, pyro, tri-, trimeta-, and tetrametaphosphates,[21] and of fluoride, chloride, bromide, and iodide ions.[22]   Selective retention of chloride ions on a resin can be achieved by using a strongly acid cation exchange resin in the form of its silver salt.[23]   This technique is analogous to methods in which, for example, an anion-exchange resin in the form of its oxalate is used to retain strontium but not cesium, or in its hydroxide form to retain zirconium and niobium but not cesium or strontium.

7.3   Chromatography of Inorganic Substances[23a]

Complex formation plays a major part in the separation of inorganic species by adsorption chromatography.   Chromatography on cellulose (including filter paper) is essentially a solvent-extraction process in which the aqueous phase is held on the cellulose and substances distribute themselves between this fixed phase and the mobile organic solvent. Typical examples are the chloro complexes formed by some metal ions such as Cu^{2+}, Bi^{3+}, Zn^{2+}, Cd^{2+}, Hg^{2+}, and Fe^{3+} in hydrochloric acid, which then disssolve in oxygen-containing solvents.   This behavior is clearly analogous to adsorption of these metals onto anion-exchange resins from hydrochloric acid solutions.   The analogy is even closer when modified cellulose columns and papers containing incorporated diethylaminoethyl groups, carboxyl groups, and phosphate groups are used in separations. Similarly, metal ions have been separated on paper chromatograms using butanol/HCNS as a solvent.[24] The species Fe(III), Co(II), Cu(I), Cd(II), Hg(II), and Ag(I) travel with the solvent front but Ni(II), Cr(II), As(III), and Pb(II) are resolved. Conversely, by impregnating a cellulose or silica gel column with a solution of dithizone in carbon tetrachloride, a fixed organic phase is produced. Percolation of water samples through such columns leads to selective removal of traces of Zn, Cd, Pb, Mn, Co, Cu, and Zn which can subsequently be recovered by progressive elution with mineral acids or ammonia (which competitively complexes with Co and Cu).[25]

The absorptive properties of filter paper lead to some of the effects, such as zone enrichment and localization of different species, that are so important for the increased sensitivity often possible in spot test analysis.

In paper chromatography it is necessary to treat the final paper with a suitable reagent when the species concerned are insufficiently colored. The reagent should be nonspecific to facilitate the location of all the cations. Passage of H_2S gas after exposure to ammonia is useful for detecting most of the heavy metals. Alternatively, a number of "wide-spectrum" organic chelating agents have been used as sprays, followed by examination under ultraviolet light.[26] These comprise o-aminobenzoic acid, 8-hydroxyquinoline, kojic acid, morin, and naphthionic acid. For detection of specific ions the usual spot test conditions are applicable. The R_F values of many cations with complex-forming mixtures and in various solvent systems are given in reference 27, together with details for the separation of metals in different groups.

Columns of powdered 8-hydroxyquinoline (also mixed with kieselguhr) permit separation of ions in the following order: VO_3^-, WO_4^{2-}, Cu^{2+}, Bi^{3+}, Ni^{2+}, Co^{2+}, Zn^{2+}, Fe^{3+}, UO_2^{2+}. The bands are readily identified by their colors[28] and the sensitivity is high (down to 2 μg for Fe^{3+}). Violuric acid has been used similarly[29] for separations of alkali and alkaline earth metals, including such pairs as Na-K, K-Mg, Ba-Ca, and Sr-Ca as well as the ions Cu^{2+}, Hg^{2+}, and Pb^{2+}. Sodium and potassium have been separated semiquantitatively on columns of 5-oxo-4-oximino-3-phenylisoxazoline.[30] Naphthoquinoline and cupferron (mixed with potato starch) have been used in columns for separating Fe, Cu, Ni, and Co.[31]

Filtration through columns of specific reagents, or spot tests on filter papers impregnated with reagents, enables small quantities of metal ions to be detected, often in the presence of large excesses of other species, by the formation of local, well-defined colored zones.[32]

Inorganic adsorbents, such as alumina, can be used to separate metals as their complexes, e.g. Bi, As, Sb, and Sn as their tartrates,[33] and Co as its nitroso-R-salt chelate.[34] The reagent is probably adsorbed on the alumina, so that it behaves essentially like the columns of pure reagents described above, although metal ions themselves can adsorb on alumina surfaces because of hydrolysis.

Aqueous solutions are not essential. Dithizone complexes of many metal ions can be adsorbed from chloroform or carbon tetrachloride solutions and eluted with acetone.[35] The α-nitroso-β-naphthol complexes of Co, Fe, Ni, and Cu can also be adsorbed from chloroform onto alumina.[36]

Organic reagents have been little used in determining inorganic anions separated by paper chromatography. Examples include diphenylamine in concentrated sulfuric acid (to detect nitrate ion), the zirconium alizarin reagent (for fluoride), fluorescein with silver nitrate (as a fluorescence technique for detecting chloride and bromide ions), diphenylcarbazide (for chromate and dichromate), turmeric (for borate), and brucine (for bromate, nitrate, and chlorate). A scheme of analysis for common anions based on paper chromatography has been described.[37]

In suitable cases, the ring oven technique[38] can be applied in the micro-determination of inorganic species. This has been used, for example, in a method for the estimation of beryllium with eriochrome cyanine R.[39]

7.4 Polarography of Metal Complexes

The basic principle of this technique is the application of a steadily increasing voltage across two electrodes (one of which usually consists of mercury drops falling slowly from a fine capillary) dipping into a solution, to obtain a characteristic current-voltage curve.[40] Provided the electrode reaction is thermodynamically reversible, the potential at the midpoint of each step in the curve (the half-wave potential, $E_{1/2}$) is characteristic of a particular ionic species, while the step height is a measure of its concentration. The half-wave potential is a reduction potential and is displaced if complex-forming species are present. It may also be pH-dependent. The shift in the half-wave potential for the reaction

$$M^{a+} + a\,e + Hg \rightleftharpoons M(Hg)$$

consequent on the complex formation

$$M^{a+} + nX^{b-} \rightleftharpoons MX_n^{(a-bn)+}$$

is given by

$$(E_{1/2})_1 - (E_{1/2})_2 = \frac{0.0591}{a} \log \beta + \frac{0.0591\,n}{a} \log [X^{b-}],$$

where β is the stability constant of the complex.

It is this shift of $E_{1/2}$ by complex formation that enables the interfering effect of one metal upon another to be overcome by producing sufficient separation between them. Thus in the presence of excess cyanide ion Cu(II) is converted to cuprocyanide ion, enabling metals such as lead and nickel to be determined polarographically in copper-base alloys without prior chemical separation. Similarly, by the addition of 1,2-diamino-cyclohexane-N,N,N′,N′-tetraacetic acid, Cu(II) and Bi(III) can be determined in the presence of Pb(II), Cd(II), and Zn(II), and Tl(I) can be determined in the presence of Pb(II),[41] whereas, in the absence of complexing species, these steps overlap.

Complex formation often leads to marked improvement in the shapes of poorly defined, irreversible waves, and to the prevention of precipitation under necessary operating conditions.

Conversely, polarographic data can be used to provide evidence about the nature and properties of complex ions as well as their structures, stabilities, and reactions.

References

1. For a brief review, see *B.D.H. Adsorption Indicators*, 3rd ed., The British Drug Houses, Poole, England, 1961.
2. Kolthoff, I. M., *Chem. Rev.*, **16**, 87 (1935).
3. Tandon, K. N., and R. C. Mehrotra, *Anal. Chim. Acta*, **27**, 15 (1962).
4. Schulek, E., and E. Pungor, *Anal. Chim. Acta*, **4**, 109, 213 (1950).
5. Rudenko, N. P., *Russ. J. Phys. Chem.*, **62**, 505 (1930).
6. Reichenberg, D., K. W. Pepper, and D. J. McCauley, *J. Chem. Soc.*, **1951**, 493.
7. Kunin, R., and R. J. Myers, *J. Am. Chem. Soc.*, **69**, 2874 (1947).
8. Ketelle, B. H., and G. E. Boyd, *J. Am. Chem. Soc.*, **69**, 2800 (1947).
9. Kunin, R., *Ion Exchange Resins*, 2nd ed., John Wiley and Sons, New York, 1958; Samuelson, O., *Ion Exchangers in Analytical Chemistry*, John Wiley and Sons, New York, 1953; Kitchener, J. A., *Ion Exchange Resins*, John Wiley and Sons, New York, 1958; *Dowex: Ion Exchange*, the Dow Chemical Co., Midland, Mich. 1959; *Ion Exchange Resins*, 4th ed., The British Drug Houses, Poole, England, 1959.
10. For typical examples, see Kraus, K. A., and F. Nelson, "Anion Exchange Studies of the Fission Products," *Proc. Int. Conf. on Peaceful Uses of At. Energy, Geneva*, 1955, Vol. 7, pp. 113, 131 (1956); Kraus, K. A., and F. Nelson, "Metal Separations by Anion Exchange," Symposium on Ion Exchange and Chromatography in Analytical Chemistry, 1956; *ASTM Spec. Tech. Publ. No.* 195 (1958).
11. Spedding, F. H., *Discussions Faraday Soc.*, **7**, 14 (1949)
12. Spedding, F. H., J. E. Powell, and E. J. Wheelwright, *J. Am. Chem. Soc.*, **76**, 612, 2557 (1954).
13. Vickery, R. C., *J. Chem. Soc.*, **1952**, 4357.

14. Werner, L. B., and I. Perlmann, "The Preparation and Isolation of Cm," *U.S. Atomic Energy Comm.* AECD, No. 1898; Thompson, S. G., R. A. James, and L. O. Morgan, "The Tracer Chemistry of Am and Cm," *U.S. Atomic Energy Comm.*, AECD, No. 1907; Street, K., and G. T. Seaborg, *J. Am. Chem. Soc.*, **72**, 2790 (1950).

15. Lederer, E., and M. Lederer, *Chromatography*, Elsevier Publishing, Amsterdam, 1954, Chapter 38.

16. Woermann, D., K. F. Bonhoeffer, and F. Helfferich, *Z. Phys. Chem. (Frankfurt)* **8**, 265 (1956); Skogseid, A., Dissertation, Oslo, 1948.

17. Cornaz, J. P., and H. Deuel, *Experientia*, **10**, 137 (1954).

18. Parrish, J. R., *Chem. Ind.*, **1956**, 137.

19. Hale, K., *Research (London)*, **9**, 104 (1956).

20. See, for example, the "resin spot test" proposed by Fujimoto, K., *Chemist-Analyst*, **49**, 4 (1960), and its application for the detection of submicro amounts of Fe(III) with 7-iodo-8-hydroxyquinoline-5-sulfonic acid. (Fujimoto, M., and Y. Nakatsukasa, *Anal. Chim. Acta*, **26**, 427 (1962). Another application is in the adsorption of $CdI_4{}^{2-}$ on beads of an anion-exchange resin, followed by a color test for Cd with glyoxal-bis(2-hydroxyanil); see West, P. W., and J. Diffee, *Anal. Chim. Acta*, **25**, 399 (1961).

21. Grande, J. A., and J. Beukenkamp, *Anal. Chem.*, **28**, 1497 (1956).

22. Atteberry, R. W., and G. E. Boyd, *J. Am. Chem. Soc.*, **72**, 4805 (1950).

23. Mackereth, F. J. H., *Proc. Soc. Water Treat. Exam.*, **4**, 27 (1955).

23a. See also Pollard, F., and J. F. W. McOmie, *Chromatographic Methods of Inorganic Analysis*, Butterworths, London, 1953.

24. Martin, E. C., *Anal. Chim. Acta*, **5**, 511 (1951).

25. Carrett, D. E., *Anal. Chem.*, **25**, 1927 (1953); Pierce, T. B., and P. F. Peck, *Anal. Chim. Acta*, **26**, 557 (1962).

26. Elbeith, I. I., J. F. W. McOmie, and F. H. Pollard, *Discussions Faraday Soc.*, 7, 183 (1949).

27. Ref. 15, pp. 321–323.

28. Erlenmeyer, H., and H. Dahn, *Helv. Chim. Acta*, **22**, 1369 (1936).

29. Erlenmeyer, H., and W. Schoenauer, *Helv. Chim. Acta*, **24**, 878 (1941); Robinson, G., *Discussions Faraday Soc.*, 7, 195 (1949).

30. Erlenmeyer, H., and J. Schmidlin, *Helv. Chim. Acta*, **24**, 1213 (1941).

31. Shemyakin, F. M., and E. S. Mitselovskii, *Zh. Analit. Khim.*, 3, 349 (1948).

32. For applications and technique, see Feigl, F., *Spot Tests in Inorganic Analysis*, Elsevier Publishing, Amsterdam, 5th ed., 1958.

33. Pinterovic, *Z. Kem. Vjestnik. (Zagreb)*, **15**, 16 (1941–42).

34. Dean, J. A., *Anal. Chem.*, **23**, 1096 (1951).

35. Erametsa, O, *Suomen Kemistilehti*, **16B**, 13 (1943).

36. Paulais, R., *Ann. Pharm. Franc.*, **4**, 106 (1946).

37. Elbeich, I. I. M., and M. A. Abou-Elnaga, *Anal. Chim. Acta*, **23**, 30 (1960).

38. Weisz, H., *Microanalysis by the Ring Oven Technique*, Pergamon Press, New York, 1961, pp. 70–76.

39. West, P. W., and P. R. Mohilner, *Anal. Chem.*, **34**, 558 (1962).

40. See, for example, Kolthoff, I. M., and J. J. Lingane, *Polarography*, Interscience Publishers, New York, 2nd ed., 1952.

41. Pribil, R., and Z. Zabransky, *Coll. Czech. Chem. Comm.*, **16**, 554 (1951).

CHAPTER 8

Visible and Ultraviolet Absorption
Spectra of Metal Complexes

Analytical methods based on measurements of spectral differences often present few manipulative difficulties, are rapid, and are usually suitable for routine work. For these reasons, such methods comprise what is probably the most important group used in the chemical analysis of inorganic species. Their importance is also a direct result of the commercial development of reliable spectrophotometers, especially those for use in the ultraviolet and visible regions. For this reason, some knowledge of factors governing the absorption and emission of light is highly desirable.

8.1 The Process of Light Absorption

Light is a form of electromagnetic radiation, and its absorption or emission by a molecule arises from transitions between two different energy levels. The wavelength of the light associated with the transition from energy E_1 to energy E_2 is given by $E_1 - E_2 = hc/\lambda$. This makes it possible to use absorption spectra to gain information about differences in energy levels in ions and molecules, and hence to increase our understanding of the strengths and types of chemical bonds that are involved. Absorption of light takes place by the interaction of the electric field which accompanies it with the dipole of the molecule in a direction perpendicular to that in which the light travels or with a dipole induced in the molecule by the electric field. Unless there is a change in the polarization of the molecule in this direction light absorption or emission cannot occur.

Among organic molecules, an indication of whether light absorption in the visible or near-ultraviolet region is likely to occur can be obtained by considering the possibility of quantum-mechanical resonance in the

143

system. For example, Pauling[1] was able to account qualitatively for the absorption bands of neutral dyes such as indigo in terms of resonance between the classical valency structures and dipolar structures of higher energy. If two (or more) canonical forms of a molecule do not differ too greatly in energy, light absorption is probable; while the longer the conjugation pathway involved, the longer the wavelength at which maximum absorption should occur.

Whereas the wavelength of the absorbed light is determined by the energy difference involved in the transition, the extinction coefficient (or, more strictly, the area under the absorption curve) is governed by the size of the absorbing species (which increases the chance a molecule has of "trapping" any given quantum of light) and by the probability of the transition.

The relation is given approximately by the equation[1a]

$$\epsilon_{max} = 9 \times 10^3 Pa$$

where P is the probability of the transition and a, in square angstrom units, is the area of the chromophore. The molecular extinction coefficient ϵ of a substance is the optical density of a $1M$ solution, 1 cm thick. Values of $\log \epsilon \geqslant 4$ are "high-intensity" absorptions, and are due to transitions of high probability ("allowed" transitions), whereas values of $\log \epsilon < 3$ are "low-intensity" absorptions and arise from transitions of low probability ("forbidden" transitions). Most of the absorption in the ultraviolet and visible regions is associated with transitions in which electrons are excited from one molecular orbital to another. The fact that spectra consist of bands rather than sharp lines, especially in solution, is due to the occurrence, at the same time, of changes in vibrational and rotational energies and to the interaction between molecules, including solvation effects.

The fact that values of $\log \epsilon$ rarely exceed 5 (corresponding to $P = 1$ and $a = 11 \text{ Å}^2$) places a limit on the obtainable sensitivity of spectrophotometric methods. A value of $\log \epsilon = 5$ for the complex of a metal of molecular weight 60 would lead to an optical density of 0.1 in a 1-cm cell for a metal concentration of 0.06 ppm. These levels are reached in the zinc complex of 2-naphthylthiocarbazone (in chloroform), in rhodamine B chloroantimonate (in benzene), and in a limited number of other examples. In general, however, most colored metal complexes absorb light at only about one-tenth to one-hundredth of this intensity. Where greater sensitivity is required it is necessary to resort to techniques such as solvent extraction, which permit preliminary concentration of the species sought.

Most commonly the excited molecule gives up its excess energy, partly as infrared radiation and partly by changes in kinetic energy resulting from collisions with other molecules. This is usually achieved by passing from a low vibrational energy in the excited state to a high vibrational energy in the ground state.

Sometimes, however, the energy absorbed by the molecule is sufficient to bring about the rupture of a chemical bond and lead to chemical change. A familiar example is the photolytic decomposition of oxalic acid by uranium salts, with the production of formic acid and carbon dioxide. Many other organic species that are able to form uranyl complexes behave similarly, especially in ultraviolet light. During the process U(VI) is reduced to U(IV), but it is reoxidized by atmospheric oxygen so that the reaction continues until the organic material is used up.

8.2 Fluorescence

In some cases the excited molecule may fall to a lower electronic state by emission of visible or ultraviolet light; that is, by fluorescence. Generally, because of some prior loss of energy by the excited molecule, the emitted light is of longer wavelength (lower energy) than the absorbed light. Fluorescence is particularly associated with complex organic molecules with rigid frameworks, such as polycyclic aromatic and hetero-cyclic compounds. One of the simplest examples is 3-hydroxy-2-naph-thoic acid, which in acid solution gives a blue fluorescence with aluminium.[2]

Consideration of the interactions between optical electrons responsible for fluorescence in a complex and the field of the metal ion[3] suggests that, in general, metal ions most likely to form fluorescent complexes are those

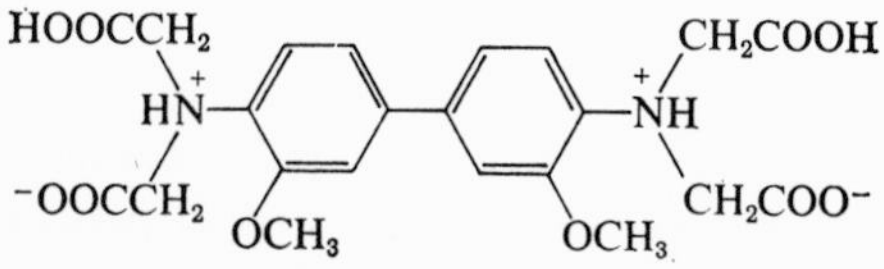

L

containing the most stable electron groupings, i.e. where shells are either full or empty. This is because the perturbation effect of the ionic field depends considerably upon the protection afforded to the optical electrons by the shells in the ion itself, and incomplete shells facilitate dissipation of fluorescence and "internal quenching" by electron promotion. Thus, cations that commonly form fluorescent complexes include Zr^{4+}, Al^{3+},

Sc^{3+}, Zn^{2+}, Mg^{2+}, Ca^{2+}, and Li^+, but not transition metal ions, although exceptions among the latter are known. The low-spin tris(5-methyl-1,10-phenanthroline) ruthenium (II) complex is such a case (possibly because the energy separations between filled and vacant d orbitals is too great to permit ready promotion of an electron), so that ruthenium can be determined fluorometrically.[4] Usually, the indicator ligand is fluorescent but its transition metal ion complex is not, so that, for example, the titration of EDTA with copper (II) in the presence of o-dianisidine-N,N,N′,N′-tetraacetic acid (L) is characterized by the disappearance of fluorescence due to (L) once the endpoint is passed and a trace of free copper (II) ion is present.[5] Mercury (II) ions behave similarly.

Fluorimetric methods are often more sensitive than the usual colorimetric ones. They are more likely, however, to be affected by the pH of the solution, the nature of the solvent, the concentration of the reagent, the temperature, and the presence of foreign molecules or ions (which may partially quench the fluorescence).[6] Metals commonly determined in this way are Be, Al, Ga, In, Sc, U, and Zr. In alkaline solution, beryllium reacts with quinizarin (1,4-dihydroxyanthraquinone) to form a red fluorescent compound. Similarly, at pH 4.5, tin (IV) forms a fluorescent complex with purpurin (1,2,4-trihydroxyanthraquinone), and in weakly acid solutions Th, Ga, and Pr give fluorescent complexes with 1-amino-4-hydroxyanthraquinone. The red bis complex of eriochrome (pontachrome) blue black R with aluminium, formed at pH 4.8 during 1

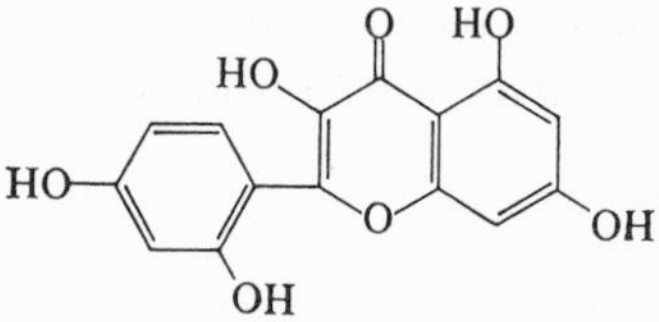

LI

hour, can be extracted, into n-amyl alcohol and determined by its fluorescence.[7] The method is sensitive to about 0.01 ppm of aluminium, but Fe, Cu, Co, V(V), and Ti all interfere seriously if present. Magnesium, zinc, aluminium, gallium, and indium[8] are sometimes determined at low concentration by the fluorescence of their 8-hydroxyquinoline and 8-hydroxyquinoline-5-sulfonate[9] complexes. 2-(o-Hydroxyphenyl)-benzoxazole is a fluorimetric reagent for cadmium.[10] Morin (LI) reacts in acid or neutral solution to form fluorescent complexes with Be, Ga, Sn(IV) > Sc > Zr, Th, Al, In, and Ce(III) > Y,[11] at concentrations down to $10^{-4} - 10^{-5}M$, probably by chelation through the —C=O group and the 3- or the 5-phenolate ion. The large number of reacting species necessitates prior separation. Determination of uranium by fluorescence is by direct ultraviolet examination of solid solutions of its salts in sodium fluoride.[12] Gallium down to 0.01 ppm can be detected as a solution of rhodamine B chlorogallate in benzene.

Some recent examples of the use of fluorescence include fluorexon as an indicator for the titration of calcium with the sodium salt of EDTA[13] and anthracene blue SVG in strong sulfuric acid for determining traces of boron in magnesium.[14]

8.3 Types of Ultraviolet and Visible Spectra of Complexes

Three types of transition giving rise to ultraviolet and visible spectra in metal complexes can be described, although in any particular case it may not be possible to distinguish clearly between them. They are:

1. Excitations within transition metal ions, generally associated within states of a d^n configuration, and referred to as d–d transitions. Similarly, in the rare earths, f–f transitions can occur.

2. Excitations within the ligand.

3. Charge-transfer transitions, involving the transfer of an electron from being mainly on the metal to being mainly on the ligand, or vice versa.

d–d TRANSITIONS

d–d Transitions produce bands in the visible, the near-ultraviolet, or the near-infrared regions, with molar extinction coefficients ranging from about 0.1 to 100, and are responsible for the colors of most of the transition metal complex ions. Although they are the best understood spectra of metal complexes,[15] their intensities are too low for them to have much analytical application. They have their origin in transitions of electrons between filled d orbitals and empty or only half-filled d orbitals which differ in energy because of the orientation of ligands about the central metal ion (in contrast to the isolated gaseous ion in which all five of the d orbitals are of equal energy). In the simplest case, that of a single d electron in an octahedral complex, splitting of energy levels is as shown in Fig. 8.1.

The doubly degenerate level E_g corresponds to the orbitals $d_{x^2-y^2}$ and d_{z^2}, and the triply degenerate level T_{2g} corresponds to d_{xy}, d_{yz}, and d_{zx}, so that the d–d spectrum consists of a single band produced by the transition $T_{2g} \rightarrow E_g$. A similar spectrum would be expected for a d^9

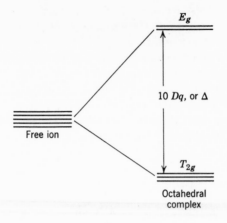

Fig. 8.1. The origin of the d–d spectrum for an octahedral complex of a cation containing only one d electron.

system, and also for d^4 and d^6 systems when the energy separation between E_g and T_{2g} is small enough that the high-spin state is maintained. Thus, in the spectra of the aquo ions listed in Table 8.1, there is a single,

TABLE 8.1

Visible Absorption Spectra of Some Transition Metal Ions[a]

Ion	Ti^{3+}	Cr^{2+}	Mn^{3+}	Fe^{2+}	Cu^{2+}
Configuration	d^1	d^4	d^4	d^6	d^9
λ_{max}, mμ	493	719	476	962	794
ϵ	4	7	5	2	12

[a] From Holmes, O. G., and D. S. McClure, *J. Chem. Phys.*, **26**, 1686 (1957).

fairly broad band in the visible or near-infrared region. The center of this band gives, directly, the energy separation, Δ or $10Dq$, between the T_{2g} and the E_g levels as 22 kcal for the Ti^{3+} aquo ion.

Replacement of water molecules in the coordination shell of a metal ion by molecules of another ligand will, because it alters the ligand-field strength, also move the d–d transition bands to longer or shorter wavelengths, depending on whether the new Δ is smaller or greater than for water. This explains why the spectrochemical series (see Chapter 4), which places ligands in order of increasing field strength for one central metal ion, can be used with confidence to predict the direction and relative amounts of wavelength shifts when complexes containing other ligands are compared with the aquo ions. This gives, taking several members of the series, λ_{max} for $I^- > H_2O > py > CN^-$. The maxima for the d^4 and d^9 systems occur at shorter wavelengths than simple theory predicts, and the observed bands are probably composite ones, broadened because of the further splitting of the d_{xy}, d_{yz}, and d_{zx} energy levels. This is a result of the Jahn-Teller effect (discussed in Chapter 3), the operation of which leads to a distorted octahedral configuration.

In all cases other than those just discussed, the energy level diagrams are complicated by the different ways in which electrons can be assigned to orbitals and because of quantum-mechanical interactions between levels of the same symmetry.[16] However, d–d transitions are "forbidden" because they do not involve a change of ± 1 in the value of the quantum number l. (Examples of transitions that meet this requirement and hence are "allowed" include $s \to p$, $p \to s$, $p \to d$, $d \to p$, and $d \to f$.) This is why d–d transitions are of such low intensity. That they occur at all is almost certainly due to the slight loss of symmetry of the complex ions, resulting from the existence of vibrations that are not themselves centrally symmetrical. This restriction does not apply to tetrahedral complexes, because they lack an inversion center, so that their extinction coefficients can be much higher. Values in the range 200–1200 have been found for the visible spectra of several compounds of formula MX_4^{2-} (M = Ni, Co, Cu; X = Cl, Br, I).[17]

Although the interpretation of rare earth metal ion spectra is not yet well investigated, transitions of the type f^n–$f^{n-1}d$ are important. Because such transitions are "permitted" they are much more intense than d–d transitions, and because these f electrons are not much affected by ligands in complex formation, their wavelengths and intensities do not change very much from one complex to another. Actinides give rise to similar spectra, but because the f electrons are less well screened, larger crystal-field effects are exerted by ligands. Analogous to the transition metal d–d transitions, both the rare earths and the actinides show f–f transitions of low intensity.

EXCITATIONS WITHIN LIGANDS

It is customary in discussing the electronic absorption spectra of organic molecules to distinguish five types of orbitals and the electrons contained in them.[18] These are, in what is commonly the order of increasing energy, bonding σ (σ), bonding π (π), nonbonding (n), antibonding π (π^*), and antibonding σ (σ^*). Thus bands due to $n \to \pi^*$ transitions will usually lie at longer wavelengths than those from $\pi \to \pi^*$ transitions.

In complexes where the bonding to the metal ion is essentially electrostatic, the metal ion will influence the spectrum in a way similar to protonation of the ligand. This will consist of displacements which are usually slight and which may be either to shorter or to longer wavelengths, with little, if any, change in the shape of the absorption curve or in the maximum extinction coefficients. With heteroaromatic ligands, such as pyridine, for example, complex formation should produce slight shifts to shorter wavelengths for bands due either to $n \to \pi^*$ or to $\pi \to \pi^*$ transitions. By their nature, such shifts are not at all specific for the cation concerned.

The electron-withdrawing effect of Mg^{2+} is greater than for a single proton, so that the absorption maximum (530 mμ) of the eriochrome black T-magnesium monoanion occurs at shorter wavelengths than for the eriochrome black T dianion (650 mμ); the intensity is also somewhat diminished.[19] The greater the stability of a series of metal chelates with this ligand (and hence the greater the electronic interaction between ligand and metal), the more the spectra of the complexes are displaced towards the ultraviolet. A similar displacement has been noted for the spectra of the murexide trianion, and the monocalcium, magnesium, zinc, and copper (II) chelates.[20]

Similar effects resulting from electronic interaction between the metal ion and the resonating system responsible for light absorption by the ligand are common to many of the colorimetric reagents for metal ions. Thus, dithiooxamide (rubeanic acid) (LII) finds application as a spot

$$HN{=}C\text{———}C{=}NH$$
$$\underset{SH}{|}\qquad\underset{SH}{|}$$

LII

test reagent because of the range of colored complexes it forms with Cu, Co, Ni, Fe(III), Ag, Bi, Hg(I), Pd, and Pt. It is also used in the colorimetric determination of ruthenium.[21]

Where strong covalent-bond formation with the metal occurs, however, including perhaps back-double-bonding by the metal's π electrons, the nature of the molecular orbitals on the ligand may be significantly changed, including both the energy levels and the probability of transition of electrons to or from other orbitals. It may not always be possible when this occurs to distinguish transitions within the ligand itself from those involving electron shifts to or from the metal ion. The most useful guide, in such cases, is to compare the complete ultraviolet and visible absorption spectra of the ligand and its metal complexes.

The metal indicator metalphthalein (XXX) is interesting in this respect, because the colors of its metal chelates are intense only for Ca(II), Sr(II), and Ba(II).   Except for Mg(II), which gives a weak color, the other metal complexes are almost colorless.   Because the red Ca, Sr, Ba, and Mg colors are similar to the completely dissociated form of metalphthalein, but occur at pH values lower than those where metalphthalein is fully ionized there is little doubt that complex formation involves the loss of the phenolic protons, corresponding to the ligand (LIII).   Apparently, if the bonding

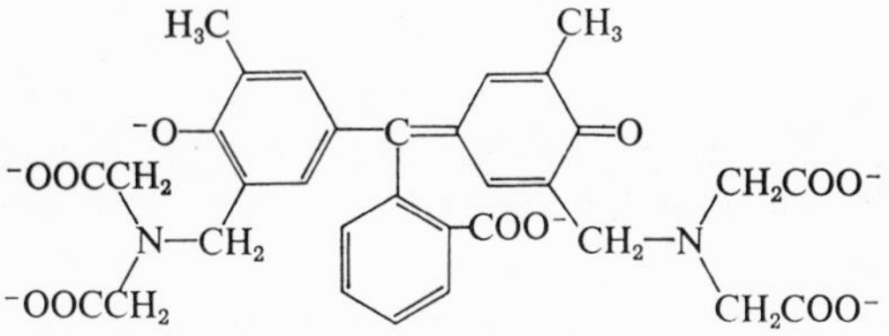

LIII

between metal ion and phenolate oxygen is mainly ionic there is not much interference with the resonating system responsible for the color in the ligand.   Covalent metal-oxygen bonding, on the other hand, grossly it, so that the red color is not observed.   Similar effects operate for calcein and thymolphthalexone.

Alizarin complexone (XXXII) solutions are yellow ($\lambda_{max} \approx 423$ mμ) at pH < 5, but at pH $\geqslant 6$ they are red ($\lambda_{max} \approx 520$ mμ).   In this form the 2-hydroxyl group is ionized whereas the 1-hydroxyl group is probably hydrogen bonded to the carbonyl oxygen at position 9.   Metal complex formation at pH 4.3–4.6 gives red products with wavelengths of absorption maxima lying in the sequence Pb $<$ Ce(III) $<$ Th(IV) $\approx$ Ni < 520 mμ, which probably also reflects the degree of ionic character of the metal-phenolic oxygen bond.   The high stability of the complexes of Al, Ce(III), Th, and Zr makes it possible to determine these metals colorimetrically in the presence of other metal ions, such as Fe(III), Mn(II), Hg(II), Ni, and Pb, using EDTA as masking agent.[22]

Dithizone and its metal complexes in carbon tetrachloride form a graded series, with approximate absorption maxima as follows:[23]

Dithizone (620 mμ) $>$ Cu(II) (545 mμ) $>$ Zn (535 mμ) $>$ Cd (520 mμ)
= Pb (520 mμ) $>$ In (510 mμ) $>$ Bi (500 mμ)
$>$ Hg(II) (490 mμ) $>$ Ag (460 mμ)

Assuming that the complexes are mono-, bis-, and tris-, depending on whether the metal ion is mono-, di-, or trivalent, an electrostatic approach would suggest that there might be a trend in λ_{max} with the reciprocal of ionic radius (rather than with ionic potential z/r).   This is found.   Except for lead, maxima are fitted, on an average, within about ± 10 mμ by the equation $\lambda_{max} = 357 + 134/r$. The equation may be considered to express a progressive change from a fully ionic form (the monoanion) to a completely charge-neutralized species (the neutral molecule). It leads to the prediction that λ_{max} for Tl(I), radius 1.47 Å, would be at 450 mμ, which coincides with a secondary maximum of dithizone itself, so that uncomplexed dithizone would interfere seriously if Tl was determined in this way. Insertion of methyl groups into the p, p'-positions of the phenyl groups in dithizone displaces maxima by about 10 mμ towards longer wavelengths. Replacement of the phenyls by naphthyl groups also displaces maxima to longer wavelengths. As a reagent, this derivative is not very different from dithizone.[24]

CHARGE TRANSFERS

A different class of absorption spectra that find use in chemical analysis are those described as *charge transfer*. They arise when the absorption of radiation causes an electronic transition between two orbitals in one of which the electron is more heavily concentrated on one atom and in the other it is mainly located on a different atom. This gives rise to a "charge-transfer transition," and the absorption band it gives rise to is a "charge-transfer band." Three general types of charge-transfer transition giving rise to absorption in the ultraviolet and visible region have been suggested.

1. Electrons from σ-bonding orbitals may be excited into empty t_{2g} or antibonding e_g orbitals. In both cases there is a net transfer of charge from the ligand to the metal. The important properties here are the oxidizing character of the central metal ion and the existence of a partly filled electron shell. The reaction is essentially a photochemical oxidation-reduction.

2. Electrons in filled π orbitals that are localized mainly on the ligands may be excited into antibonding orbitals formed by combining ligand orbitals with the s, p, or e_g orbitals on the metal. This transition again involves charge transfer from ligand to metal.

3. Electrons from bonding σ orbitals may be excited into vacant π orbitals which are localized very greatly on the ligands. This leads to a modest charge transfer from metal to ligand.

These spectra are "Laporte allowed" (because the transitions are between states of opposite parity) and so are generally far more intense than are d–d transitions, but at present there are very few cases in which the exact nature of the transition has been determined. Thus, the ferric thiocyanate complex owes its intense red color to the transfer of an electron from the CNS$^-$ ion to the Fe^{3+} ion with the formation of a CNS radical and a Fe^{2+} ion,[25] so that it is, in fact, a photochemical oxidation-reduction reaction. The likelihood of this transition increases when further thiocyanate ions are located around the metal ion, so that the bis complex has approximately twice the molecular extinction coefficient of the mono complex.[26] (The intensification of the color of an aqueous solution of ferric and thiocyanate ions when acetone is added is probably due mainly to displacement of equilibria towards more complete complex formation as expected in ionic systems when the dielectric constant is lowered) Similar explanations probably apply to the origins of the blue color of the cobalt, the amber color of the molybdenum (V), and the yellow colors of the uranium (VI), niobium (V), tungsten (V), and rhenium (VI?) thiocyanate complexes, all of which find analytical application. These complexes are often extracted into ethers, esters, or other oxygen-containing organic solvents as neutral species or thiocyanate acids. Alternatively, to repress dissociation of the complexes by lowering the dielectric constant, acetone is added to their aqueous solutions. It is possible that at least part of the spectra of the square planar $Ni(CN)_4^{2-}$ and $Pd(CN)_4^{2-}$ ions are due to electron transfer into their vacant $d_{x^2-y^2}$ orbitals.

The vanadium (IV) ion VO^{2+}, in its complexes such as the aquo ion $VO(H_2O)_5^{2+}$, shows strong tetragonal distortion because of the short vanadium-oxygen π bond. This makes possible two low-energy charge-transfer bands in which an electron from the oxygen π orbital is transferred into a half-filled orbital and an antibonding orbital on the metal.[27] Tetrahedral Ni(II) complexes, such as $[Ni(Ph_3AsO)_2Br_2]$ and $NiI_2(PPh)_2$, are not very common. The green or red color of some of these complexes is due to a charge-transfer band which tails into the visible region from the ultraviolet.

Charge transfer in the uranium oxalate complexes leads to the photochemical decomposition of oxalate ion to formate ion.

Many anions in aqueous solution have a very strong absorption band ($\log \epsilon \approx 4$) in the ultraviolet, usually in or near 2000–2500 Å, although in some cases, such as NO_2^- (366 mμ), NO_3^- (302 mμ), and SO_3^{2-} (300 mμ), the wavelength maximum occurs nearer the visible. Examples include Cl^-, Br^-, I^-, OH^-, SH^-, SCN^-, OCl^-, CN^-, ClO_2^-, NO_2^-, ClO_3^-, NO_3^-, SO_3^{2-}, and SO_4^{2-}. This band has been interpreted as a charge-transfer band in which absorption of light by the hydrated negative ion leads to the formation of a free radical and a hydrated electron;[28] thus $Cl^-(H_2O)_n \rightarrow Cl(H_2O)_n^-$. Carboxylate ions, such as formate, acetate, oxalate, and succinate, also absorb in this region. Although the alkali metal and alkaline earth metal ions do not show any charge-transfer bands in the ultraviolet or visible, the hydrated ions of many other metals do, their maxima also lying in the region 2000–2500 Å. Some examples are

Cr^{2+} (log ϵ = 2.8), V^{2+} (log $\epsilon \approx$ 2.0), and Fe^{2+} (log ϵ = 1.5). Rabino-witch[29] suggested that if the cation is easily oxidized the charge-transfer absorption of longest wavelength is from the ion to the solvent, whereas if the cation is easily reduced it is from the solvent to the ion. For example, $Fe^{2+}(H_2O)_n \rightarrow Fe^{3+}(H_2O)_n{}^-$, and $Fe^{3+}OH^- \rightarrow Fe^{2+}OH$.

Similarly, the complexes $PbCl^+$ ($\lambda_{max} \approx$ 230 mμ), $PbBr^+$ (235 mμ), and PbI^+ (275 mμ) have absorption intensities of log ϵ between 4.1 and 4.4. With complexes containing more than one halide ion, absorption moves to longer wavelengths, indicating that less energy is required to bring about electron transfer. In the ferric chloride, bromide, and thiocyanate complexes, the charge-transfer band associated with the production of free radicals occurs in the visible or near-ultraviolet. Cupric halides behave similarly. The instability of ferric and cupric iodides suggests that, in these substances, thermal energy is sufficient to bring about such a charge transfer.

Little has been done to interpret in this way the spectra of more compli-cated species. Complexes of $[Co(NH_3)_6]^{3+}$ and $[Cr(NH_3)_6]^{3+}$ have strong absorption below 2500 Å, and progressive replacement of the ammonia molecules by halide ions moves the absorption to longer wave-lengths.[30] The extent of the shift increases in the order I > Br > Cl > F. The bands are probably due to the transfer of an electron from the anion to the cobaltic ion.

A similar explanation is likely for the yellow color of $[Ir(NH_3)_6]^{3+}3I^-$. It is suggested that the phenolic reagents such as tiron, used in the esti-mation of Fe^{3+}, Cu^{2+}, and V^{4+}, as well as thioacetic and sulfosalicylic acids used for Fe^{3+}, produce characteristic spectra in their metal complexes because of charge-transfer processes involving electron shifts from ligands to metal ions. It is noteworthy that these ligands readily undergo oxi-dation-reaction reactions.[25] It is also roughly true that in the complexes of a given ligand with different metals the charge-transfer bands move to longer wavelengths as the oxidizing power of the metal ions increases. The increased stability of higher valencies of ions in the later rows of the periodic table (e.g. Fe $\rightarrow$ Ru $\rightarrow$ Os) leads, for the same reason, to a pro-gressive movement of these bands to shorter wavelengths in passing from the first to higher rows of any series. The intense colors of the Cu(I) and Fe(II) 1,10-phenanthroline, α,α'-bipyridine and related complexes have been ascribed to transitions involving the transfer of metal electrons to ligand π orbitals.[31] This is probably also true of the colored complexes formed by beryllium alkyls and halides with α,α'-bipyridine, and of these and similar complexes with aromatic amines given by Be, Zn, Cd, Al, and Ga alkyls.

The binding of the two pyridyl rings of each α,α'-bipyridine molecule in the same plane when they are coordinated to a metal ion greatly increases the possibility of resonance stabilization of the molecule: This explains why light absorption by the Fe(II) and Cu(I) complexes of α,α'-bipyridine is not very much less than for the corresponding complexes with 1,10-phenanthroline. This planarity is important. 3,3′-Dimethyl substitution in α,α'-bipyridine introduces steric hindrance, leading to some distortion from a planar structure. The color of its tris ferrous complex is only one-fifth of the intensity of the parent complex.[32] Substitution of methyl groups into the 4,4′ or 5,5′ positions does not lead to steric interaction and does not affect the color of the tris ferrous complex. Possibly because the groups are larger, 3,3′-dicarboxy-α,α'-bipyridine does not form a colored complex with ferrous ion:[33] However, the base-weakening effect of the carboxyl groups may also be important. The estimation of Ti^{4+} by the use of hydrogen peroxide depends on a charge-transfer band for the species $Ti^{4+}O_2H^-$.

Charge-transfer spectra of purely organic molecular complexes are also well known, but they lie outside the scope of this book. Such spectra can also arise in organic solvents containing nonmetallic inorganic species; thus an intense band ($\log \epsilon \sim 4$), with λ_{max} lying between 290 and 380 mμ, results when I_2 is dissolved in benzene or its methylated derivatives.[34] Bromine behaves similarly.

8.4 On Designing Ligands to Give Colored Metal Complexes

Ligands of suitable complexing ability but of unsatisfactory spectral characteristics can be "tailored" to give spectra which are increased in intensity and displaced to longer wavelengths. To do this the conjugation

TABLE 8.2

Common Chromophores

$-\overset{|}{C}=\overset{|}{C}-$ < $-\overset{|}{C}=O$ < $-\overset{|}{C}=S$ < $-CH=N-$ <
(carbonyl) (thione) (azomethine)

$-N=N-$ < $-\underset{\underset{O}{\downarrow}}{N}=N-$ < $-N=O$ < $-NO_2$ <
(azo) (azoxy) (nitroso) (nitro)

$=\overset{|}{C}-\overset{|}{C}=\overset{|}{C}-$ <
(quinonoid)

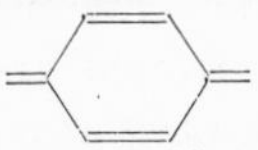

path in the ligand must be extended to result in greater π-electron delocalization by incorporating one or more of the common chromophores like those listed in Table 8.2, or by increasing the number of aromatic rings. For example, replacement of the p-nitrobenzene group in p-nitrobenzenediazo-aminoazobenzene ("cadion") by 4-nitronaphthalene (to give "cadion 2B") shifts its color towards blue and increases the contrast with the "lake" cadmium hydroxide forms with it. (This "lake" is red because coordination of the cadmium through the nitrogen atoms decreases the extent of π-electron delocalization in the ligand.)

An analogous process has been used in the colorimetric determination of aluminium. The precipitate of aluminium as the 8-hydroxyquinoline complex is dissolved in dilute alcoholic hydrochloric acid and converted to a diazo compound with sulfanilic acid and sodium nitrate, to give a yellow-red solution on addition of sodium hydroxide.[35]

An extreme example of the extension of the conjugation pathway in a ligand to shift absorption spectra to longer wavelengths is provided by stilbazo (stilbene-4,4'-bis(1-azo-3,4-dihydroxybenzene)-2,2'-disulfonate) (LIV), which, as a modified pyrocatechol, has been proposed as a reagent for aluminium.[36]

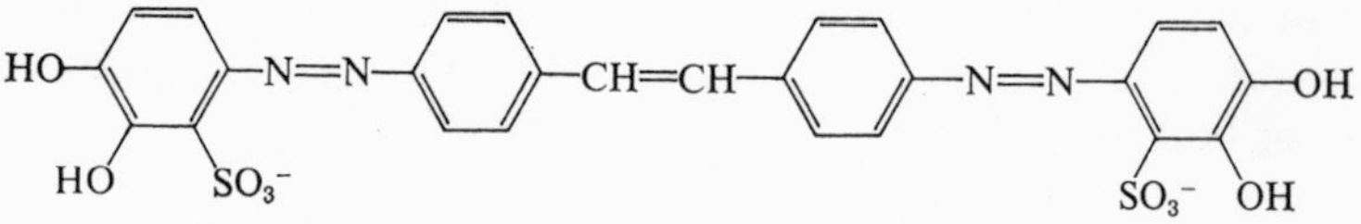

LIV

In indo-oxine (LV) the desired shift from ultraviolet to visible absorption

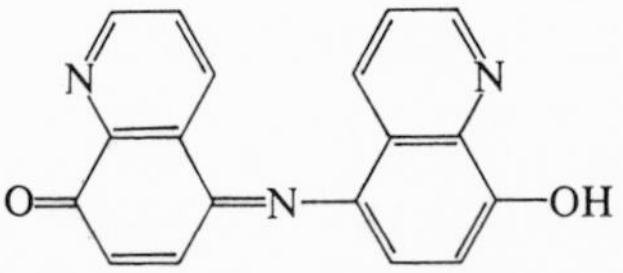

LV

has been achieved by "doubling up" the 8-hydroxyquinoline molecule, so that the corresponding metal complexes are mainly blue or violet.[37] Substances absorbing in the visible region offer more convenient methods than those absorbing only in the ultraviolet region.

A bathochromic shift in the spectra of metal complexes with 8-hydroxyquinoline is produced by insertion of a 7-iodo group into the ligand, while a 5-sulfonic acid group confers water solubility on the complexes. The resulting molecule, 7-iodo-8-hydroxyquinoline-5-sulfonic acid ("ferron"), is used as a reagent for ferric ion, with which it forms a soluble, green, tris complex in slightly acid solutions.

Phenylarsonic acid forms a white precipitate with zirconium. If, however, a suitable chromophoric group is attached to the organic residue, the precipitate is colored. Thus p-dimethylaminobenzeneazophenyl-arsonic acid (LVI) has a long conjugation pathway that is modified when metals form complexes through its arsonic acid portion, leading to a color change. The reagent is used as a colorimetric spot test reagent for zirconium, with which it gives a brown precipitate. (Tantalum behaves similarly.)

LVI

In general, however, a useful colorimetric reagent must interact with a metal ion to produce a complex having a characteristic intense absorption band which does not occur in either the free reagent or the free ion. Reactions which result only in a displacement of absorption maxima when a proton is displaced by a metal ion are likely to be less specific than those reactions which invoke some particular property of the cation concerned. This difficulty can often be minimized by incorporating masking reagents in the solution or by carrying out preliminary separations. Specificity is less important in metal indicators in complexometric titrations, so long as the log stability constants of the metal indicator complexes vary in roughly the same way as the log stability constants of the corresponding metal titrant complexes. A profitable avenue of exploration would be one concerned with the production of ligands that give rise in their complexes, particularly with transition metal ions, to intense charge-transfer spectra.

In some cases small changes in the ligand may lead to greater specificity. This is well illustrated in the 1,10-phenanthroline series. The bis(1,10-phenanthroline) ferrous complex has a rather low stability constant, and its d electrons exist in a high-spin state. It very readily adds another molecule of 1,10-phenanthroline to form the stable tris complex in which all the d electrons are paired up. This complex is intensely colored because of a charge transfer in which one of the d electrons in the filled t_{2g} orbitals is placed in a π^* orbital of the phenanthroline.[38]   In 2,9-dimethyl-1,10-phenanthroline (LVII), however, the methyl groups prevent the formation of the tris complex with ferrous ion for steric reasons, so that this characteristic absorption band is not found. They do not interfere in the formation of the tetrahedral bis complex with cuprous ion, which, like the bis complex of (unsubstituted 1,10-phenanthroline) copper (I), has an intense yellow color and probably also involves a transition from filled t_{2g} to π^* orbital. The weakness of the metal-ligand bonding in the bis(2,9-dimethyl-1,10-phenanthroline) ferrous complex and its lack of color make it possible to use 2,9-dimethyl-1,10-phenanthroline (neo-cuproine) as a sensitive copper-selective reagent even in the presence of high concentrations of ferrous ion. The steric effect prevents tris ferrous complex formation while still permitting the bis cuprous complex to exist if positions ortho to the nitrogen atoms are points of fusion of aromatic rings, as in cuproine (2,2'-biquinoline) (LVIII). Cuproine is rather less sensitive, but more readily prepared, than 6,6'-dimethyl-2,2'-bipyridine (LIX), which can also be used in this way.

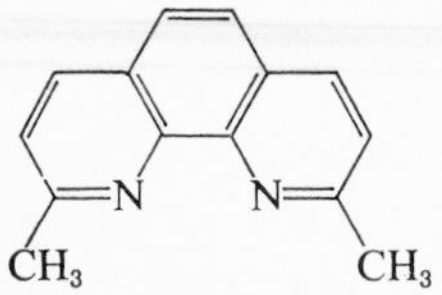

LVII 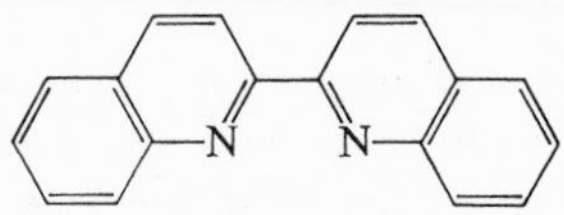   LVIII 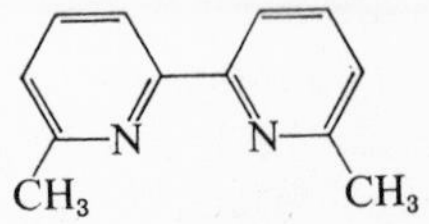   LIX

Metal complex formation by 2,2'-bipyridines and 1,10-phenanthrolines and the effects of substituents have been thoroughly investigated, so that in some cases it is possible to predict quite closely not only the absorption maxima of some of the metal complexes, but also the corresponding molecular extinction coefficients.[39] For example, the substitution of methyl groups for hydrogen atoms is an additive function for both the wavelengths of maximum absorption of the ferrous and copper complexes and their molecular extinction coefficients.[40] By insertion of phenyl groups into positions 4 and 7 of 1,10-phenanthroline, the conjugation pathway in the ligand is extended, doubling the molecular extinction coefficient of the ferrous complex. The increase in the hydrophobic nature of the ligand also makes it possible to extract the ferrous complex from aqueous solution with amyl alcohol or n-hexyl alcohol, whereas the corresponding complex of 1,10-phenanthroline requires nitrobenzene for its extraction (as the perchlorate). Alternatively, if cyanide ion is added to solutions containing the tris complexes of 1,10-phenanthroline or 4,7-diphenyl-1,10-phenanthroline with iron (II), neutral dicyano-bis complexes that can be extracted into chloroform are produced. (Because the colorless complex ion $Cu(CN)_3{}^{2-}$ is more stable than the cuprous-phenanthroline complex, it is possible to determine traces of iron in copper samples.[41])

The selectivity for Cu(I) of 2,9-dimethyl-1,10-phenanthroline and the color enhancement of 4,7-diphenyl substitution is combined in bathocuproine[42] (LX).

To overcome the poor solubility of bathocuproine and the batho-phenanthroline in water, especially in the presence of perchlorate ion, the corresponding disulfonic acids can be used without loss of sensitivity:[43] They are much more freely soluble in water but are not extractable by

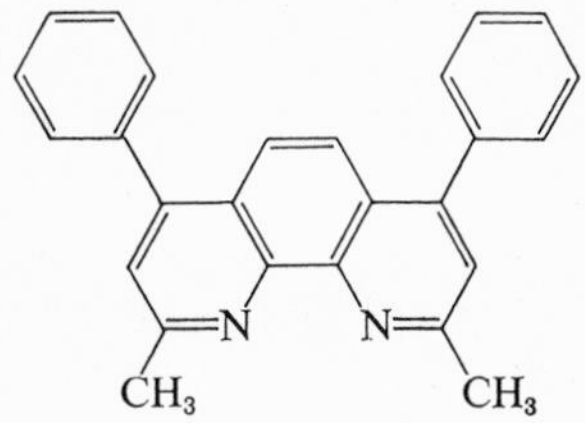

LX

organic solvents. Similarly, insertion of a sulfonic acid group into positions 3 or 5 in 1,10-phenanthroline renders the corresponding tris ferrous complexes soluble in perchlorate solutions without significantly altering their absorption spectra.[44]

Other substances proposed as colorimetric reagents for iron, and containing the same N—C—C—N chain, include the 4,4′,4″-triphenyl derivative of terpyridyl (LXI), which is about four times as sensitive as 2,2′-bipyridine and is also useful as a reagent for cobalt,[45] 2-(2-pyridyl)-

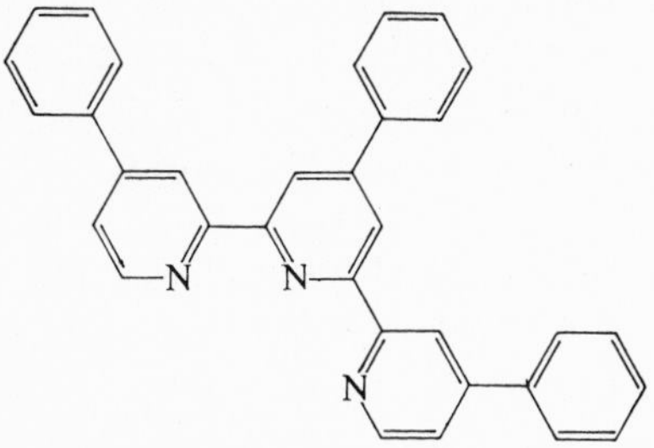

LXI

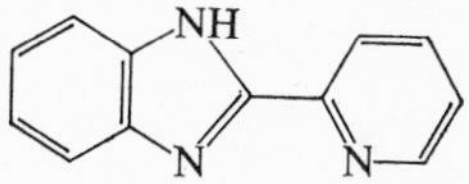

LXII

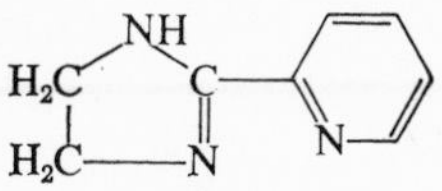

LXIII

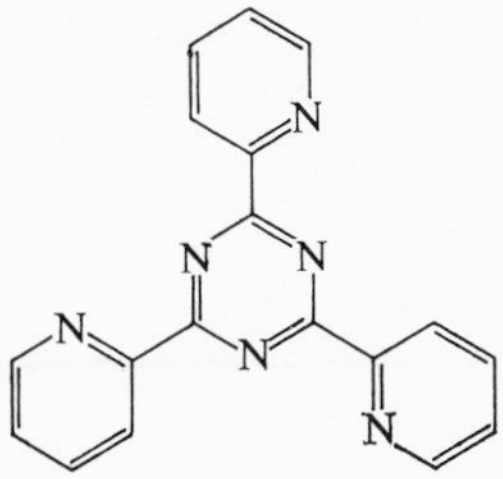

LXIV

benzimidazole (LXII), and 2-(2-pyridyl)-imidazoline (LXIII).[46] 2,4,6-Tripyridyl-1,3,5-triazine (LXIV), is as sensitive a reagent for iron as is bathophenanthroline, and in the presence of perchlorate ion its blue ferrous complex can be extracted into nitrobenzene.[47] Absorption spectral differences are such that iron and copper can be determined on the same solution by using bathocuproine (for cuprous ion) and then adding 2,4,6-tripyridyl-1,3,5-triazine.

2-Pyridyl-1,3,5-triazine behaves as a bidentate chelate, resembling 2,2-bipyridine in forming a tris complex with iron, but 2,4-dipyridyl-1,3,5-triazine, like terpyridyl, is terdentate and gives a bis complex.   The third pyridyl group in 2,4,6-tripyridyl-1,3,5-triazine does not contribute to the metal binding.   Insertion of phenyl groups into the 4' positions of the pyridines improves the spectral properties of the iron (II) complexes, in the same way as for the 1,10-phenanthroline and 2,2'-bipyridine series, but this advantage is offset by a resulting sparing solubility in water.[48]

Phenyl-2-pyridyl ketoxime (LXV), which also contains the N—C—C—N

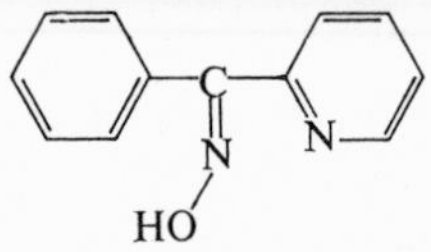

LXV

chain, has been proposed as a colorimetric reagent for iron, with which it gives a red color which is extractable into amyl alcohol.[49]   The corresponding orange-yellow chelate of palladium (II) is highly soluble in chloroform: Its formation has been suggested as a spot test for palladium.[50] Gold (III) reacts similarly.   Replacement of the phenyl group by methyl, to give methyl-2-pyridyl ketoxime, does not greatly alter the complexing ability of the reagent.   However, it increases the water-solubility of the reagent and its metal complexes, the absorption maxima of which are shifted to shorter wavelengths, so that the tris complex with ferrous iron is orange-red in acid solutions.   (In alkaline solution, the ligand loses a proton so that the corresponding red-violet nitrone complex (LXVI) is formed.[51] Copper (I) forms a yellowish-green bis complex.)

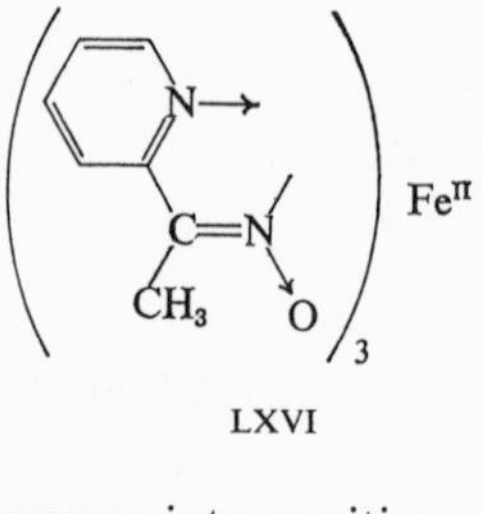

LXVI

Insertion of hydroxyl groups into positions 4 and 7 of 1,10-phenanthroline greatly weakens its complex-forming ability with ferrous iron in neutral or weakly acid solution.   This is probably due to the existence of the tautomerism (LXVII) ⇌ (LXVIII), in which the amide form, (LXVIII), is greatly favored.   For example, in the analogous 4-hydroxy-quinoline the ratio of amide to enolic form is 24,000 to 1.[52]   Complex

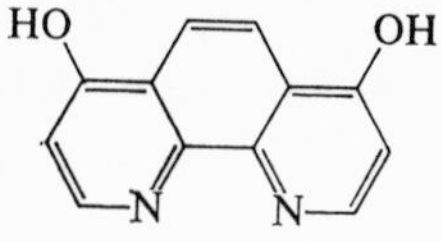

LXVII

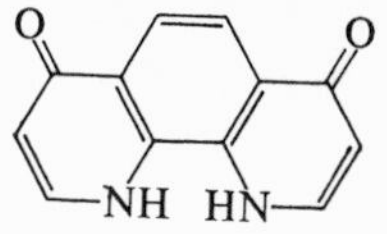

LXVIII

formation by such amides would be very weak.   However, in strongly alkaline solutions the phenolic groups are fully ionized and the dianion of 4,7-dihydroxy-1,10-phenanthroline becomes a sensitive reagent for ferrous iron.[53]   The increased electron density on the nitrogen atoms, relative to the unsubstituted 1,10-phenanthroline complex, leads to a small increase in light absorption (ϵ_{max} = 15,000 as against 11,000) and a slight shift to longer wavelengths (λ_{max} = 520 mμ, instead of 509 mμ).

Salicyclic acid can be used as a colorimetric reagent for U(VI).   The spectral properties of the complex are improved by inserting suitable groups into the ligand.   Examples include the following substituents in the p-position; amino- (or better) p-nitrobenzeneneazo- (to give alizarin yellow R), m-nitrobenzeneazo- (to give alizarin yellow GG), and benzene-azo-.[54]   These substituted salicyclic acids contain substituents that increase the color intensity of their complexes and displace maxima to longer wavelengths.

Another group of colorimetric reagents in which there has been some "tailoring" of the molecule is derived from fluorone.   9-Methyl-2,3,7-tri-hydroxyfluorone (LXIX) ("methyl fluorone") has been proposed as a colorimetric reagent for Sb(III), with which it forms an intensely red-

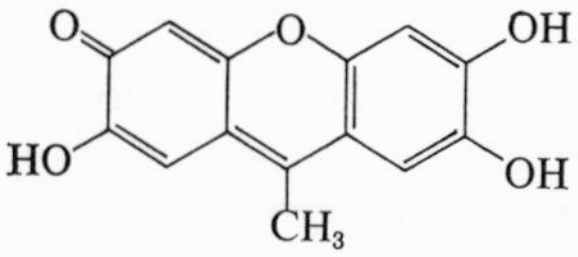

LXIX

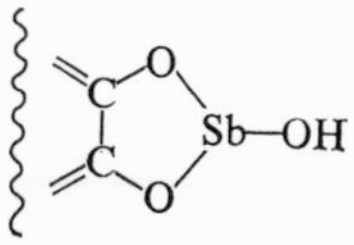

LXX

colored cyclic ester of the type (LXX), within the pH range 2–4.[55]   (Inter-ference by other ions is avoided by prior separation as gaseous stibine.) Light absorption is due to a transition within the ligand, the spectrum of the antimony complex being similar to that of methyl fluorone in alkaline solution.   Replacement of the methyl group by phenyl gives "phenyl

fluorone," which is used for the spectrophotometric estimation of germanium,[56] with which it forms an insoluble, red-colored bis complex.
Fluorone and its derivatives are too polar for solvent extraction to be
possible, so the complex has to be stabilized in aqueous solution by addition of a dispersing agent. Many species such as Ga(III), Sn(II), Sn(IV),
Sb(III), Zr(IV), MoO_4^{2-}, Ti(IV), As(III), Bi(III), Fe(III), and AsO_4^{3-}
also react, but these interferences are easily overcome by first isolating
the germanium as the tetrachloride either by distillation or by extraction
from about $9M$ hydrochloric acid by carbon tetrachloride. The corresponding nitroderivatives, 9-(3-nitrophenyl)- and 9-(4-nitrophenyl)-2,3,7-
trihydroxylfluorone have been suggested as sensitive colorimetric reagents
for zirconium[57] and tin (IV),[58] respectively. 9-(4-Dimethylaminophenyl)-
2,3,7-trihydroxyfluorone, originally suggested as a reagent for germanium,
with which it forms a complex soluble in ethanolic hydrochloric acid
solution,[59] is now used to determine tantalum in zirconium and niobium.[60]

8.5   Chemiluminescent Indicators

A small number of substances are known to emit light as a direct
result of chemical reaction. Sometimes this property of chemiluminescence can be used as an indicator in an analytical process. Suitable substances of this type include siloxene (which is a derivative of calcium
silicide) and luminol (3-aminophthalic acid cyclic hydrazide),[61] lophine (2,
4,5-triphenylimidazole),[62] and lucigenin (N,N'-dimethyl-biacrydiliumdini-
trate).[63]   Luminol (LXXI) is oxidized by a free-radical mechanism to a

LXXI

transannular peroxide dianion which then emits a quantum of light as it
decomposes to aminophthalic acid and nitrogen.[64]   Metal ions catalyze
the decomposition of hydrogen peroxide by a free-radical mechanism.
Hence when an ammoniacal copper (II) solution is titrated in the presence
of luminol with an EDTA solution containing 0.01% hydrogen peroxide,
the mixture emits light until an excess of EDTA is present, whereupon the
light disappears. Conversely, lucigenin reacts with hydrogen peroxide
but not with free radicals, so that during similar titrations it emits only
short flashes of light so long as free metal ions are present. When the endpoint is reached and the hydrogen peroxide is no longer decomposed

catalytically, the lucigenin exhibits a steady chemiluminescence. A mechanism has been suggested for the reaction and for the production of light.[64] Lucigenin can also be used as an adsorption indicator for argentometric titrations of iodide ions. So long as it is adsorbed on the surface of the negatively charged silver iodide precipitate no light is emitted, even in the presence of hydrogen peroxide. Desorption when the charge on the surface is changed leads to sudden luminescence.

Such indicators have applications in turbid, opaque, or dark solutions.

References

1. Pauling, L., *Proc. Natl. Acad. Sci.*, **25**, 577 (1939).
1a. Braude, E. A., *J. Chem. Soc.*, **1950**, 379.
2. Kristiansen, H., *Anal. Chim. Acta*, **25**, 513 (1961).
3. Yuster, P., and S. I. Weissman, *J. Chem. Phys.*, **17**, 1182 (1949).
4. Veening, H., and W. W. Brandt, *Anal. Chem.*, **32**, 1426 (1960).
5. Belcher, R., D. I. Rees, and W. I. Stephen, *Talanta*, **4**, 78 (1960).
6. For further details, see Dankwortt, P., and J. Eisenbrand, *Luminiszenz-Analyse in Filtrieten Ultravioletten Licht*, Akad. Verlag, Leipzig, 6th ed., 1956; Radley, J. A., and J. Grant, *Fluorescent Analyses in Ultraviolet Light*, Chapman and Hall, London, 4th ed., 1954; Willard, H. H., L. L. Merritt, and J. R. Dean, *Instrumental Methods of Analysis*, 3rd ed., Van Nostrand, New York, 1958, Chapter 3; White, C. E., *Anal. Chem.*, **28**, 621 (1956); **30**, 729 (1958); **32**, 47R (1960); **34**, 81R (1962).
7. Weissler, A., and C. E. White, *Ind. Eng. Chem. (Anal. Ed.)*, **18**, 530 (1946); Ishibashi, M., T. Shigematsu, and Y. Nishikawa, *Japan Analyst*, **6**, 568 (1957).
8. Ishibashi, M., T. Shigematsu, and Y. Nishikawa, *Nippon Kagaku Zasshi*, **77**, 1474 (1956).
9. Schachter, D., *J. Lab. Clin. Med.*, **58**, 495 (1961).
10. Evcim, N., and L. A. Reber, *Anal. Chem.*, **26**, 936 (1954).
11. Charlot, G., *Anal. Chim. Acta*, **1**, 233 (1947).
12. Papish, L., and L. E. Hoag, *Proc. Natl. Acad. Sci. U.S.*, **13**, 726 (1927).
13. Hofman, J., *Casopis Lekaru Ceskych*, **100**, 1171 (1961).
14. Gordievskii, A. V., and G. P. Ustyugov, *Izv. Vysshikh Uchebn. Zavedenii, Khim. i Khim. Tekhnol.*, **4**, 366 (1961).
15. See, for example, Jørgensen, C. K., *Absorption Spectra and Chemical Bonding in Complexes*, Pergamon Press, Oxford, 1962.
16. This is discussed more fully by Dunn, T. M., in *Modern Coordination Chemistry*, Lewis, J., and R. G. Wilkins, eds., Interscience, New York, 1959, pp. 229–300.
17. Gill, N. S., and R. S. Nyholm, *J. Chem. Soc.*, **1959**, 3997.
18. For recent review, see Mason, S. F., *Quart. Rev.*, **15**, 287 (1961).
19. Schwarzenbach, G., and W. Biedermann, *Helv. Chim. Acta*, **31**, 678 (1948).
20. Schwarzenbach, G., and H. Gysling, *Helv. Chim. Acta*, **32**, 528, 1108, 1314 (1951); Schwarzenbach, G., *Anal. Chim. Acta*, **7**, 141 (1952).
21. Ayres, G. H., and F. Young, *Anal. Chem.*, **22**, 1281 (1950).
22. Leonard, M. A., and T. S. West, *J. Chem. Soc.*, **1960**, 4477.
23. Fischer, H., and W. Weyl, *Wiss. Veröffentl. Siemans-Konzern*, **14**, No. 2, 41 (1935).

24. Hubbard, D. M., *Ind. Eng. Chem.* (*Anal. Ed.*), **12**, 768 (1940).
25. Orgel, L. E., *Quart. Rev.*, **8**, 422 (1954).
26. Perrin, D. D., *J. Am. Chem. Soc.*, **80**, 3852 (1958).
27. Ballhausen, C. J., and H. B. Gray, *Inorg. Chem.*, **1**, 111 (1962).
28. Franck, J., and G. Scheibe, *Z. Physik. Chem.*, **139A**, 22 (1929).
29. Rabinowitch, E., *Rev. Mod. Phys.*, **14**, 112 (1942).
30. Linhard, M., and M. Weigl, *Z. Anorg. Chem.*, **266**, 49 (1951).
31. Orgel, L. E., *An Introduction to Transition Metal Chemistry*, Methuen, London, 1960, p. 101.
32. Cagle, F. W., and G. F. Smith, *J. Am. Chem. Soc.*, **69**, 1860 (1947).
33. Richter, F. P., Ph.D. thesis, Univ. of Illinois, 1941.
34. Burgers, J., M. A. Hoefnagel, P. E. Verkade, H. Visser, and B. M. Wepster, *Rec. Trav. Chim.*, **77**, 491 (1958).
35. Alten, F., H. Weiland and H. Loofman, *Angew. Chem.*, **46**, 668 (1933).
36. Kuznetzov, V. I., G. C. Karanovich, and D. A. Drapkina, *Zavodsk. Lab.*, **16**, 7. 87 (1950); through *CA*, **45**, 972g (1951).
37. Berg, R., and E. Becker, *Z. Anal. Chem.*, **119**, 81 (1940).
38. Ref. 16, p. 270.
39. McCurdy, W. H., and G. F. Smith, *Analyst*, **77**, 846 (1952); Smith, G. F., *Anal. Chem.*, **26**, 1534 (1954).
40. Brandt, W. W., and G. F. Smith, *Anal. Chem.*, **21**, 1313 (1949); Smith, G. F., and W. H. McCurdy, *Anal. Chem.*, **24**, 371 (1952).
41. Diehl, H., and E. B. Buchanan, *Talanta*, **1**, 76 (1958).
42. Smith, G. F., and D. H. Wilkins, *Anal. Chem.*, **25**, 510 (1953).
43. Blair, D. E., and H. Diehl, *Talanta*, **7**, 163 (1961).
44. Blair, D. E., and H. Diehl, *Anal. Chem.*, **33**, 867 (1961).
45. Schilt, A. A., and G. F. Smith, *Anal. Chim. Acta*, **15**, 567 (1956).
46. Walter, J. L., and H. Freiser, *Anal. Chem.*, **26**, 217 (1954).
47. Collins, P. F., H. Diehl, and G. F. Smith, *Anal. Chem.*, **31**, 1862 (1959).
48. Diehl, H., E. B. Buchanan, and G. F. Smith, *Anal. Chem.*, **32**, 1117 (1960).
49. Trusell, F., and H. Diehl, *Anal. Chem.*, **31**, 1978 (1959).
50. Sen, B., *Anal. Chim. Acta*, **22**, 22 (1960).
51. Banerjea, D. K., and K. K. Tripathi, *Anal. Chem.*, **32**, 1197 (1960).
52. Albert, A., and J. N. Phillips, *J. Chem. Soc.*, **1956**, 1294.
53. Schilt, A. A., G. F. Smith, and A. Heimbuch, *Anal. Chem.*, **28**, 809 (1956).
54. Baiulescu, Gh., and I. C. Cuirea, *Z. Anal. Chem.*, **166**, 5 (1959).
55. *Organic Reagents for Metals*, Hopkin and Williams, Chadwell Heath, Essex, England, 5th ed., 1955, Vol. 1, p. 103.
56. Cluley, H. J., *Analyst*, **76**, 523, 530 (1951).
57. Sano, H., *Talanta*, **2**, 187 (1959).
58. Lebedova, N. V., and V. A. Nazarenko, *Anal. Abstr.*, **9**, 8 (1962).
59. Kimura, K., and M. Asada, *Bull. Chem. Soc. Japan*, **29**, 812 (1956).
60. Nazarenko, V. A., and M. B. Shustova, *Zavodsk. Lab.*, **23**, 1283 (1957); Nazarenko, V. A., and N. V. Lebedeva, *ibid.*, **25**, 899 (1959).
61. Kenny, F., and R. B. Kurtz, *Anal. Chem.*, **29**, 543 (1957).
62. Erdey, L., and I. Buzas, *Anal. Chim. Acta*, **15**, 322 (1956).
63. Erdey, L., *Acta Chim. Acad. Sci. Hung.*, **3**, 81, 95, 105 (1953); Erdey, L., and I. Buzas, *Acta Chim. Acad. Sci. Hung.*, **6**, 77, 127 (1955).
64. Erdey, L., and I. Buzas, *Anal. Chim. Acta*, **22**, 524 (1960).

CHAPTER 9

Solubility of Complexes

9.1 Factors Governing Solubility in Water

Water is a highly polar solvent which, because of strong hydrogen bonding between molecules, is also highly associated. For a substance to be readily soluble in water, it must be able to break up some of the water structure and become solvated. The smaller organic molecules such as the simpler alcohols, aldehydes, amines, carboxylic acids, and ketones achieve this result mainly through hydrogen bonding. Sulfur is much less effective than oxygen in hydrogen-bond formation, so that replacement of O by S in compounds of the same structure always leads to lower solubility in water. Nitrogen, on the other hand, is only a little less strongly hydrogen bonding than oxygen. Aliphatic hydrocarbon chains and aromatic rings, unable to react in this way, decrease the solubility of molecules in water, the effect increasing in any series as the chains are lengthened or more rings are added. Ions and highly polar substances, on the other hand, exert sufficient electrostatic attraction to orient water molecules around them, and these, in turn, are hydrogen bonded to more of the solvent molecules. This is why a neutral molecule which may be only slightly soluble in water may dissolve readily in alkaline solution

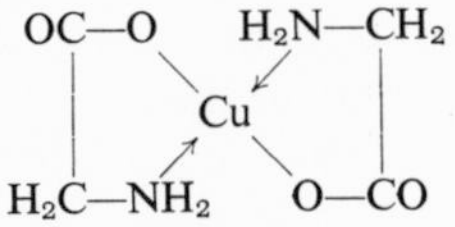

$$
\begin{array}{c}
\text{OC---O} \qquad \text{H}_2\text{N---CH}_2 \\
\quad | \qquad \diagdown \quad \diagup \qquad | \\
\qquad \qquad \text{Cu} \\
\quad | \qquad \diagup \quad \diagdown \qquad | \\
\text{H}_2\text{C---NH}_2 \qquad \text{O---CO}
\end{array}
$$

LXXII

(because of anion formation) or in acid solution (because of cation formation). This property is often important in determining the conditions under which organic reagents can be used. Qualitatively, then, the process involved in dissolving a substance consists in part in orienting solvent molecules around it so that the surface of the solvated molecule resembles the bulk phase. Solubility in water might therefore be expected

165

where substances are highly polar or where they already resemble water in structure.

The bis(glycino)-copper (II) complex (LXXII), which has no net charge, owes its water solubility to its highly polar nature and small hydrocarbon content. The same comment applies to metal-EDTA complexes, and also explains why such complexes are not extracted by organic solvents from aqueous solution.

The latter properties are to be contrasted with conditions in the insoluble copper complexes of quinaldinic acid (quinoline-2-carboxylic acid) (LXXIII), anthranilic acid (LXXIV), and α-amino-n-caproic acid, in all

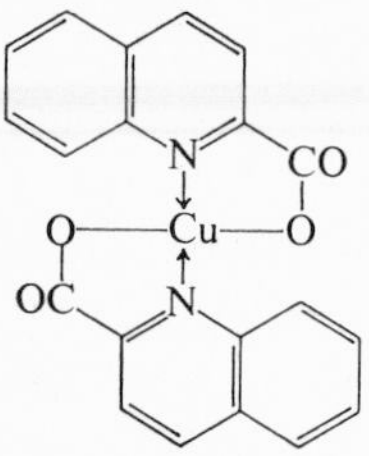

LXXIII 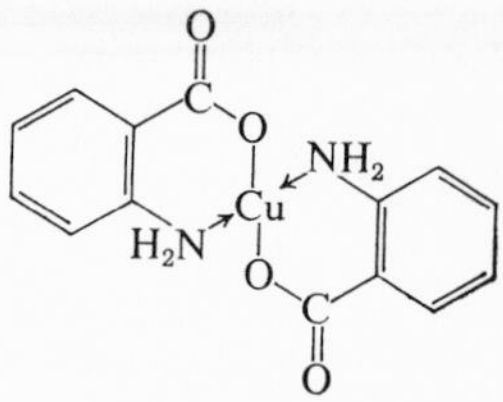   LXXIV

of which the metal-ligand binding is qualitatively similar to that in metal-glycine complexes.

An alternative, qualitative explanation of the insolubility of many inorganic salts, such as carbonates and phosphates, is that these anions have lattice-building properties. They combine with metals in such a way as to form a large network of metal ions and anions, and the size of this structure contributes to its insolubility. This is also likely to be the case in the antimony and bismuth complexes with pyrogallol, two of the phenolic oxygens in any given ligand molecule being bonded to one metal ion whereas the third oxygen is bonded to another metal ion, each of the metal ions, in turn, being linked to further pyrogallol moieties. (It is sterically impossible for all three oxygens to be linked to the same metal ion.) The resulting complexes are much less soluble than those derived from pyrocatechol.

Steric effects can operate to prevent the formation of insoluble complexes. The bis complex of 2-methyl-8-hydroxyquinoline with aluminium carries a positive charge and is water soluble, but the small size of the aluminium ion does not permit another 2-methyl-8-hydroxyquinoline anion to be packed around it to form the expected uncharged insoluble tris complex. This has analytical applications in the separation of aluminium from zinc and larger cations.

Where water solubility of a metal complex is desired, for example in colorimetric methods not based on extraction into organic solvents, this can be often achieved by inserting sulfonic acid or other strongly ionized groups into the ligand. For example, the tris complex of 8-hydroxy-quinoline with ferric ion has no net charge and is insoluble in water, whereas the corresponding complex of 8-hydroxyquinoline-5-sulfonic acid is readily soluble. Compare, also, metal complexes of pyrocatechol and tiron. The water solubility of metal complexes with a bulky ligand such as thoron (used as a colorimetric reagent for Th, Pu, Zr, U, Be, Np, and Bi) is a direct consequence of the sulfonic acid groups. Similarly, whereas the copper dialkyldithiocarbamate complexes are almost insoluble in water, the carboxylic group in 3-carboxy-pentamethylene-dithiocarba-mate (LXXV) leads to water-soluble copper complexes.

$$\text{Na}^+ \,\,^-\text{OOC}-\overset{\displaystyle \text{H}_2\text{C}-\text{CH}_2}{\underset{\displaystyle \text{H}_2\text{C}-\text{CH}_2}{\text{CH}}}\,\,\,\text{N}-\text{CSS}^- \,\,\text{Na}^+$$

LXXV

The sulfonate group in unithiol (sodium 2,3-dimercaptopropane sul-fonate) confers solubility on its metal complexes so that unithiol is recom-mended as a masking agent for ions of mercury, lead, and zinc which show preferential binding with sulfur-containing ligands.[1] Insertion of a *p*-dimethylamino group into phenylfluorone makes its metal complexes soluble in acid solution.[2]

Among a series of related ligands such as the anions of 8-hydroxyquino-line and its 5,7-dichloro and -dibromo derivatives the increasing insolu-bility of the metal complexes in water with increasing size of the reagent affects equilibria in complex formation. Quite apart from any effect on stability constants of the metal complexes, the larger reagents are more effective precipitants than the parent substance in more acid solutions.

Theoretically, the solubility of electrolytes in water can be calculated by means of a thermodynamic cycle in which ions in the solid crystal are vaporized and then hydrated. The work required in the first process is equal to the lattice energy of the crystalline solid,[3] while the second step involves the heats of hydration of the gas ions.

In practice, however, the calculations are not helpful in obtaining absolute values of solubilities because they depend on differences in these very large quantities. They do, on the other hand, enable some qualitative predictions to be made. For example, according to Born, the change in free energy involved in taking a sphere of charge *ze* from a vacuum and inserting in a cavity of radius r in a solvent of dielectric constant D is given by the equation

$$-\Delta G = \frac{(ze)^2}{2r}\left(1 - \frac{1}{D}\right)$$

The Born treatment also predicts that the entropies and hence the heats of hydration will vary with $(ze)^2/r$. This leads to the expectation that solubilities of ions will be less in solvents of low dielectric constant than in water. Further, it predicts that if, in a related series of metal ions, the crystal lattice energies are comparable, solubilities will decrease with increasing size of cation. (Melting points provide a useful guide to lattice energies.) The increase in solubility with increasing temperature is due to increased ionic vibrations in crystals, so that less energy is required to separate crystals into their component species.

A further consquence of the dependence of solubility on crystal-lattice energy is that if a substance can exist in two crystalline forms the metastable form will be the more soluble. This is partly why, for example, many precipitates become less soluble on aging. (Another reason is that, because of surface-tension effects, small particles are more soluble than large particles. This leads to a slow growth of the larger particles at the expense of the smaller ones, with a gradual drop in solubility.)

In nonpolar solvents such as carbon tetrachloride, benzene, and petroleum ether intermolecular forces are much smaller. These solvents dissolve nonpolar substances much more readily than they dissolve electrolytes and polar molecules, partly because of their chemical similarity and partly because the former lack the strong electrostatic forces that stabilize the solid state in the latter.

9.2   Effect of pH on the Solubility of Metal Complexes and Salts

The *solubility product* K_s of a substance A_aB_b, dissociating in solution into the species A and B, is given by the identity $K_s = (a_A)^a(a_B)^b$, where the a's denote the thermodynamic activities for equilibrium with solid A_aB_b. For the purposes of discussion, activity coefficients are assumed equal to unity. (That is, ionic-strength effects will be ignored. The activity coefficient of an ion in dilute solution is given approximately by the Debye-Hückel relation, $-\log f = Az^2\mu^{1/2}/(1 + B\mu)$, where A and B are constants, z is the charge on the ion, and μ is the ionic strength.) So that $K_s \simeq [A]^a[B]^b$ under these conditions. The solubility of A_aB_b, on the other hand, is the maximum concentration of this species that can exist in a particular solution. For A_aB_b alone in a solvent this is given by $(K_s/a^ab^b)^{1/(a+b)}$, but if [B] is increased $[A]_{max}$ is decreased.

Thus the solubility product of AgCl is 1.2×10^{-10}, so that the solubility of AgCl in distilled water is $1.1 \times 10^{-5} M$: in $0.01 M$ KCl solution, however, the solubility of AgCl is only $1.2 \times 10^{-8} M$ because of the *common ion* effect of the additional chloride ion. In the titration of a mixture of chloride and iodide ions, silver iodide ($K_s = 1.7 \times 10^{-16}$) will precipitate first because its solubility product is very much smaller than that of silver chloride. The point at which silver chloride begins to precipitate is reached when the silver chloride and iodide concentrations fit the simultaneous equations:

$$[\text{Ag}^+][\text{Cl}^-] = 1.2 \times 10^{-10}$$
$$[\text{Ag}^+][\text{I}^-] = 1.7 \times 10^{-16}$$

that is, when the iodide concentration is only 1.4×10^{-6} times the chloride concentration. It is this large factor which makes possible the quantitative titration of iodide ion in the presence of chloride, using either suitable adsorption indicators or a silver electrode.

The addition of complex-forming reagents to such systems may greatly alter the solubility of individual species. Important applications in chemical separations arise because one ionic species may, by conversion to a complex ion, be retained in solution under conditions where other components are precipitated. Or, conversely, the desired species may precipitate as an insoluble complex whereas other substances remain in solution. The sulfides of Cu^{2+}, Cu^+, and Cd^{2+} are almost insoluble ($K_s = 6 \times 10^{-45}$, 2×10^{-47}, and 1×10^{-28}, respectively) but by adding cyanide ion to neutral solutions of Cu^{2+} and Cd^{2+} to form the complexes Cu(CN)_4^{3-} (a cuprous complex) and Cd(CN)_4^{2-} (with log stability constants of 27.7 and 16.9, respectively), precipitation of Cu_2S, but not of CdS, is prevented. The reason for this discrimination is apparent if the equilibria governed by solubility products and stability constants are examined quantitatively.

The principles involved in such cases can be expressed mathematically, and some representative cases have been discussed.[4] These may be summarized as follows.

Ligands are proton acceptors, and, if K_{a1}, K_{a2}, ... are the acid dissociation constants for the mono-, di-, ... protonated species HL, H_2L, ... (charges omitted), at any pH the ligand concentration is related to the total concentrations of ligand plus protonated species by the equation

$$[\text{L}]\left(1 + \frac{[\text{H}^+]}{K_{a1}} + \frac{[\text{H}^+]^2}{K_{a1}K_{a2}} + \cdots\right) = [\text{L}]_{\text{total}} \tag{1}$$

For convenience, let us designate the portion in parentheses as α. This equation is quite general and applies whether L is an anion or a neutral molecule. If $[\text{M}]_{\text{total}}$ is the total concentration of a given metal, and f

is the fraction of the metal precipitated at a given pH by a precipitant, it can be calculated[4] that

$$\{[M]_{total}(1 - f)\}^m\left([L]_{total} - \frac{n}{m}f[M]_{total}\right)^n = K_s \cdot \alpha^n \qquad (2)$$

where the precipitated complex is M_mL_n.

Inspection of equation (1) shows that α increases rapidly as the hydrogen ion concentration is raised (pH is lowered) and hence, from equation (2), the amount of complex precipitated at constant $[M]_{total}$ and $[L]_{total}$ decreases. That is, the solubility of metal complexes increases in acid solutions, often making it possible, by judicious selection of pH values, to separate quantitatively two or more metals as their complexes. At pH 2.0, $0.001M$ Cu^{2+} can be precipitated quantitatively from a solution $0.001M$ in Cd^{2+} and Zn^{2+} by $0.003M$ quinaldinic acid: The solubility products of the 1:2 complexes are 1.6×10^{-17}, 5.0×10^{-13}, and 1.6×10^{-14}, respectively, and the pK_a of the ligand is about 5.[5]

A further consequence of equation (2) is that for ligands of the same types the higher the ligand-to-metal ratio in a complex the greater will be the effect of pH change on the solubility of metal complexes.

If a ligand is added to a solution to form stable complexes with a metal ion so as to prevent its precipitation by another species, X, as M_mX_n, the effect of raising the pH is to reduce α and hence to increase the total concentration of the metal that can be present in solution. The equation is

$$\begin{aligned} [M]_{total} &= [M] + [ML] + [ML_2] + \cdots \\ &= [M](1 + K[L] + \beta_2[L]^2 \cdots) \\ &= [M] \cdot \gamma \end{aligned} \qquad (3)$$

Precipitation cannot occur so long as $[M] < (K_s/[X]^n)^{1/m}$. Where the ligand is polydentate, like EDTA, and forms only a 1:1 complex, the amount of ligand that must be added to prevent precipitation is given by

$$[L] = \frac{1}{K_1}\left[\left(\frac{[X]^n}{K_s}\right)^{1/m} \cdot [M]_{total} - 1\right] \qquad (4)$$

The relation of $[L]$ to $[L]_{total}$ is given by equation (1). This process of "tying up" a metal ion so as to prevent the formation of a precipitate is sometimes called "sequestration."

Equations (3) and (4) apply directly to the hydrolysis of metal ions $(X = OH^-)$, provided mixed hydroxy-ligand metal complexes are not formed. However, equation (2) no longer holds if the pH region is one in which hydrolysis of metal ion is important. Because hydrolysis reduces the concentration of free metal ion, higher concentrations of precipitants would be required than equation (2) predicts. At sufficiently high pH values, the metal hydroxide, itself, will precipitate. Because polynuclear species are often produced in hydrolytic equilibria, no attempt will be made to examine in further detail the mathematical equations applicable to such systems.

Provided further complexes are not formed, the solubility of a sparingly soluble species is depressed if excess precipitant is added.

9.3 Applications to Alkali Metal Salts and Complexes

These general considerations explain why, in the alkali metals, the larger the cation, the more numerous are its insoluble salts. Sodium has very few insoluble salts, the most important being the mixed Na,Zn and Na,Mg uranyl acetates which precipitate from dilute acetic acid. These salts are used in quantitative determinations of sodium, the sodium (molar) concentration in the precipitate being assumed equal to that of the uranium, which can be determined as the yellow uranyl thiocyanate. Other difficultly soluble salts of sodium include the antimonate, fluosilicate, and aluminium fluoride. The sparing solubility of its DL-(α-methoxy)-phenylacetate can also be used in the gravimetric estimation of sodium.[6]

Sodium perchlorate is readily soluble in water, but the perchlorates, periodates, and hexachloroplatinates of K, Rb, and Cs are rather insoluble in water and virtually insoluble in 90% ethanol (dielectric constant and solvent effects). Similarly, lithium and sodium tetraphenylboron are moderately soluble in water and useful for precipitating the tetraphenylborates of K, Rb, and Cs from neutral or faintly acid aqueous solutions.[7] This precipitation is generally used as a gravimetric method for these metals.[8] Alternatively, direct titration is possible using an amperometric technique to detect the endpoint.[9] As would be expected from the nonselective nature of the reaction, other large univalent ions such as Ag^+, Tl^+, and Cu^+, as well as many nitrogen bases, also form insoluble

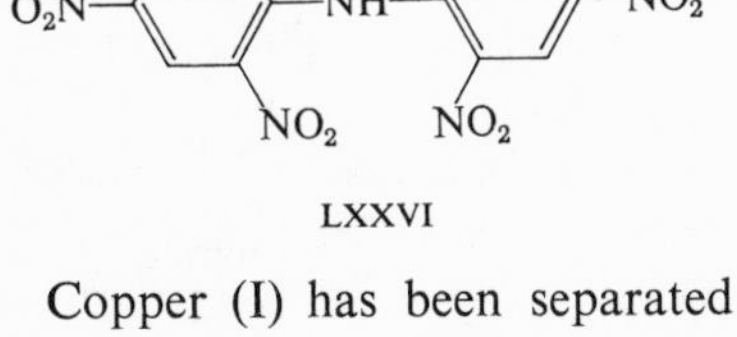

LXXVI

tetraphenylborates. Copper (I) has been separated in this way, using ascorbic acid as a reducing agent.[10] If lithium tetraphenylboron is used, sodium can be determined subsequently by precipitation using lithium tetra-*p*-tolylboron.[11]   K, Rb, and Cs can also be precipitated by the cobaltinitrite ion $[Co(NO_2)_6]^{3-}$ and various other large anions.

One such reagent is hexanitrodiphenylamine (dipicrylamine) (LXXVI), which is used in the form of its lithium, sodium, or magnesium salt.[12] Replacement of hydrogen atoms in aromatic rings by halogen atoms or nitro groups leads to a decrease in water solubility, so that the K, Rb, Cs, Tl(I), and NH_4 salts of dipicrylamine are all only slightly soluble.   To repress hydrolysis it is necessary to work in alkaline solutions.   The precipitates are finally dissolved in water for colorimetric estimation. The anion of picric acid has also been used in this way, but its salts are more soluble.

Similar considerations explain why 6-chloro-5-nitrotoluene-3-sulfonic and 2-bromo-3-nitrotoluene-5-sulfonic acids form soluble lithium or sodium salts but precipitate the larger potassium and rubidium ions as their sparingly soluble salts.

However, although an interpretation of solubilities of salts and complexes in terms of solvation effects and ionic size is undoubtedly qualitatively correct, some anomalies exist.   Dihydroxytartaric acid and its potassium and rubidium salts are readily soluble in water but in spite of the number of hydroxyl and carboxylate groups in the anion its sodium and lithium salts are only sparingly soluble.

Lithium ion, because of its smaller size and hence its greater ionic potential, shows differences from the other alkali metal ions in the solubilities of its salts, so that it can be precipitated as the fluoride, carbonate, and phosphate, as well as in mixed salts such as lithium potassium ferric periodate, $LiKFeIO_6$.   Choline phosphate in 50% isopropanol is a convenient precipitant for lithium as phosphate.[13]

9.4   Alkaline Earth Metal Species

The alkaline earth metal ions behave rather similarly.   With large anions, such as $S_2O_3^{2-}$, SO_4^{2-}, IO_3^-, BrO_4^-, CrO_4^{2-}, oxalate^{2-}, and NO_3^-, solubilities of the salts decrease in the order $Mg^{2+} > Ca^{2+} > Sr^{2+} > Ba^{2+}$.

Nitro groups in aromatic and heterocyclic molecules make them less hydrophilic so that the anion of picrolonic acid (1-*p*-nitrophenyl-3-methyl-4-nitropyrazol-5-one) (LXXVII) forms insoluble salts with Mg, Ca, Sr, Ba, Mn, Fe, Pb, Cu, and Th.   Calcium can be determined gravimetrically in this way by precipitation in neutral solution, or colorimetrically by oxidation of the precipitate to pyrazole blue.[14]

Variations in crystal structure, and hence in lattice energies, explain some of the irregularities that are observed, such as $Ba^{2+} > Mg^{2+} \approx$

$Sr^{2+} > Ca^{2+}$ for the solubilities of the fluorides. Apart from such exceptions, solubilities of series such as the alkaline earth halides would be expected to be least when the radius of the anion approaches, and is

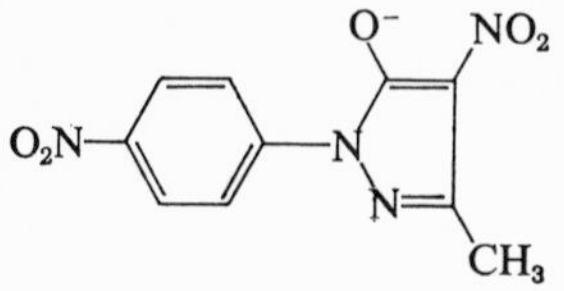

LXXVII

only slightly greater than, the radius of the cation, or more correctly of the cavity the cation occupies in the solution. (According to Latimer, Pitzer, and Slansky,[15] this cavity is in all cases 0.85 Å greater than the crystal radius for cations, while the anion cavity is greater by 0.25 Å.) In agreement with this expectation, LiF is the least soluble of the alkali fluorides, the sequence being LiF < NaF < KF.

The large size of the monoanion of bis(*p*-chlorophenyl) phosphoric acid leads to the precipitation of insoluble salts from neutral solutions of many cations, including those of Mg, Ca, Sr, Ba, Fe, Co, Ni, Cu, Cd, Al, Cr, Pb, and Sn(IV).

9.5 Complexes Bonding through Sulfur Anions

Another factor that becomes important among the transition metal ions is the crystal-field stabilization energy which, by increasing the lattice forces, would be expected to decrease solubility in simple ionic salts. This would be true only where the crystal field due to the anion was greater than that due to water. For example, the solubility of the sulfides lies in the sequence $MnS > FeS > CoS > NiS > CuS < ZnS$. In general the converse applies, because ions such as I^-, Br^-, Cl^-, and F^- have lower field strengths than water, so that the hydrated ions gain in stability, and solution in water is facilitated. High field strengths occur among anions only where covalent-bond formation may be expected, as in NO_2^- and CN^-. Where complexes rather than hydrated ions are

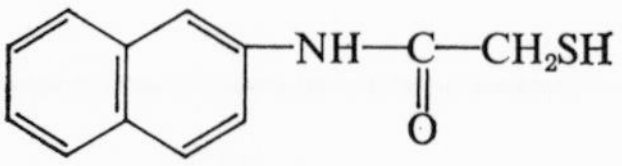

LXXVIII

present, their ligand-field stabilization energies must be considered. However, covalent bonding, especially if it leads to charge neutralization, is likely to produce much greater effects, usually by decreasing solubility.

The insolubility of many metal sulfides is a familiar example. This is true, similarly, of thioglycolic-β-aminonaphthalide (thionalide) (LXXVIII), which can be used to precipitate metals from dilute mineral acid solutions by bonding through its sulfur atom. As would be expected, such reagents are most suitable for heavy metals that form their strongest complexes with sulfur anions (for example, Cu, Ag, Au, Hg, As, Sb, Bi, Pt, Pd, Ru, and Rh > Cd, Pb, Ni, Co, Mn, Tl). Because it is so readily oxidized, thionalide is often used in the presence of a suitable reducing agent such as hydrazine. In many cases, coordination through the oxygen or the nitrogen atom to form a five-membered chelate ring in metal-thionalide complexes appears likely. The precipitates find restricted use for gravimetric determinations. The analog, thioglycolic acid anilide, has the same grouping and is also used in this way, but because it contains a phenyl in place of a naphthyl group its metal complexes are more soluble.

Other precipitants depending on complex formation through anionic sulfur include mercaptobenzothiazole, 2-mercaptobenzimidazole, and 1-phenyl-tetrazoline-5-thione, the anion of which (LXXIX) has been suggested for the gravimetric determination of cadmium.[16] As would be expected, cations of Co, Ni, Zn, Ag, Hg, and Pb also give precipitates. Bismuthiol I (LXXX, R = H), and bismuthiol II (LXXX, R = phenyl)

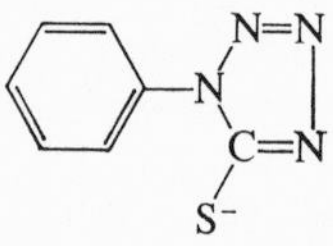

LXXIX

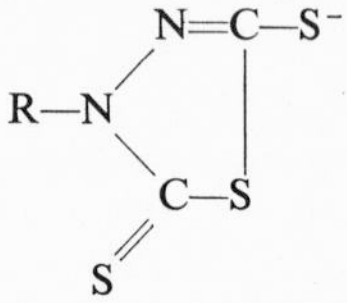

LXXX

are other examples of this class of precipitants. The former has been used in this way for precipitating Fe, Cu, Pd, Ag, Au, Cd, Hg, Tl, Pb, As, Sb, Bi, Se, and Te, the necessary selectivity being obtained by pH control and the presence of suitable masking agents. Extraction with organic solvents makes it possible to use these reagents in spectrophotometric methods.

Ligands giving rise to insoluble bidentate metal chelates by five-membered ring formation through sulfur atoms include the anions of toluene-3,4-dithiol (dithiol) and 1-chloro-3,4-dimercaptobenzene. Here, also, the colored precipitates are soluble in organic solvents. These reagents are stronger reducing agents than H_2S so that Sn(IV) is reduced to Sn(II) during precipitation. Dithiooxamide (rubeanic acid), which can be used as a precipitant for Cu, Ni, Co, Pd, Pt, and Au, belongs to this group. It also readily undergoes hydrolysis to H_2S, so that Zn, Cd, Ag, Pb, and Hg are precipitated by rubeanic acid as their sulfides.

However, —SH groups in organic molecules are prone to oxidation to stable disulfides, R—S—S—R, so that as a rule mercaptans and allied reagents tend to be unstable.

9.6   p-Dimethylaminobenzylidene-rhodanine

The presence of polar groups able to form hydrogen bonds with water, although a necessary condition for the solubility of organic molecules in water, is not in itself sufficient.   Pteridine (LXXXI) is very soluble in

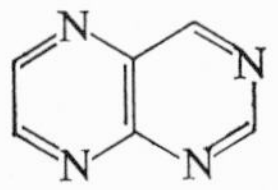

LXXXI

water, but progressive replacement of the hydrogens by hydroxyl or amino groups makes the molecule less and less soluble.   This is because the increasingly uneven π-electron distribution over the molecules greatly increases intermolecular attractions, leading to much stronger crystal-lattice forces, as shown by the infusible nature of the solid materials.

These considerations probably explain the slight water solubility of 5-(p-dimethylaminobenzylidene)rhodanine (LXXXII) (melting point greater than 200°), which is used in acid solution as a precipitant for silver, mercury (I and II), copper (I), gold, and palladium.   (The reagent is

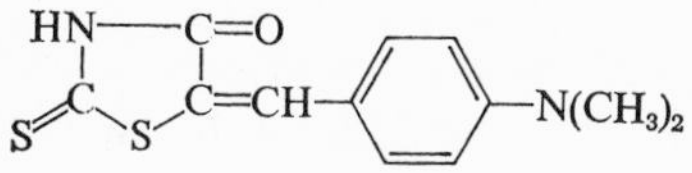

LXXXII

added as an alcoholic solution.)   The location of the NH group between CO and CS greatly increases its acidic character, making it a stronger acid than o-nitrophenol (pK_a 6.15 and 7.22, respectively).   Complex formation by a metal ion involves the negatively charged nitrogen in the anion of (LXXXII).   In acid solution only those metal ions that are highly polarizable, usually because of low valency and filled, or almost filled, d shells, will react.   This group includes Ag(I), Au(I), Cu(I), Pd(II), and Pt(II). In neutral or alkaline solutions, where the ratio of ligand to total reactant is much greater, many other cations interfere.   Suspensions of the freshly formed precipitates serve as colorimetric methods for silver (red),[17] copper (I) (violet), mercury (I) (purple),[18] and mercury (II) (red)[18] that are sensitive to about 0.5 ppm.   Probably because of the dimethylamino group on the ligand, the palladium bis complex is soluble in formic, hydrochloric, and propionic acid solutions: Its use as a sensitive spectrophotometric method for palladium has been suggested.[19]

Other substances having a CS group adjacent to the NH group as in rhodanine also form slightly soluble silver salts. Examples include 2-thiohydantoin and its condensation products with p-dimethylamino-benzaldehyde and nitrosodiphenylamine,[20] and 2-thio-5-keto-4-carbethoxy-1,3-dihydropyrimidine.[21]

9.7   Precipitation of Anionic Complexes with Large Cations

The Born equation predicts that the hydration energies of large ions are low, so that large cations or cationic complexes are precipitated if large anions are present. This behavior is shown, for example, in the precipitation of Th^{4+} as its tetra(m-nitrobenzoate); in the use of the benzidine cation to precipitate sulfate, phosphate, and tungstate ions; and in the formation of insoluble ion pairs between tetraphenylarsonium cation and perchlorate, periodate, permanganate, and perrhenate ions, as well as anionic chloro complexes of zinc, cadmium, and mercury. The corresponding species from tetramethylammonium ion and anionic gold chloro complex has been used in gravimetry.[22]

Amino derivatives of triphenylmethane, such as parafuchsine, methyl violet, crystal violet, and malachite green, can form trications in which each of the amino groups is protonated. This indicates that each of the amino groups is also available for metal complex formation, and it is suggested[23] that in the insoluble precipitates formed with $PdCl_2$ and $AuCl_3$ two amino groups are coordinated as neutral molecules to different molecules of $PdCl_2$ or $AuCl_3$, whereas the third amino group is protonated and available for ion pair formation with $PdCl_4^{2-}$ or $AuCl_4^{-}$.

It is likely that the insolubility of the tetrakis complex of mandelic acid (phenylglycolic acid) with zirconium is due in part to this size factor and in part to the ability of a carboxylic oxygen and the hydroxyl group in each ligand anion to occupy two of the eight coordination sites round the cation, so that each zirconium ion is held in four five-membered chelate rings.

The water insolubility of tris(1,10-phenanthroline) iron (III) perchlorate, although ferric perchlorate is very soluble, arises in this way and parallels the behavior of many alkaloids and heterocyclic organic bases. If the anions used are long-chain alkyl sulfates or sulfonates, the resulting compounds can be extracted by chloroform from water.

Similarly, the bis-ethylenediamine copper (II) complex forms, with the complex ions $[HgI_4]^{2-}$ and $[CdI_4]^{2-}$, the salts [Cu en$_2$][HgI$_4$] and [Cu en$_2$] [CdI$_4$], which are insoluble in water, ethanol, and ether. The red-violet precipitate of [Fe(bipy)$_3$] [CdI$_4$] is one of the most sensitive tests for cadmium.[24] β-Naphthoquinoline and the quaternary base, phenyltrimethylammonium ion, can also be used in this way to precipitate cadmium as $[BH^+]_2[CdI_4{}^{2-}]$ and $[B^+]_2[CdI_4{}^{2-}]$, respectively. Similarly, slightly acid solutions of bismuth salts in the presence of iodide ion give an orange-red precipitate of the type $[BH^+][BiI_4{}^-]$ with cinchonine and many other alkaloids.

Cations of bases such as methyl violet and rhodamine B form sparingly soluble salts with anionic thiocyanato zinc and copper complexes. When p-dimethylaminostyryl-β-naphthiazole methiodide is used as the cation, the resulting complexes can be determined spectrophotometrically.[25] The characteristic crystals formed by cobalt, iron (III), and zinc using acridine as the base have been suggested as of use for spot tests.[26]

In some cases, the same result is achieved by replacing water in the coordination shell of the metal ion by pyridine: These water-insoluble complexes are extractable by chloroform. Examples typical of metals such as Cu(II), Cd, Fe(II), Mn, Zn, Ni, and Co are Cu $py_2(SCN)_2$, Ni $py_4(SCN)_2$ and Co $py_4(SCN)_2$, all of which are colored. Benzidine also forms crystalline complexes of the form $MR_2(SCN)_2$ with Cd, Cu, Hg, and Zn.

Germanium can be isolated by conversion to the trioxalatogermanic acid, which forms insoluble salts with large bases such as quinine, strychnine, and β-naphthoquinoline.[27]

9.8   Hydrophobic Character and Charge Neutralization in Inner Complexes. Representative Examples

At a suitable pH, the apparent solubilities of complexes of a given ligand with a series of metal ions can be expected to parallel the stability constants of the complexes, so that the nature of the binding groups— whether nitrogen, oxygen, or sulfur, and whether aromatic or similar stabilization is involved—becomes important in discussing suitable pre-cipitants for particular types of cation. Also, if insoluble complex, as distinct from ion pair, formation is to occur, the ligand must usually be an anion so that the necessary charge neutralization can be achieved.

Exceptions occur, for example among "inert" complexes and salts where replacement of coordinated water by ligand may lead to insolubility. Formation by $PdCl_2$ of the bis complex of β-furfuraldoxime is an example in which the inorganic species is already a neutral molecule. Another precipitant for $PdCl_2$ is p-nitrosodiphenylamine. In this instance, formation of the bis complex may involve bonding through either the amino or the nitroso groups.

An ion pair can be distinguished from an inner-sphere complex by the fact that there is no contact between the central metal ion and the ligand in the ion pair; that is, the water molecules solvating a metal ion, or other groups immediately surrounding it, are not replaced as a result of ion pair formation.   On the other hand, the process of complex formation by a metal ion in aqueous solution involves the partial or complete replacement of water molecules immediately surrounding the metal ion by one or more ligand molecules.   If the resulting complex has no net electronic charge and also lacks hydrophilic groups, it can be expected to be sparingly soluble in water.

Sulfonic acid groups help to increase solubility in water, whereas aromatic groups decrease it.   The sulfinic acid radical, $-SO_2H$, is less effective because it has fewer lone pairs of electrons available for hydrogen-bond formation with water.   This is probably why the ferric and quadrivalent metal ion salts of benzenesulfinic and benzeneseleninic acids (and their derivatives) are insoluble whereas the salts of the corresponding sulfonic acids are soluble.   The increased hydrophobic character also explains the solubility of aromatic sulfinic acids in benzene and ether.

Once a metal chelate with a large hydrophobic surface (for example the tris complex of 8-hydroxyquinoline with aluminium) has precipitated from aqueous solution it exists in a form not readily wettable by water, so that it is relatively resistant to dissolution into even quite strong acids. This is less likely to occur where some of the coordination sites round the metal ion remain occupied by water molecules, as in bis complexes of bidentate chelates with a divalent metal ion that forms octahedral complexes.

CUPFERRON

Cupferron (LXXXIII) is readily soluble in water because of its nitroso group and its anionic oxygen.   Tris complex formation with Fe(III), Bi(II), or Ga(III) through the two oxygen atoms makes these groups unavailable for hydration, produces a complex, such as (LXXXIV), having

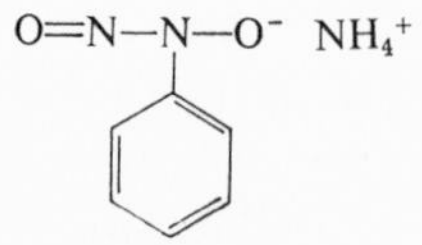

LXXXIII 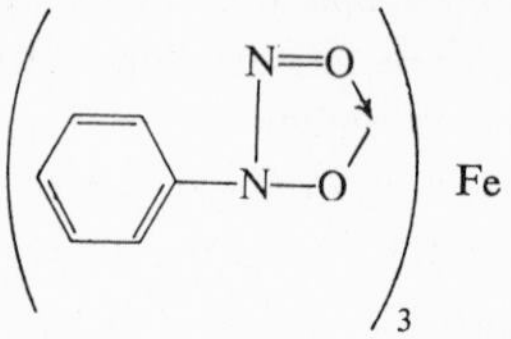   LXXXIV

no net charge, and at the same time leaves the aromatic ring portions projecting into the solvent.   The metal complex precipitates.   Other metals precipitating in acid solution include Sn, Ti, U(IV), V, and Zr. As would be expected, these are all metals that form their strongest complexes with oxygen-type ligands. In less acid solutions, Cu(II) precipitates as the neutral bis complex: Separation from other divalent ions such as Mn, Co, Ni, and Zn depends, in part, on the higher stability constant of the Cu complex and, in part, on the weakness with which Cu(II) binds water in its fifth and sixth coordination sites. Cupferron also precipitates Nb and Ta.

The solubility of complexes is even further reduced if neo-cupferron, in which the phenyl group is replaced by a naphthyl group, is used instead.

This is another example of the decreased solubility in water that is generally observed as the hydrophobic fraction of a solute is increased. Similarly, the solubility of the Cu(I) complex of thioglycolic acid, $CuSCH_2COOH$, is decreased to one-twentieth if the acid is converted to its anilide and to one-fiftieth if the α-naphthylamide derivative is used. In the same way, Bi forms a sparingly soluble selenite, but water solubility is much depressed if aryl groups are attached to the selenium to give, for example, benzene and naphthalene selenonic acids, both of which have been suggested for the gravimetric determination of Bi as their tris complexes.[28]

This kind of comparison must be made with some care. For example, comparison of sulfates and phenylsulfonates is not likely to be helpful because the former ion is divalent and shows lattice-building properties whereas the phenylsulfonate ion is monovalent. This is why the alkaline earth sulfates are insoluble in water, whereas their phenylsulfonates are soluble. Diphenylation of arsenic, phosphoric, and boric acids produces similar effects.

Other precipitants forming five- or six-membered chelate rings with metal ions by binding through oxygen atoms show qualitatively similar behavior to cupferron. Examples include pyrogallol, gallic acid, 9-methyl-2,3,7-trihydroxy-6-fluorone, chloranilic acid, and rhodizonic acid. In general, trivalent metal ions form neutral, insoluble tris complexes, and bivalent metal ions give neutral bis complexes which are commonly insoluble if the metal has a preference for four-coordinate structures. The reagents are usually nonselective, with higher-valent cations forming the most stable complexes.

SALICYLALDOXIME

Other examples of uncharged, sparingly soluble metal complexes include the bis complexes such as (LXXXV) formed by salicylaldoxime with many divalent metal ions. Salicylaldoxime, itself, is only sparingly soluble in water, and in its metal complex the single —OH group per ligand molecule is insufficient to confer water solubility. Metal bonding takes place through a nitrogen and an anionic oxygen, so that salicylaldoxime functions as a "wide-spectrum" precipitant that is very pH-dependent in its analytical applications. Alkylation of the phenolic group destroys

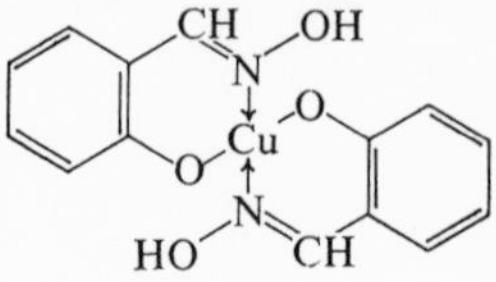

LXXXV

its chelating ability. Its use as a selective precipitant for copper (II) at about pH 2.6–3.3 depends mainly on the observation that Cu(II) complexes are commonly much more stable than those of most other divalent metal ions. Thus with increasing pH the following metals are precipitated by this reagent: Ni(II), Pb(II), Hg(II), Co(II), Ag(I), Zn(II), Cd(II), Bi(III), Fe(II), Mn(II), and Mg(II). The neutral Pb(II) complex contains a ligand-to-metal ratio of 1:1, and under suitable conditions similar copper and zinc complexes are formed. These complexes require the loss of 2 protons per metal ion, and the structure (LXXXVI) is suggested, with water probably occupying the forth coordination site round the metal ion. The possibility cannot be excluded, however, that in these complexes the oxime reacts as the nitrone tautomer to give complexes such as (LXXXVII).

Here again the precipitation characteristics of the reagent can be

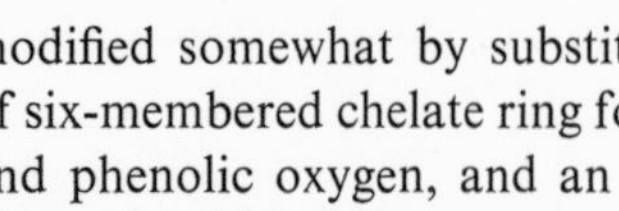

LXXXVI

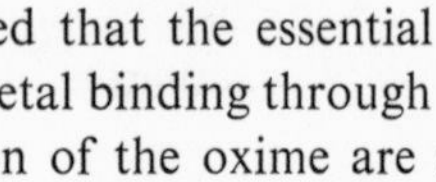

LXXXVII

modified somewhat by substitution, provided that the essential features of six-membered chelate ring formation by metal binding through nitrogen and phenolic oxygen, and an α-configuration of the oxime are retained. Thus the following are some of the oximes resembling salicylaldoxime (all R's = H in (LXXXVIII)) in giving precipitates with copper ions: (in all cases R's = H unless indicated)

$R_1 = C_6H_5$; $R_1 = CH_3$; $R_1 = CH_3$, $R_3 = OH$; $R_1 = CH_3$,
$R_4 = OH$; $R_1 = CH_3$, $R_3 = OCH_3$; $R_1 = CH_3$, $R_4 = OCH_3$;

$R_1 = CH_3,\ R_5 = OCH_3;\quad R_1 = CH_3,\ R_2R_3 = C_6H_4;$

$R_1 = CH_3,\ R_3R_4 = C_6H_4;\quad R_1 = CH_3,\ R_2R_3 = C_6H_4,$

$R_5 = COOH$ [29]

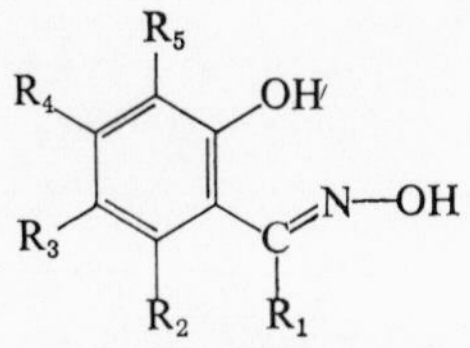

LXXXVIII

The color-enchancing effect of nitro groups makes nitrosalicylaldoxime a better spot test reagent.

Reagents in this group require that the complex-forming hydroxyl must either be phenolic or else be present in a group such as an acyloin oxime (in which case the ligand is a dianion); hydroxyl groups in aliphatic and alicyclic systems are not sufficiently acidic to be able to give rise to the necessary type of anionic ligand.

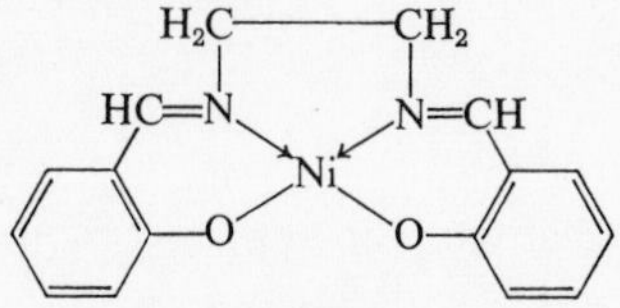

LXXXIX

Schiff's base formation with o-hydroxy aldehydes yields reagents having similar complex-forming properties. An example is salicylaldehyde-ethylenediamine, which has been suggested for the gravimetric determination of nickel, with which it forms the insoluble complex (LXXXIX). Although Schiff's bases are readily hydrolyzed in water (to give aldehyde

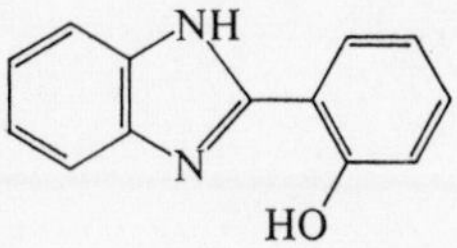

XC

and amine), the presence of cations which form stable complexes can displace this equilibrium by withdrawing the Schiff's base as its insoluble metal complex. For this reason, a mixture of salicylaldehyde and copper (II) in ammoniacal solution precipitates the copper as its bis salicylaldimine complex.

Other precipitants involving six-membered chelate ring formation through a phenolic oxygen and a doubly bound nitrogen are 2-(o-hydroxy-phenyl)benzimidazole (XC) for mercury,[30] and 2-(o-hydroxyphenyl)-benzoxazole, for cadmium.[31]

α-BENZOINOXIME

The insoluble 1:1, uncharged, copper complex with α-benzoinoxime (cupron), possibly (XCI) or (XCII), owes its insolubility to the high ratio of phenyl groups to groups able to coordinate to water molecules. Alternatively, if the anionic oxygens are able to "donate" electrons to a second

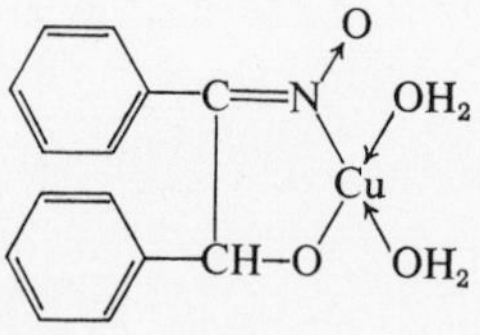

XCI 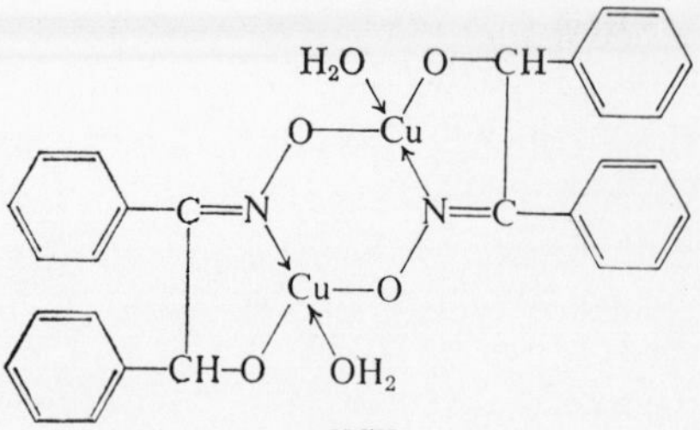   XCII

copper, a three-dimensional macromolecule would be possible. The reagent shows good selectivity for copper, but in acid solutions it also gives precipitates (of unknown structure) with molybdates, tungstates, vanadates, and uranyl salts. In this group it seems likely that bonding will be through oxygens to give six-membered chelate rings. The sparing solubility of α-benzoinoxime, itself, may be due to internal hydrogen bonding between the two —OH groups.

Qualitatively similar behavior towards copper in ammoniacal solution is shown by many other acyloin oximes, including the following, which contain no aromatic rings—acetoin oxime, acetol oxime, butyroin oxime, and fructose oxime. However, the complexes in the latter group are less stable and are dissociated if the ammonia concentration is increased.

ARSONIC ACIDS

The use of arsonic acids (XCIII) as selective precipitants for tetravalent metal ions such as Sn(IV), Hf(IV), Th(IV), Ce(IV), Ti(IV), U(IV), and WO^{4+} is readily explicable in terms of the foregoing discussion. Taking as an example Zr(IV) with phenylarsonic acid ((XCIII), R = C_6H_5), the usual condition for precipitation is from a solution about $1M$ in hydrochloric or sulfuric acid. In such a solution Zr^{4+} and its chloro or sulfato complexes are the predominant zirconium species,[32] so that electrostatic interaction with anionic ligands is high. This makes it possible for phenylarsonic acid (pK_1 3.6, pK_2 8.5) to act as a bidentate chelate, giving the uncharged and sparingly soluble bis complex, (XCIV). Phenylarsonic acid also precipitates Nb and Ta.

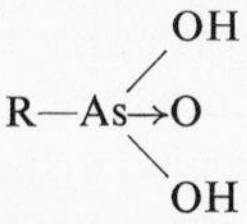

XCIII 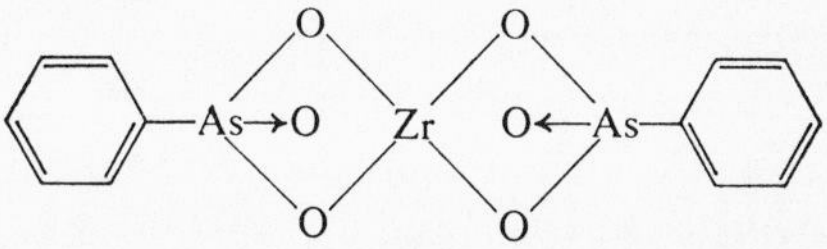   XCIV

The greater hydrophobic character of a phenyl group than an *n*-propyl group probably accounts for the ability of phenyl-, but not *n*-propyl-, arsonic acid to precipitate Ti(IV). In somewhat less acid solution, the partially hydrolyzed metal ions such as ZrO^{2+} can still form an insoluble complex; in this case the metal-to-ligand ratio is 1:1. The selectivity of the reagents is a consequence of the conditions under which they are used, which lie so far on the acid side of the ligand pK values that only the most stable complexes (involving highly charged cations) can be formed. The possibility of having a mixture of 1:1 and 1:2 complexes in the precipitate, leading to variation in composition, makes it necessary to ignite to the metal oxide or use some other method for quantitative determination.

This is why a spectrophotometric method based on the determination of the amount of *p*-dimethylaminobenzeneazophenylarsonic acid contained in its precipitate with zirconium[33] is unlikely to be quantitative.

This objection does not apply to the use of thoron (XCV), which forms soluble red 2:1 complexes with thorium and zirconium in fairly strongly

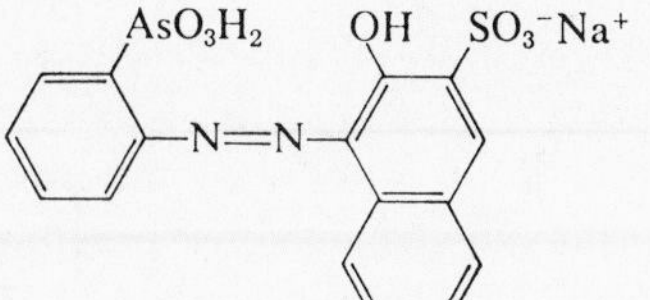

XCV

acidic solutions and which finds application in their colorimetric determination.[34] Similarly, *o*-arsonophenylazochromotropic acid has been proposed as a colorimetric reagents for thorium.[35]

Inclusion of chromophoric groups such as dimethylaminophenylazo into precipitants such as phenylarsonic acid, which usually give white or pale-colored precipitates with metal ions, facilitates analytical manipulations of small quantities, because the precipitate is more clearly visible, and improves the accuracy of spot tests.

(Thoron also reacts in strongly alkaline solution to form an orange complex with lithium, which is soluble and suitable for use in a colorimetric method sensitive to about 0.1 ppm.[36] The color is intensified by acetone, but the nature of the bonding in the complex is unknown.)

Further increase in the water-repelling properties of the ligand in the arsonic acid series and the use of somewhat less acid solutions enable other cations to be separated.   Examples include Fe(III), probably as $FeOH^{2+}$ in a 1:1 complex with p-(n-butylphenyl) arsonic acid, and Cd^{2+} (from acetic acid solutions) with 3-nitrophenylarsonic acid: precipitation of Fe(III) by such reagents is prevented if more strongly complexing species such as fluoride, phosphate, tartrate, or citrate are present.

That the coordinately bonded oxygen atom in arsonic acids does not play an important part in metal complex formation is suggested by the observation that arsinic acids ($-As(OH)_2$) can also be used as precipitants. (Compare sulfonic and sulfinic acids.)

8-HYDROXYQUINOLINE

The same general comments apply to the use of 8-hydroxyquinoline to form sparingly soluble bis complexes with Mg, Mn, Co, Ni, Cu, Zn, Cd, Pb, and In, tris complexes with Al, Fe, Bi, and Ga, and tetrakis complexes with Th and Zr, which are representative of the many metals precipitated by this reagent, but here again the effect is less sharply obvious because the ligand itself is only sparingly soluble.   (This is because the hydroxyl group and the heterocyclic nitrogen in 8-hydroxyquinoline form an intramolecular hydrogen bond, so that there is much less solvation, and a lower solubility, than in quinoline.)   Because the ligand is an anion of a weak acid, the complexing ability of 8-hydroxyquinoline is strongly pH dependent.   This is important in the selective precipitation of metal-oxine complexes, because the lower the stability constant of any particular metal complex the higher must be the pH of the solution for satisfactory precipitation.   Selectivity, which is thus achieved by pH control, is further improved by the use of appropriate masking reagents.   Many of the oxine complexes are nonstoichiometric in composition because of some coprecipitation of oxine and also, possibly, because of some hydrolysis of metal ion.   Nevertheless, they find extensive analytical use.

The 8-hydroxyquinoline molecule has been modified by insertion of groups such as chloro and bromo, usually into positions 5 and 7. This leads to increased acid stability of metal complexes but otherwise does not have a very great effect. Insertion of a sulfonic acid group confers solubility in water, as in the case of 7-iodo-8-hydroxyquinoline-5-sulfonic acid ("ferron"), which forms an intensely blue, soluble, tris complex with ferric ion. With more weakly complexing cations, however, salt formation can occur through the sulfonic acid group, leading to insolubility.

Where metal-oxine precipitates are stoichiometric they can be used in direct gravimetric determinations; alternatively, the 8-hydroxyquinoline content of the precipitates can be determined titrimetrically by oxidation or by bromination, or by suitable spectrophotometric techniques using solutions in acids or organic solvents. Otherwise, ignition to the oxide may be necessary.

4-Hydroxybenzthiazole (XCVI), which forms insoluble complexes with copper, nickel, and zinc,[37] shows complexing behavior similar to that of 8-hydroxyquinoline, but because the lone pairs of electrons on sulfur have some tendency towards hydrogen-bond formation with water, metal complexes of 4-hydroxybenzthiazole are somewhat more soluble.

XCVI

Complex formation involving a five-membered chelate ring in which the metal ion is bound to an anionic oxygen and a heteroaromatic nitrogen can also occur with α-carboxylic acids of nitrogen heterocycles. Examples include α-picolinic, quinaldic, and isoquinaldic acids, and, as expected, they form insoluble complexes with the same cations as 8-hydroxyquinoline. The α- and o-aminoacids can also conveniently be grouped with this class, although they lack the π-bonding possibilities through the nitrogen atom that exist when nitrogen is part of a heterocyclic system. These reagents are nonselective as precipitants, but, because of the much greater stability of copper complexes and the relative weakness with which water is held in the coordination sites above and below copper ions in square planar complexes, copper can be selectively precipitated as its bis complex from acid solutions of aminoacids such as anthranilic acid. (The corresponding complexes of most of the other divalent metals are more soluble because of octahedral stereochemistry involving much stronger partial solvation of the metal ions in their complexes.)

DIOXIMES

The bis(dimethylglyoxime) nickel complex appears, at first sight, to be anomalous in being highly insoluble, because the complex contains two hydroxyl groups and two oxygen atoms that might be expected to hydrate readily.   Crystallographic analysis shows that the complex has the planar configuration (XCVII), in which the —OH and the —O⁻ are strongly

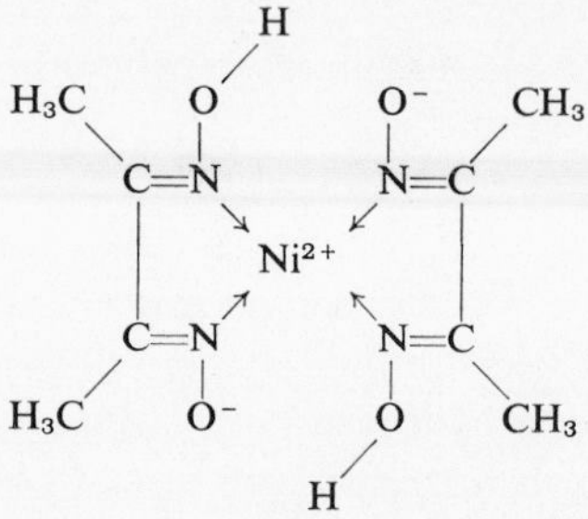

$$
\begin{array}{c}
\text{H} \\
\text{H}_3\text{C} \quad \text{O} \qquad \text{O}^- \quad \text{CH}_3 \\
\text{C}=\text{N} \qquad \text{N}=\text{C} \\
\text{Ni}^{2+} \\
\text{C}=\text{N} \qquad \text{N}=\text{C} \\
\text{H}_3\text{C} \quad \text{O}^- \qquad \text{O} \quad \text{CH}_3 \\
\text{H}
\end{array}
$$

XCVII

internally hydrogen bonded[38] and hence are less readily solvated.   Such a structure is possible only if each molecule of dimethylglyoxime (or other dioximes used in this way) have the oxygen atoms in each molecule of ligand in the trans configuration, i.e., directed away from each other.   The residual —OH groups in the nickel complex (and also of the complexes with other metals) contain ionizable protons, so that the complex is a dibasic acid which forms salts in alkaline solution.

This planar structure and the tendency of Ni to form weak metal-to-metal bonds in the solid state explain the greatly increased insolubility relative to, say, Cu(II) where such bonding does not occur.   (The Cu(II) complex actually has a higher stability constant than the Ni(II) complex,[39] but it has quite a different structure, in which the two rings in the molecule do not lie in the same plane.[40])   The Pd(II) complex is similar to Ni, both in structure and in insolubility, and in both cases one can visualize a pair of electrons in a d_{z^2} orbital of a metal ion forming a bond with a vacant p orbital on the metal ion above it.   Similar comments apply to complexes of α-furildioxime (XCVIII), heptoxime (XCIX), and 4-methylcyclohexane-1,2-dioxime (C, R = CH₃), which, in their α geometric configuration, are also used for the gravimetric determination of Ni(II) and Pd(II). The advantages of these precipitants lie, mainly, in their being more water soluble than dimethylglyoxime.   (They also give a larger weight of precipitate for a given weight of Ni or Pd.)   The related species, 1,2,3-cyclohexanetrione trioxime, also gives an insoluble bis complex with nickel: The suspension, stabilized in gelatine solution, has been suggested for use in the spectrophotometric determination of nickel.[41]   Only two of the oxime groups per ligand molecule are concerned in metal bonding.

Where the oxime groups are attached to an unsaturated ring, as in α,β-naphthoquinonedioxime and o-quinonedioxime, the reagents act as dibasic acids, precipitating many metal ions from neutral solutions.[42]

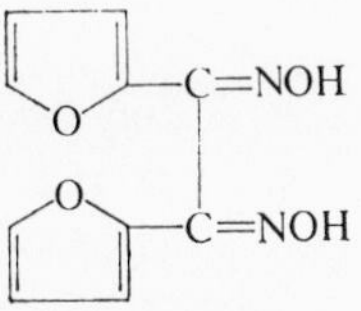

XCVIII 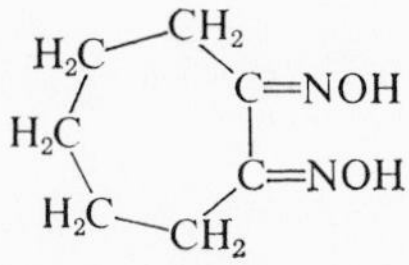   XCIX 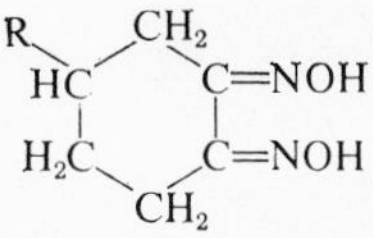   C

The furyl groups of α-furildioxime should make it a stronger acid than dimethylglyoxime, so that the effective ligand (monoanion) concentration of the former is greater in acid solution.   This enables α-furildixime to be used down to pH 4.3, whereas dimethylglyoxime is useful only at pH values above about 5.1.   Removal of freedom of rotation about the link joining the two carbon atoms to which the nitrogens are attached considerably increases the stability of the resulting metal complexes, so that nioxime (C, R = H), although its pK_a values are similar to those of dimethylglyoxime, can be used in solutions down to pH 3.4.

Oxamidoxime (CI) can be looked upon as a derivative of dimethylglyoxime, which it resembles in forming an insoluble bis complex with nickel and also a soluble complex with cobalt that can be used for its quantitative estimation.[43]   Nitrosoguanidine can also be considered in this way.

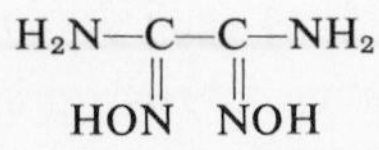

CI 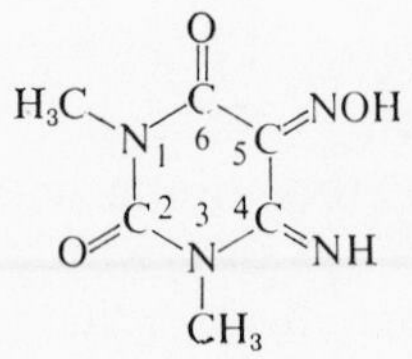   CII

1,3-Dimethyl-4-imino-5-oximino-alloxan (CII) has been suggested as an organic reagent for metals.[44]   The oximino group on C_5 and the imino group on C_4 lead to chelate-ring formation, as in the dioximes, with Ni and Pd(II), whereas, with Fe(II), Cu(II), and Co(II), the groups on C_5 and C_6

can lead to metal binding through a nitrogen and an oxygen. In both systems, complex formation leads to the production of color.

Complex formations similar to that with dimethylglyoxime are possible, also, in the case where one of the nitrogen atoms is part of a heterocyclic

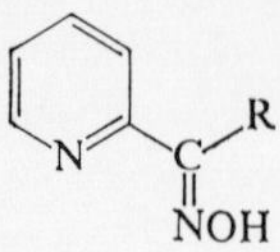

CIII

ring, as in 2-pyridyl methyl ketoxime (CIII, R = CH₃) and 2-pyridyl phenyl ketoxime, (CIII, R = C₆H₅), both of which form insoluble nickel chelates.

NITROSONAPHTHOLS

The insolubility of the tris(α-nitroso-β-naphthol) cobalt (III) complex (CIV) is readily explained, and so is the solubility of the corresponding complex of nitroso-R-salt which differs only in having six sulfonate groups.   Reagents such as α-nitroso-β-naphthol are not specific, but react similarly with Fe(III), Zr(IV), Cr(III), W(VI), and a number of other tri- and higher-valent ions.   The relatively weak ligand-field effects to be expected in such complexes, where half of the bonding to the metal is through oxygen atoms, and the predominantly electrostatic nature of this

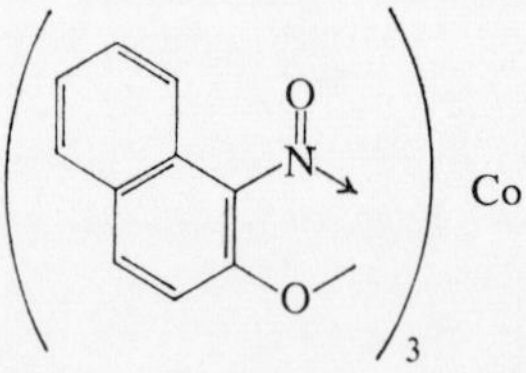

CIV

part of the metal-ligand interaction, explain why the bis complexes of these reagents with most of the divalent metal ions have lower stability constants than the tris, low-spin Co(III) complexes, so that in acid solutions they do not interfere.   For example, Co(III) can be determined in the presence of large concentrations of Ni.   In less acid solutions other metal ions are precipitated.

Similarly, in dimethylformamide solution, Cu(II) and Ni(II) can be determined by spectrophotometric titration with α-nitroso-β-naphthol,[45] with which they form stable, colored complexes.   The low-spin state of the Co (III) complexes is probably the reason why, once the complex with nitroso-R-salt is formed, it is kinetically inert so that the solution can be strongly acidified to dissociate complexes with other metals whereas the Co(III) complex remains intact.

Competing effects govern the solubility of octahedral complexes formed from divalent cations. The hydrophobic character of the aromatic portions such as naphthalene residues will be partly offset by the water molecules still coordinated to the metal ion in its bis complex. Thus, whereas the ferrous complex with α-nitroso-β-naphthol is insoluble in water, replacement of naphthalene by benzene gives o-nitrosophenol, which forms a soluble ferrous complex. Similarly, hydration of the metal ion prevents the extraction of the complex into petroleum ether, although the reagent itself goes preferentially into this solvent.

Precipitates obtained by using reagents in this group often contain more than theoretical quantities of the precipitant, and, as they are also unstable to drying, it is usual to ignite and weigh the metals as their oxides.

CHLORANILIC ACID

It is sometimes convenient to determine the concentration of a cation by adding a known excess of the reagent, removing the precipitate, and and then obtaining the concentration of unused precipitant. The determination of calcium using chloranilic acid, based on spectrophotometric measurement of the unused red chloranilate ion, is an example.[46] A variation of this technique is the use of barium chloranilate for the colorimetric determination of sulfate ions.[47] When sparingly soluble barium chloranilate is shaken in a buffered solution containing sulfate ions, double decomposition occurs. The less soluble barium sulfate is precipitated and an equivalent quantity of chloranilate ion passes into solution. After filtration, the chloranilate concentration is determined spectrophotometrically, the limit of detection corresponding to 0.06 ppm of sulfate. The same technique uses mercuric chloranilate to determine chloride,[48] and the chloranilates of lanthanum,[49] thorium,[50] and strontium[51] for the determination of fluoride ion. Calcium has also been determined using bromanilic acid.[52] Lathanum chloranilate has also been suggested for use in this way to determine phosphate.[53]

Alternatively, the insoluble chloranilate can be filtered off, washed, and dissociated by a more powerful complexing agent, the liberated chloranilic acid being determined spectrophotometrically. (This technique is capable of wide application. For example, calcium can be precipitated as its naphthalhydroxamate which, in turn, is dissolved in EDTA, and the free naphthalhydroxamate ion is measured.[54])

It is likely that in its metal complexes chloranilic acid (CV), like rhodizonic acid (CVI), forms five-membered chelate rings through pairs of phenolic and adjacent quinonoid oxygens. Both of these reagents can be used as rather unselective precipitants in spot tests based on colored complex formation with metals. From its similarity to chloranilic acid,

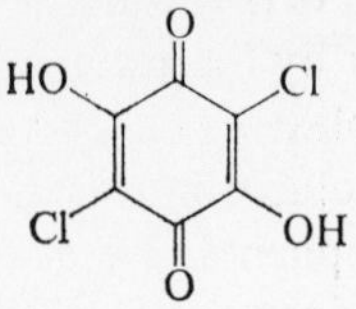

CV

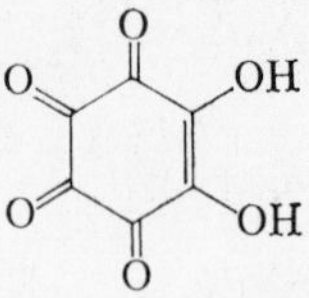

CVI

tetrahydroxy-*p*-quinone should also react with metals in the same way, but the complexes should be more water soluble. The hydroxyanthraquinones, such as alizarin, also belong to this class of reagents, except that bonding to metal ions generally involves six-membered ring formation, the oxygen atoms being peri to each other. However, this group shows a tendency to colloidal aggregation by the reagent, so that it is often doubtful whether the precipitates (which are often colored) with metals are to be ascribed to true complex formation or to the adsorption of metal ions on the surfaces of the particles to give "color lakes."

SOME RECENTLY INTRODUCED PRECIPITANTS

bis (Allylthiocarbamido)hydrazine (dalzin) (CVII), forms insoluble 1:1 complexes (CVIII) with Cu, Hg, Ni, Pb, Pd, and Zn by bonding through the sulfur atoms and the hydrazine nitrogens. The reactions are suitable

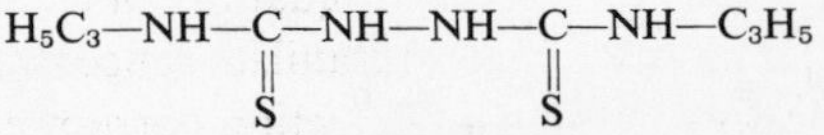

CVII

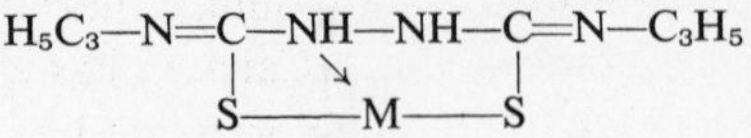

CVIII

for gravimetric use.[55] Alternatively, dalzin can be used to determine Cu(II) by amperometric titration.[56]

Ligands related to the dioximes in forming five-membered rings by coordination of nickel ion through the nitrogen atoms have been suggested for use as precipitants. Where structures analogous to the bis(dimethylglyoxime) complex can be written, an insoluble nickel complex is obtained.

Examples include nitrosoguanidine (CIX), the three dimethylglyoxime derivatives corresponding to R = H, CH_3, and OCH_3 in formula (CX), and quinoline 2-aldoxime (CXI). A reagent belonging to the same class is phenyl-α-pyridyl ketoxime (CXII), which has been proposed for use in

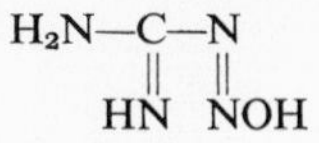

$$H_2N-C-N$$
$$\underset{HN}{\|}\quad\underset{NOH}{\|}$$

CIX

$$H_3C-C-C-CH_3$$
$$\underset{HON}{\|}\quad\underset{N-R}{\|}$$

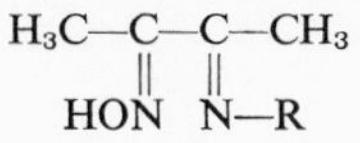

CX

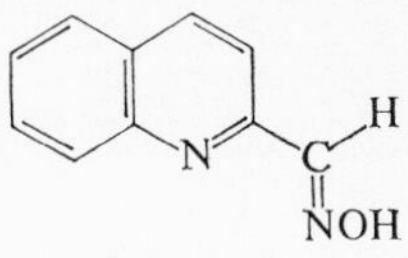

CXI

spectrophotometric determinations of palladium,[57] gold (III),[58] and iron (II).[59] The water-insoluble, orange-yellow complex with gold is soluble in chloroform.

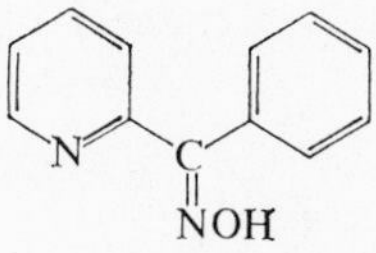

CXII

Metal-binding through anionic nitrogens is uncommon but is found, for example, in the bis-o-(p-toluylsulfonamido) aniline complex with Cu(II) (CXIII) that has been suggested for use in the gravimetric determination of cupric ion.[60] The analogous 8-sulfonamidoquinolines have

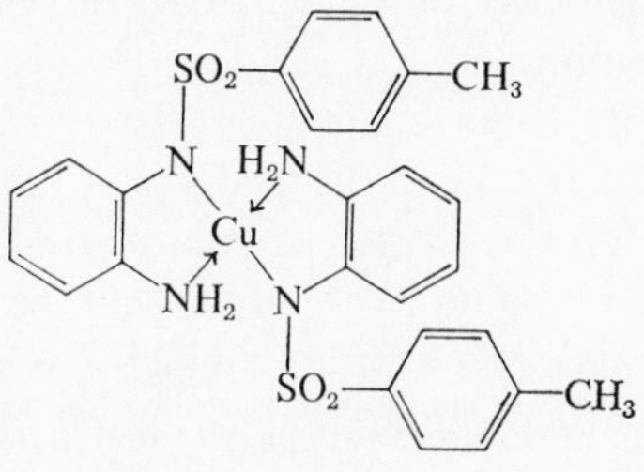

CXIII

also been examined as possible metal precipitants.[61] As would be expected in ligands binding through two nitrogens, these reagents are much more selective than either 8-hydroxyquinoline or 8-mercaptoquinoline, preferred cations being Ag^+, Cu^{2+}, Zn^{2+}, Pb^{2+}, Co^{2+}, and Hg^{2+}. The sulfonamide grouping makes the complexes insoluble in organic solvents. Another example is benzo-1,2,3-triazole (CXIV), the anion of which forms water-insoluble complexes with Cu(II), Cd, Co, Fe(II), Ni, and Zn.[62]

To avoid some of the defects of cupferron, N-benzoyl-N-phenylhydroxyl-amine (CXV) has been suggested as an alternative precipitant.[63] In both cases, metal binding leads to the formation of five-membered chelate rings in which an anionic oxygen and a doubly bonded neutral oxygen are involved, so that similar complex formation is to be expected. N-

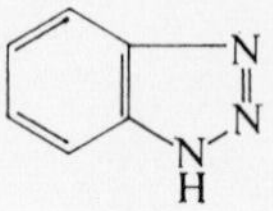

CXIV

Benzoyl-N-phenylhydroxylamine forms insoluble complexes with many cations that prefer anionic oxygen-type bonding, such as Be, Al, Sc, Fe(III), Ti(IV), Zr, Th, Sn, Nb, and Ta, V, Mo(VI), and U(VI). Their selective precipitation depends on the pH of the solution.[64] In many

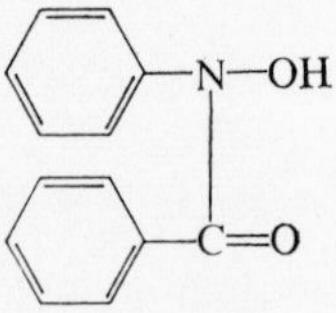

CXV

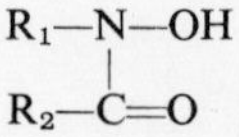

$$R_1-N-OH$$
$$R_2-C=O$$

CXVI

cases (such as the tris complex with scandium) these neutral metal complexes are extractable into organic solvents.

This reagent is a member of the general class shown in (CXVI) of which other members, including $R_1 = C_6H_5$ or H, $R_2 = C_6H_4OH$, C_6H_5, $C_6H_5CH=CH$, or C_9H_6N have been described. The main differences resulting from these changes lie in the acidities of the N—OH groups and the electron densities on the oxygen atoms of the C=O groups (except that the phenolic group in salicylhydroxamic acid, because of its increased solubility in water, makes this reagent a much less efficient precipitant). These differences lead to corresponding variations in pH values for opti-

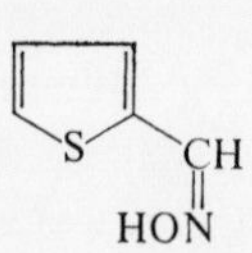

CXVII

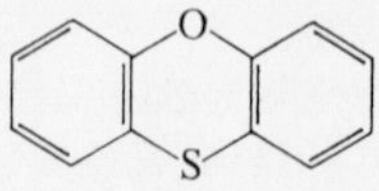

CXVIII

mum separation of metal ions. Thus, like N-benzoyl-N-phenylhydroxyl-amine, both cinnamylhydroxamic acid and N-cinnamoyl-N-phenyl-hydroxylamine have been proposed as precipitants for Nb and Ta.[65]

The suggestion that 2-thiophene-trans-aldoxime (CXVII) can be used as a precipitant for palladium[65] is interesting; it is apparently one of the few analytically useful chelating agents in which a hetero atom of sulfur participates in metal binding.   This behavior is comparable with that of β-furfuraldoxime which can also be used for the gravimetric determination of palladium.   Another example is phenoxithine (CXVIII), which, in weakly acid solutions, forms an insoluble bis complex with palladium (II) chloride.

9.9   Solubility in Organic Solvents

Many complexes that are insoluble in water because of their nonpolar character dissolve readily in nonpolar solvents.   Thus the ferric-oxine and the nickel-dimethylglyoxime complexes are soluble in chloroform, while the water-soluble ferric-oxine sulfonic acid complex is not.   Feigl[67] has concluded that "excellent solubility in chloroform is a characteristic of only those inner complex compounds whose molecules contain no free acidic or basic groups," where such groups include $C=O$, $-N=O$, $-OH$, and $=N-H$.

The effect of solvents containing hydrophilic groups, like acetone and the lower alcohols, on the solubility of some complexes in aqueous systems can be readily understood in terms of the tendency of these groups to act as donors and displace water molecules from coordination sites in the complexes.   Alternatively, the lowering of the dielectric constant and the fact that the solvent molecule has a better chemical resemblance than water to parts of the structure of the complex may be responsible for these effects.   The latter effects seem the more likely in explaining why copper dialkyldithiocarbamate complexes are appreciably soluble in upwards of 40% ethanol but not in water.

9.10   Collectors

Where a metal ion that forms an insoluble complex is present only in trace amounts, it may be convenient to add a larger quantity of another metal which also forms an insoluble complex with the same reagent. The latter may act as a *collector*, in the same way that copper sulfide carries down with it any small quantities of Mo, Zn, Pb, Sb, and other metals in a solution.   Thus Fe^{3+} and Al^{3+} can be used as collectors in precipitations with 8-hydroxyquinoline, and similarly the complex of Fe^{3+} with cupferron recovers traces of Ti, V, and Zr from solution.[68]   The collector may sometimes be chemically quite different: Precipitation of barium sulfate in a solution containing traces of nickel and dimethylglyoxine carries the nickel-dimethylglyoxime complex down with it.   In general, Fajans' precipitation rule operates.   This states that the lower the solubility of the compound formed by the minor constituent (if it is a cation) with the anion of the precipitate, the greater will be the amount of it carried down by the precipitate.

An elegant variation of this technique, which is applicable for separating ultramicroquantities, is to use the precipitant itself as collector, by working under such conditions that the precipitant crystallizes out.[69]   Examples of this are the collection of traces of Ag, Au, and Hg with 2-mercapto-benzimidazole (added to the aqueous phase as an ethanolic solution),[70] and of the determination of uranium in sea water using α-nitroso-β-naphthol.[71]

Thus, "collection" takes advantage of the property of co-precipitation, which is usually undesirable in chemical analysis.   Two main types of coprecipitation can be distinguished.   In the first there is mechanical entrainment or physical absorption on the surface of the precipitate. In the second, interpenetration of the crystal lattice can occur.   An example of this is probably the induced precipitation of $CaSO_4$ in the presence of $BaSO_4$.   As the size of the $BaSO_4$ crystals grow, suitably oriented sulfate groups provide spatially favorable arrangements for incorporating either calcium or barium ions, whereas in pure $CaSO_4$ solutions no such solid phase is available.   Once the calcium ions are incorporated into the crystal lattice it is no longer possible to remove them without complete destruction of the solid phase.   The same effect is frequently observed in precipitations using organic reagents, metal ions coprecipitating as their complexes in pH regions where they are ordinarily soluble.

The use of mercurous chloride as a collector for traces of Au, Pt, Pd, Se, and Te salts in acid solution should be considered a special case; reduction to the free element occurs on the mercurous chloride surface.

9.11   Micelle Formation

In the extreme case of an organic molecule, such as a long-chain hydro-carbon, with an ionic group attached at one end, micelle formation can occur.   The common soaps, which are the sodium salts of long-chain fatty acids, are familar examples.   Above a low concentration (usually very low), soaps cease to be entirely molecularly dispersed in aqueous solution.   Instead they form micelles, which are colloidal aggregates, in which the hydrophilic groups are on the outside in contact with the aqueous phase, whereas the hydrocarbon chains make up the interior. In nonaqueous solvents the directions of the micelles are reversed, with the polar groups in the central region and the hydrocarbon chains in the solvent.

These detergents can be cationic (e.g. cetylpyridinium chloride), non-ionic (e.g. tetradecyl-deoxy-polyethyleneglycol) or anionic (e.g. sodium lauryl sulfate and the sodium salts of long-chain fatty acids). Metal-containing anionic detergents for nonpolar solvents include[72]:

1. The alkali and alkaline earth soaps of naphthenic and sulfonic acids from petroleum and hydrocarbons (e.g. alkylnaphthylenesulfonic acids), and of alkyl phenolates and alkyl phosphates.

2. Aluminium soaps of oleic, 2-ethyl-hexanoic, naphthenic, and C_8-C_{18} normal fatty acids.

3. Soaps of transition metal ions, including Cu^{2+}, Zn^{2+}, Fe^{2+}, Ni^{2+}, and Co^{2+}, with oleic, 2-ethyl-hexanoic, naphthenic, and C_8-C_{18} normal fatty acids.

Detergent solutions are able to solubilize many organic compounds that are ordinarily of only low solubility in the solvent. This property may have analytical applications. It has been used, for example, to obtain porphyrins and their metal complexes in monomolecular dispersion for studies of their spectra and metal-binding behavior.[73]

9.12 Factors Governing the Selection of a Precipitant for Inorganic Cations

The ideal precipitant for any particular species should have certain characteristics. It should yield a complex that is sparingly soluble, and that preferably should be capable of being obtained in an analytically pure condition. Above all, it should be *specific*, giving a precipitate only with the species being determined. In practice, an organic reagent ordinarily reacts with a wide range of metal ions, and it is necessary to select particular experimental conditions if only one ion is to be precipitated as its complex. This may entail pH control or the addition of other complex-forming species to the solution to "mask" cations that would otherwise interfere.

Factors that govern the nature and composition of a precipitate, and its suitability or unsuitability for analytical purposes, are numerous and not well understood quantitatively. Their nature can be seen by considering precipitation as a time sequence. Initially the solution becomes super-saturated, and sooner or later a number of nuclei suitable for initiating crystal formation will be produced. Depending on the rate of formation of more nuclei and the rate of growth of crystals, the final precipitate will range from microcrystalline to large and granular.   On standing, crystal size will slowly increase because small crystals are more soluble than large ones, so that the latter grow at the expense of the former.   The overall picture is less simple than this.   Adsorption and coprecipitation may occur, and the precipitate may be deposited in an amorphous condition.   Again, it may appear initially in a colloidal form, necessitating the addition of surface-active materials to induce coagulation.   Often it may be desirable to recrystallize a precipitate to reduce the concentrations of undesirable contaminants.   All these factors are also clearly dependent on many physical parameters such as the conditions of temperature, pH, concentration, rate of addition of reagents, and the efficiency of mixing.   Precipitation from homogeneous solutions reduces this complexity, but the processes are, to a large extent, still empirical.   Again, the sensitivity of spot tests based on precipitation can sometimes be greatly increased if there is adsorption of a colored material on to a colorless or only slightly colored precipitate so as to render it more readily detected by the human eye.   (An example is the adsorption of p-nitrobenzeneazo-α-naphthol onto the white $Mg(OH)_2$ precipitate.)

Nevertheless, the following principles can be used as guides in selecting possible precipitants for use in analytical chemistry.

1. The complex should have no net electronic charge and should also lack polar groups that are capable of hydrogen bonding with water molecules.   The most important uncomplexed groups that should be avoided in the ligand are those with lone pairs of electrons on nitrogen or oxygen.

It must be remembered, however, that if a lone pair on, say, an $-\overset{|}{N}H$ or an $-NH_2$ group is used in metal binding, it is not available to coordinate with the solvent so that solubility is decreased on complex formation. This applies, for example, to metal complexes of iminodiacetic acid.

2. The complex should have a high stability constant.   This almost invariably involves chelate ring formation, particularly through ligand atoms for which the metal ion has greater affinity.   (This aspect is discussed in Chapter 3.)   Estimates, at least as to orders of magnitude, can be made for stability constants with new ligands using published data for analogous substances.   Among the transition metal ions, differences in stability constants will be greatest for species with high ligand fields.   Precipitation of Mn(II), which has no ligand-field stabilization in its "high-spin" complexes, from other transition metal ions is likely to require an oxygen-containing ligand, in the presence of a nitrogen-containing ligand to "mask" other metal ions in the series.   The same principle operates, but in reverse, in the precipitation of Ni(II) with dimethylglyoxime in the presence of Fe(III), Al(III), and Bi(III).

For electrostatic reasons, addition of oxygen-containing di- or tri-anions such as tartrate or citrate strongly favors formation of complexes with the trivalent cations, whereas complex formation with the divalent cations is much less strong, but is, nevertheless, often important in analysis. This nonselectivity of reagents such as the β-diketones and cupferron is only slightly improved in ligands such as 8-hydroxyquinoline and anthranilic acid where bonding is through an oxygen anion and a nitrogen atom. Conversely, the high ligand-field strength and covalent bonding associated with the four nitrogens in a bis-dimethylglyoxime complex increases the stability of the Ni(II) complex (a d^8 system) but not of any complex with Fe(III) (which is d^5) or the nontransition metal ions.

In general, it is to the ligands containing nitrogen and sulfur donor atoms (such as dithizone and diethyldithiocarbamate) that one must look for selective precipitants or extractants of cations with filled or partly filled d shells.

To secure precipitates that are highly insoluble it is often advantageous to use ligands such as dithiooxamide that, by bonding to a different metal ion at each end of the ligand, are able to act as bridging agents and give rise to polynuclear complexes. Alizarin blue (CXIX) is another example of this type.

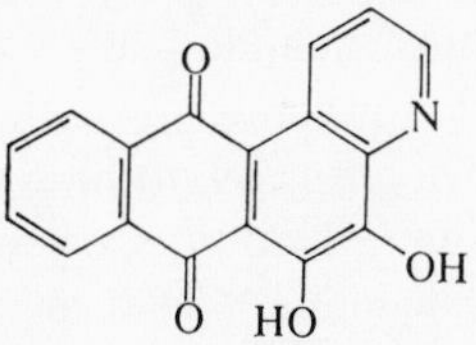

CXIX

In strongly acid solution, alizarin blue is reported to be a specific reagent for copper (II) which forms a blue crystalline precipitate.[74] This reagent can be looked upon as being both a substituted 8-hydroxyquinoline and a substituted 1-hydroxyanthraquinone, the complexing groups in each case being independent. The affinity of 8-hydroxyquinoline for Cu(II) is well known, and the 1-hydroxyanthraquinone copper complex precipitates from ammoniacal solution.[75] There seems little doubt that each molecule of alizarin blue coordinates two copper ions which, by linking with other ligand molecules, build up a very large and highly insoluble polynuclear complex. Consistent with this interpretation is the failure of sulfide or cyanide ions to decompose the complex. In fact, if the reagent is added to a cyanide solution containing copper (I), autoxidation occurs and the alizarin blue-copper (II) complex precipitates.[74] Similar polynuclear complex formation is much less likely where the metal ions bind strongly to either the oxine moiety or the hydroxyanthraquinone portion, but not both, or where the two phenolic groups are involved.

3. To minimize the coprecipitation of ligand molecules with the metal complex, the former should be much more soluble than the latter.

4. It may be advantageous to incorporate structures into the ligand that will make possible a subsequent spectrophotometric or volumetric determination as an alternative to gravimetry. For example, quantitative bromination can be used in volumetric methods with complexes of anthranilic acid, benzoin oxime, dimethylglyoxime, 8-hydroxyquinoline, and salicylaldoxime. A spectrophotometric procedure was described in the section on chloranilic acid.

5. Where gravimetric procedure is intended, the metal complex should not only have a definite composition but should also be stable to drying. Thermolytic studies using a thermobalance can be used to provide evidence for this stability and to delineate suitable operating temperatures.

6. The technique of homogeneous precipitation often leads to greater purity of precipitates, which are analytically in a more convenient form (e.g. as larger and more uniform crystals).[76] It also permits finer control of precipitation conditions. Hydrolysis to generate the precipitant may be used, as in 8-acetoxyquinoline which is thus converted to 8-hydroxyquinoline.[77] Similarly, thioacetamide has come into use as a substitute for hydrogen sulfide, which it generates by hydrolysis, so that it is applied as a reagent for the precipitation of metal sulfides from homogeneous solution.[78] Ethylammonium ethyldithiocarbamate can also be used in this way as a source of sulfide ions.[79] Hydrolysis of urea in acid solution, giving ammonia, serves as a means of raising the pH of a solution slowly.

Other applications of this technique include displacement from masking agent, oxidation of masking agent, reduction, and evaporation of masking agent or solubilizing solvent. In some cases it has been possible to synthesize the precipitant *in situ*.[80]

References

1. Vol'f, L. A., *Zavodsk. Lab.*, **25**, 1438 (1959).
2. Kimura, K., K. Saito, and M. Asadra, *Bull. Chem. Soc. Japan*, **29**, 640 (1956).
3. For discussion of lattice energies and their significance in inorganic chemistry, see Waddington, T. C., *Adv. Inorg. Chem. Radiochem.*, **1**, 157 (1959).
4. Leussing, D. L., in *Treatise on Analytical Chemistry*, I. M. Kolthoff and P. J. Elving, eds., Interscience, New York, 1959, Vol. 1, Part 1, Chapter 17, p. 675.
5. Flagg, J. F., *Organic Reagents*, Interscience, New York, 1948, p. 63.
6. Reeve, W., and I. Christoffel, *Anal. Chem.*, **29**, 102 (1957); Reeve, W., *Anal. Chem.*, **31**, 1066 (1959).
7. Kohler, M., *Z. Anal. Chem.*, **138**, 9 (1953); Gloss, G. H., *Chemist-Analyst*, **42**, 50 (1953).

8. Raff, P., and W. Brötz, Z. Anal. Chem., **133**, 241 (1951).
9. Smith, D. L., D. R. Jamieson, and P. J. Elving, Anal. Chem., **32**, 1253 (1960).
10. Davis, D. G., Anal. Chem., **32**, 1321 (1960).
11. Sazonova, V. A., and V. N. Leonov, Zh. Anal. Khim., **14**, 483 (1959).
12. See, for example, Lewis, P. R., Analyst, **80**, 768 (1955).
13. Caley, E. R., and G. A. Simmons, Anal. Chem., **25**, 1386 (1953).
14. Erdey, L., and L. Jankovits, Acta Chim. Hung., **4**, 235 (1954).
15. Latimer, W. M., K. S. Pitzer, and C. M. Slansky, J. Chem. Phys., **7**, 108 (1939).
16. Moore, C. E., and T. A. Robinson, Anal. Chim. Acta, **23**, 533 (1960).
17. Schoonover, I. C., J. Res. Natl. Bur. Std. U.S., **15**, 377 (1935).
18. Strafford, N., and P. F. Wyatt, Analyst, **61**, 528 (1936).
19. Ayres, G. H., and B. D. Narang, Anal. Chim. Acta, **24**, 241 (1961).
20. Dubsky, J. V., Mikrochem. Mikrochim. Acta, **28**, 145 (1940).
21. Sheppart, S. E., and R. H. Brigham, J. Am. Chem. Soc., **58**, 1046 (1936).
22. Maynard, J. L., Ind. Eng. Chem. (Anal. Ed.), **8**, 368 (1936).
23. Feigl, F., Chemistry of Specific, Selective and Sensitive Reactions, Academic Press, New York, 1949, p. 311.
24. Feigl, F., and L. I. Miranda, Ind. Eng. Chem. (Anal. Ed.), **16**, 141 (1944).
25. Krumholz, P., and E. Krumholz, Mikrochem., **19**, 47 (1935).
26. Martini, A., Mikrochem., **8**, 144 (1930).
27. Tchakirian, A., Ann. Chim., **12**, 415 (1939); Willard, H. H., and C. W. Zuehlke, Ind. Eng. Chem. (Anal. Ed.), **16**, 322 (1944).
28. Sotnikov, V. S., and I. P. Alimarin, Talanta, **8**, 588 (1961).
29. Feigl, F., and A. Bondi, Ber., **B64**, 2819 (1931); Ephraim, F., Ber., **B64**, 1210, 1215 (1931).
30. Walter, J. L., and H. Freiser, Anal. Chem., **25**, 127 (1953).
31. Walter, J. L., and H. Freiser, Anal. Chem., **24**, 984 (1952).
32. Larsen, E. M., and P. Wang, J. Am. Chem. Soc., **76**, 6223 (1954).
33. Feigl, F., P. Krumholz, and E. Rajmann, Mikrochem., **9**, 395 (1931).
34. Thomason, P. F., M. A. Perry, and W. M. Byerly, Anal. Chem., **21**, 1239 (1949); Mayer, A., and G. Bradshaw, Analyst, **77**, 154 (1952); Banks, C. V., and C. H. Byrd, Anal. Chem., **25**, 416 (1953); Horton, A. D., Anal. Chem., **25**, 1331 (1953).
35. Ishabashi, M., and S. Higashi, Japan Analyst, **4**, 14 (1955).
36. Thomason, P. F., Anal. Chem., **28**, 1527 (1956).
37. Erlenmeyer, H., and E. H. Schmid, Helv. Chim. Acta, **24**, 1159 (1941).
38. Rundle, R. E., and L. E. Godycki, Acta Cryst., **6**, 487 (1953); Rundle, R. E., J. Phys. Chem., **61**, 45 (1957).
39. Charles, R. G., and H. Freiser, Anal. Chim. Acta, **11**, 101 (1954).
40. Frasson, E., R. Bardi, and S. Bezzi, Acta Cryst., **12**, 201 (1959).
41. Frierson, W. J., and N. Marable, Anal. Chem., **34**, 210 (1962).
42. Feigl, F., Ind. Eng. Chem. (Anal. Ed.), **8**, 401 (1936).
43. Pearse, G. A., and R. T. Pflaum, Anal. Chem., **32**, 213 (1960).
44. Burger, K., Talanta, **8**, 77 (1961).
45. Takahashi, I. T., and R. J. Robinson, Anal. Chem., **32**, 1350 (1960).
46. Frost-Jones, R. E. U., and Y. T. Yardley, Analyst, **77**, 468 (1952); Tyner, E. H., Anal. Chem., **20**, 76 (1948); Gammon, N., and R. B. Forbes, Anal. Chem., **21**, 1391 (1949).
47. Bertolacini, R. J., and J. E. Barney, Anal. Chem., **29**, 281 (1957); Barney, J. E., and R. J. Bertolacini, Anal. Chem., **30**, 202 (1958).
48. Barney, J. E., and R. J. Bertolacini, Anal. Chem., **29**, 1187 (1957).
49. Fine, L., and E. A. Wynne, Microchem. J., **3**, 515 (1959).

50. Hensley, A. L., and J. E. Barney, *Anal. Chem.*, **32**, 828 (1960).
51. Bertolacini, R. J., and J. E. Barney, *Anal. Chem.*, **30**, 202 (1958).
52. Erdey, L., and L. Jankovits, *Acta Chem. Hung.*, **4**, 245 (1954).
53. Hayashi, K., T. Danzuka, and K. Ueno, *Talanta*, **4**, 244 (1960).
54. Banerjee, D. K., C. C. Budke, and F. D. Miller, *Anal. Chem.*, **33**, 418 (1961).
55. Dutt, N. K., and A. Dutta Ahmed, *Mikrochim. Acta*, **1961**, 571.
56. Jacobsen, E., and C. Hansteen, *Anal. Chim. Acta*, **28**, 249 (1963).
57. Sen, B., *Anal. Chem.*, **30**, 881 (1958).
58. Sen, B., *Anal. Chim. Acta*, **21**, 35 (1959).
59. Trussel, F., and H. Diehl, *Anal. Chem.*, **31**, 1978 (1959).
60. Billman, J. H., N. S. Janetos, and R. Chernin, *Anal. Chem.*, **32**, 1342 (1960).
61. Billman, J. H., and R. Chernin, *Anal. Chem.*, **34**, 408 (1962).
62. Curtis, J. A., *Ind. Eng. Chem. (Anal. Ed.)*, **13**, 349 (1941).
63. Shome, S. C., *Analyst*, **75**, 27 (1950).
64. For examples of gravimetric methods using this reagent, see Das, J., and S. C. Shome, *Anal. Chim. Acta*, **27**, 58 (1962) (for U(VI)); Das, J., and S. C. Shome, *Anal. Chim. Acta*, **24**, 37 (1961) (for Be); and Langmhyr, F. J., and T. Hongslo, *Anal. Chim. Acta*, **22**, 301 (1960) (for Nb, Ta, Ti).
65. Majumdar, A. K., and A. K. Mukherjee, *Anal. Chim. Acta*, **22**, 514 (1960).
66. Tandon, S. G., and S. C. Bhattacharya, *Anal. Chem.*, **32**, 194 (1960).
67. Reference 23, p. 407.
68. Strock, L. W., and S. Drexler, *J. Opt. Soc. Am.*, **31**, 167 (1941).
69. Weiss, H. V., and M. G. Lai, *Anal. Chem.*, **32**, 475 (1960).
70. Weiss, H. V., and M. G. Lai, *Anal. Chim. Acta*, **28**, 242 (1963).
71. Weiss, H. V., M. G. Lai, and A. Gillespie, *Anal. Chim. Acta*, **25**, 550 (1961).
72. Singleterry, C. R., *J. Am. Oil Chemists' Soc.*, **32**, 446 (1955).
73. Phillips, J. N., *Rev. Pure Appl. Chem.*, **10**, 35 (1960).
74. Feigl, F., and A. Caldas, *Anal. Chim. Acta*, **8**, 339 (1953).
75. Reference 23, p. 203.
76. Gordon, L., M. L. Salutsky, and H. H. Willard, *Precipitation from Homogeneous Solution*, John Wiley and Sons, New York, 1959.
77. Howick, L. C., and W. W. Trigg, *Anal. Chem.*, **33**, 302 (1961).
78. See, for example, Flaschka, H., and H. Jacobljevich, *Anal. Chim. Acta*, **4**, 356 (1950); Burriel-Marti, F., and A. M. Vidan, *Anal. Chim. Acta*, **26**, 163 (1962); Bowersox, D. F., D. M. Smith, and E. H. Swift, *Talanta*, **2**, 142 (1959); **3**, 282 (1960).
79. Sen, B. N., *Anal. Chim. Acta*, **24**, 386 (1961).
80. See, for example, Heyn, A. H. A., and N. G. Dave, *Talanta*, **5**, 119 (1960); Heyn, A. H. A., and P. A. Brauner, *Talanta*, **7**, 281 (1961).

CHAPTER 10

Extraction into Organic Solvents

Extraction of a metal complex from one solvent, usually water, into another often permits a considerable concentration of the complex to be achieved, with consequent increase in the effective sensitivity of an analytical procedure. It is also sometimes a very useful means of securing separations from interfering substances. Examples of its analytical application include the extraction of thiocyanate complexes of Fe(III) and Mo(V) from water by hydroxylic solvents, of Fe(III) from strong hydrochloric acid solutions by ethyl ether, of Cu(II) diethyldithiocarbamate into amyl acetate, and of Ag, Hg, Cu, Pd, Bi, Pb, Zn, and Cd complexes of dithizone into chloroform or carbon tetrachloride. The solute may then be determined spectrophotometrically, or recovered quantitatively by evaporating the solvent or by back-extraction into an aqueous phase. This back-extraction may be made possible by the addition of oxidizing, reducing, or specific complexing substances, or by change of pH. There is a large and rapidly growing literature on solvent extraction [1] and its applications dealing mainly with the separation and purification of actinides and nuclear fission products. A related technique which finds application in qualitative analysis, especially for spot tests, consists in the accumulation of a reaction product at the interface of two immiscible liquids: Traces of nickel dimethylglyoxime in aqueous ammonia gather at the interface following shaking with kerosene.

10.1 Types of System

Solvent extraction systems finding application in analytical chemistry can be divided conveniently into several groups.

1. Metal chelate complexes that carry no net electronic charge often behave as if they were organic molecules, especially if, at the same time, all coordination sites around the metal ion are occupied by the complexing

species. Such complexes are usually readily soluble in inert organic solvents.

2. Where the coordination sites around the metal ion are incompletely filled by organic ligands, neutral complexes can sometimes be extracted into organic solvents, provided the solvents are of such types that they can coordinate strongly to the metal ion. It is this property that leads to the sharp distinction between oxygen-containing solvents such as alcohols, esters, ethers, and ketones and nonpolar solvents such as benzene and carbon tetrachloride. In the extreme case of very strongly solvating species, for example tri-n-butyl phosphate in higher alcohols, ionic species such as cobalt perchlorate can be extracted because of the solvation of the cation itself.

3. Provided their internal bonding is covalent, some neutral inorganic molecules distribute themselves between inert organic solvents and water. Examples include iodine, osmium and ruthenium tetroxides, and arsenic and lead chlorides.

4. Related to the metal halides of the previous group are the complex acids formed by some of the metal halides and pseudohalides in fairly strongly acid solutions. Examples are $HAuBr_4$ and $H_2Ce(NO_3)_6$. Extraction of such species requires solvents that are capable of protonation, such as ethyl ether, amyl alcohol, or methyl isobutyl ketone. More probably, however, in such "oxonium" extraction systems, the hydrogen ion is present as the hydrated hydronium ion, $H(H_2O_4)^+$, (CXX), which is the cation forming an ion pair with the extracted anion.[2] The cation is stabilized by hydrogen bonding to the solvent, so that the coordinating ability of the solvent is very important.

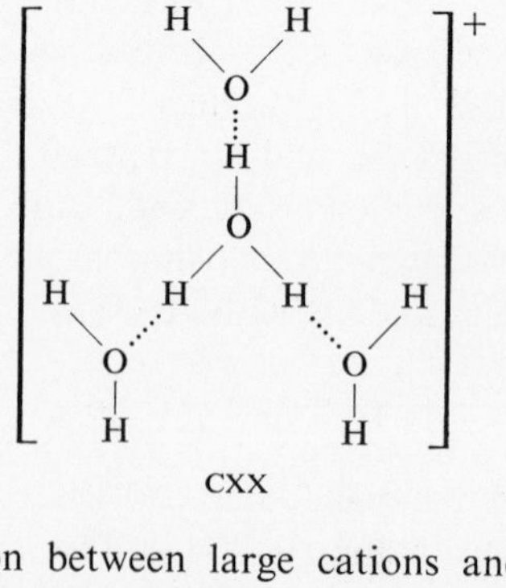

CXX

5. Ion-pair formation between large cations and anions can confer solvent extractability on pairs of species which, individually, often cannot be extracted from water. Examples include the tetraphenylarsonium cation with the perrhenate ion, and rhodamine B cation with many chloroanions.

6. A sixth group, which cannot always be sharply distinguished from the others, comprises reagents or solvents often soluble in, and used in, nonpolar solvents that behave as ion exchangers. For example, tri-isooctylamine is immiscible with water but extracts an anionic uranyl sulfate complex, as an ion pair, from acid solution. Conversely, organic phosphonic acids act as cation extractants, so that dibutylhydrogen-phosphate in kerosene will remove cations of the rare earth elements from water.

10.2 General Discussion

The distribution coefficient λ of a species between an organic solvent and water (each saturated with the other) is given by the equilibrium concentration ratio of this species in the two media. Strictly, λ becomes constant only when the species being distributed is present at low concentration and so does not significantly affect the activity of the solvent in either phase. Variations of λ with concentration are, however, often quite small. Thus the distribution coefficient of $GaCl_3$ between ethyl ether and $6M$ hydrochloric acid varies from 17.8 ± 0.3 to 16.9 as the $GaCl_3$ concentration changes from 10^{-12} to $1.6 \times 10^{-3}M$. (The species extracted is $HGaCl_4$, in which the proton is solvated.) In some cases, however, by increasing the ionic strength of the aqueous phase, λ may change considerably, because of alterations in the activities of species (including water), and in the mutual solubilities of water and organic solvent. This change may give rise to the phenomenon of "salting out" or, less commonly, of "salting in."

Attempts have been made to interpret these effects in terms of electrical effects[3] and internal pressures.[4] Another factor that modifies the distribution of a species between organic and aqueous phases is the presence of competitive complex-forming ions and molecules. Extraction of thorium nitrate into 40% tributyl phosphate in xylene is decreased if phosphate is present, because inextractable thorium phosphate complexes are formed. (This interference can be overcome by adding ferric nitrate to complex with the phosphate.[5])

Where an electrostatic treatment is applicable, for example with alkali halides, the Born equation (Chapter 9) leads to the deduction that the distribution of an ion between water and a solvent of lower dielectric constant favors the aqueous phase. This has been confirmed for the system water-ethanol.[6] However, especially with organic ligands and complexes derived from them, not only the dielectric constant but also the nature of the solvent itself becomes important. Thus, the distribution of anions of the long-chain fatty acids—lauric, myristic, palmitic, and stearic—

between water and ethanol is from 200–10,000 to 1 in favor of ethanol, whereas benzoate and nitrobenzoate anions favor the aqueous phase.[6] If benzene had been used instead of ethanol it seems a reasonable expectation that benzoate rather than fatty acid anions would have been extracted.

The situation is much more complicated than this because, in solvents of low dielectric constant, electrolytes are present as ion pairs, and equilibria are different from those in water. Whereas in water lithium perchlorate is less soluble than sodium perchlorate, in oxygen-containing nonaqueous solvents such as aldehydes, ketones, alcohols, and ethers the position is reversed. Lithium ion coordinates strongly to the oxygen atom of the solvent[7] and is readily soluble in ethyl ether, whereas sodium perchlorate is insoluble. This property is used to separate lithium chloride from the chlorides of sodium, potassium, rubidium, and cesium, using extraction of the solids with alcohol-ether mixture, pyridine, isobutyl alcohol, acetone, dioxane, or n-propyl alcohol saturated with HCl gas. Alternatively, the chlorides are dissolved in a small amount of water and addition of a suitable organic solvent such as 2-ethylhexanol[8] leaves only lithium chloride in solution. Beryllium ion, as beryllium chloride, also dissolves in many oxygen-containing donor solvents.

Silver perchlorate resembles lithium perchlorate in this way and, in addition, is highly soluble in benzene because of complex formation. Nevertheless, its distribution between water and benzene strongly favors the aqueous phase. With aniline, on the other hand, coordination of silver ion by the solvent is so strong that silver perchlorate is extracted from water. The increased solubility of iodine in some solvents, including acetone, is due to the reduction of free iodine concentration in the solvent, resulting from the formation of a charge-transfer complex. For reasons such as these it is necessary to consider somewhat empirically any system in which more than one solvent is present.

Although in the present discussion only two main groups of solvents— nonpolar (e.g. carbon tetrachloride) and polar (mainly oxygen-bonding types, e.g. ethyl ether)—are mentioned, some gradations of properties are observed. Chloroform is a polar solvent but does not coordinate strongly to metal complexes, and hence it is considered an "inert" solvent. Benzene, on the other hand, although nonpolar is highly polarizable, and hence is capable of weak bonding because of ion-induced dipole interaction.

10.3 Metal Halides and Their Complex Acids

Among purely inorganic species that are extractable from aqueous solution by organic solvents are numerous metal chlorides. These include, in decreasing ease of extraction from 6M hydrochloric acid by ethyl ether, the chlorides of Fe(III), Ga(III), Au(III), Tl(III), Mo(VI), Sb(V), As(III), Ge(IV), Te(IV), Sn(II), Sn(IV). In this series the percentage extracted falls from 99% to 15%, while Sb(III), Ir(IV), As(V), Zn, and Hg(II) are only weakly extracted.

These figures serve only as guides, however. The distribution coefficient varies with hydrochloric acid and chloride ion concentrations, passing through a maximum at about $7M$ HCl for Fe(III) with ethyl ether as extractant, about $3M$ for Sb(III), $4M$ for Sn(IV), and, in most other cases, increasing with acid concentration. Results also vary with the organic solvent, and for ferric iron, with the total Fe(III) concentration: The latter variation may be due to the formation of polynuclear complexes in the ether phase. The picture is probably one of successive complex formation in the aqueous solution with one, or at most perhaps two, of the complexes such as MCl_3 and $HMCl_4$ being extractable. At higher halide concentrations, formation of anionic complexes (as distinct from uncharged complex acids) can be expected to diminish the ease of extraction. Extraction of SbI_3 by benzene falls off above an iodide concentration of about $0.01M$ because nonextracted SbI_4^- is formed.

Species resulting from the association of metal ions with suitable inorganic anions are extracted into solvents such as ether, but not into benzene or carbon tetrachloride. This is because oxygen-containing solvents, including ethers, and higher alcohols and ketones, can be protonated and can also be coordinated to a metal ion in a complex if coordination sites are available. In extracted species, such as $HFeBr_4$, $HInCl_4$, $HInBr_4$, $HTlCl_4$, $HGaCl_4$, $HGaBr_4$, $HAuCl_4$, and $HAuBr_4$, the proton is solvated (and possibly hydrated) in the organic phase with the formation of an ion pair, whereas in the anions the four halogen ions are disposed tetrahedrally about the metal ion and no further solvation is required. These species are extracted most efficiently under highly acid or salting-out conditions. On the other hand, in a neutral complex such as $FeCl_3$ either one or three of the coordination sites around the central metal ion must ordinarily be occupied by water molecules to give iron one of its preferred coordination numbers. In such a case, extraction requires that one or more of these water molecules can be replaced by a polar organic solvent. Where the coordination requirements of the metal are already satisfied by the ligands, for example in $HgBr_2$, the complex may be extractable into nonpolar solvents.

On the other hand, where the species might be expected to have a strongly covalent character, as in $AsCl_3$, $GeCl_4$, SbI_3, $HgBr_2$, and SnI_4, other solvents such as carbon tetrachloride, chloroform, and benzene can also be used. Analytical applications include the separations of Ga from Al, In, and Tl(I); of Fe(III) from most of the transition metal ions;

of Mo(VI) from Cr and W; and, in very dilute hydrochloric acid, of Tl(III) from Fe(III) and Ga(III). $AuCl_3$, or possibly $HAuCl_4$, is also quite readily extracted from dilute hydrochloric acid. Bismuth iodide is extracted quantitatively by isoamyl alcohol and isoamyl acetate from sulfuric acid solutions.[9]

Solvent extraction of fluorides is much more limited. Nb and Ta can be extracted as fluoro complexes from acid aqueous solutions using diisopropyl ketone, cyclohexanone, methyl ethyl ketone, hexone, or other ketones.[10]

Ethyl ether extracts bromides of the following metals from $6M$ hydrobromic acid:[11]

$$In > Tl(III) > Au(III) > Fe(III) > Ga \gg Tl(I) > Te(IV)$$

In $4M$ hydrobromic acid, Sb(V), Sn(II), and Sn(IV) are readily extracted into ethyl ether, while As(III) > Mo(VI) > Se(IV) are partly extracted in $6M$ hydrobromic acid.[12] Tl(III) is readily extracted from $0.1M$ hydrobromic acid.

For extraction data on metal bromides with other solvents see reference 12.

The extraction of $HAuBr_4$ from 2.5–$3M$ hydrobromic acid by isopropyl ether has been suggested[14] as an analytical method for gold: Under these conditions relatively little iron is extracted.

From $6.9M$ hydriodic acid, ethyl ether extracts the metal iodides (or their halogen acids) of Sb(III), Hg(II), Cd(II), Au(III), Sn(II) $\gg$ Bi(III) > Zn(II) > In(III) $\approx$ Mo(VI) $\approx$ Te(IV). For a 4:1 ether-to-water ratio the extraction range varies from effectively complete to about 5.5%.[15] Extraction of InI_3 from 0.5–$2M$ hydriodic acid, using ethyl ether, has been suggested as an analytical separation step[16]: At higher acidities the less readily extracted $HInI_4$ is formed.

Any attempt to interpret quantitatively the equilibria in such systems of metals and halide ions requires consideration of a number of factors. If, with increasing metal ion concentration, distribution favors either the organic or the aqueous phase, polymerization in that phase may be occurring. Alternatively, it may be that self-salting out or in may be involved. Dissociation of species such as HMX_4 may occur in the organic as well as in the aqueous phase.[17]

10.4 Thiocyanate Complexes

Thiocyanate ion resembles halide ions by forming colored complexes extractable into alcohols, ethers, and esters with Fe(II), U(VI), Bi(III), Re, Co(II), W(III), Mo(V), and Nb(III); in the presence of pyridine thiocyanate ion also forms chloroform-soluble complexes of type Cu

$py_2(SCN)_2$ with Co, Ni, Cu, Zn, and Cd. Colorless extractable complexes are formed with Zn, Sn(IV), Be, Al, In, and Sc[18]; this has enabled scandium to be separated from Mg, Ca, Mn, Y, rare earths, and thorium.[19] Similarly, zirconium has been separated from hafnium[20]; isobutyl methyl ketone preferentially extracts hafnium thiocyanate from a mixture of zirconium and hafnium thiocyanate in hydrochloric acid solution.[21]

Analytical applications include the ethyl ether extraction of Sn(IV) (99% extracted), and Zn (96%) from $1M$ ammonium thiocyanate and $0.5M$ hydrochloric acid, Ga (99%) and Co (75%) from $7M$ ammonium thiocyanate, and Fe(III) (89%) from $0.5M$ ammonium thiocyanate (optimum concentration for extraction).[18]

10.5 Inorganic Nitrates

The extractability of uranyl nitrate from water by ethyl ether is well known. It arises because U(VI) has a coordination number of 8, so that in $UO_2(NO_3)_2$ four sites round the uranium atom are available for filling by solvent molecules. Solvent coordination to the complex is obviously important in the extraction of uranyl nitrate from aqueous solution. A wide range of solvents, all containing oxygens capable of acting as donor atoms, and including ethers, ketones, alcohols and esters, and also organic phosphine oxides, can be used, but solvents such as benzene or carbon tetrachloride cannot.[22] Uranyl chloride, and to a lesser extent sulfate and phosphate, are also extractable. Similar behavior is shown towards ethyl ether by the following metal nitrates in $8M$ nitric acid[23]:

$$Au(III), \ Ce(IV) > Th(IV) \gg As(V), \ Tl(III), \ Bi(III), \ Zr$$

Zirconium nitrate can be separated from hafnium nitrate by extraction into tributyl phosphate in xylene.[24]

Salting-out effects can be very important. Whereas only 0.1% scandium nitrate is extracted from $8M$ nitric acid, the figure increases to 83% if the solution is saturated with lithium nitrate at 35°. Similarly, thorium extraction is enhanced by the nitrates of Li, Mg, Ca, Zn, Al, and Fe(III), but not of Na, K, NH_4, Sr, or Ba. In general, the salting-out effect can be attributed to a lowering of the activity of the water consequent on the hydration of the added salt, so that the formation of the extractable species is facilitated. It is feasible to separate the nitrates of Nd and La by solvent extraction.[25] Thorium nitrate is extracted preferentially from aqueous neodymium nitrate in the presence of ammonium thiocyanate, using n-amyl alcohol.[26] In some cases, such as $H_2Ce(NO_3)_6$

and $HAu(NO_3)_4$, the extracted species is probably a complex nitrato acid.

For separating metal ions such as those of the rare earths, which form complexes with similar extraction behavior, countercurrent distribution is advantageous. It has been used, for example, to separate praseodymium and neodymium nitrates in $13.8M$ nitric acid with tributyl phosphate as extractant.[27] In general, however, this technique finds application in preparative, rather than analytical, chemistry. Much more commonly, analytical methods are based on "batch" extraction procedures, with or without back-washing: Such procedures give only poor separations of material having similar distribution coefficients.

10.6   Quantitative Aspects of Extraction Equilibria

Equilibria between an organic phase and an aqueous solution in which there is stepwise complex formation have been studied by Rydberg.[28] In the case of a charged ligand A^- and a metal ion B^{n+}, in which only the uncharged complex BA_n is soluble in the organic phase, the ratio of $[BA_n]$ in the organic phase to the total concentration of B is given by

$$\frac{[BA_n]_{org}}{[B]_{total, aq}} = d = \frac{\lambda\beta_n[A]^n}{1 + K_1[A] + K_1K_2[A]^2 + \cdots + \beta_n[A]^n} \tag{1}$$

where $\lambda = [BA_n]_{org}/[BA_n]_{aq}$ is the distribution coefficient of the species BA_n between the organic phase and water. Equation (1) is not significantly altered if it is modified to include extraction of the uncharged species, HA, into the organic phase. The most important single factor determining the extractability of such complexes from water is the quantity λ, with which the remainder of this discussion is concerned. High values of λ are to be expected where BA_n is an uncharged complex, lacking polar groups, especially if the organic solvent is nonpolar and shows chemical resemblance to the nonpolar part of the ligand A.

The dependence of d in equation (1) on values of λ can readily be obtained if the stepwise formation constants are known. As examples, Figs. 10.1 and 10.2 show the variations of the observed distribution coefficient of a bis and a tris complex for several assumed ratios of stability constants as a function of ligand concentration. If, at still higher ligand concentration, anionic complexes are formed, these curves will descend again.

The application of these curves is illustrated by considering the ferric-thiocyanate system, for which $K_1 = 140$ and $K_2 = 12$ at $18°$ and at an ionic strength of 0.6.[29] It is believed that the main complex extracted into amyl alcohol is $Fe(SCN)_3$, first because this is an uncharged species

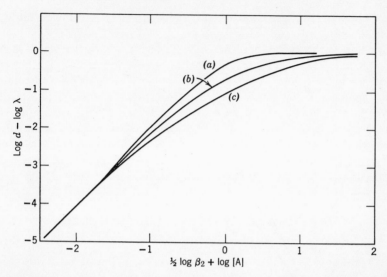

Fig. 10.1. Variation with ligand concentration (in the aqueous phase) of the apparent distribution coefficient for a 1:2 metal complex. It is assumed that two complexes MA and MA$_2$ are formed but only the latter is extractable. Curves (a), (b), and (c) are for ratios of successive formation constants, K_1/K_2, of 0 (i.e., [MA] is negligible), 9, and 100.

and second because the observed extinction coefficient maximum of 13,800 is close to what would be expected for the tris complex. (Values for ϵ_{max} of FeSCN^{2+} and Fe(SCN)$_2{}^+$ are 5000 and 9800, respectively.) The assumption that $K_1/K_2 \approx K_2/K_3$ leads to an estimate of K_3 of about 1, so that log β_3 is about 3.2. Examination of Fig. 10.2 shows that in such a system high thiocyanate concentrations are necessary if the apparent distribution coefficient is to approach its maximum possible value. Even in $1M$ thiocyanate solution, it is still only about two-thirds of this. However, by the time this concentration is reached, higher and less extractable complexes are also being formed. Log β_3 for the 1:3 molybdenyl thiocyanate complex appears to be much higher, and the ratios K_1/K_2, K_2/K_3 smaller, than for ferric iron,[30] so that conditions for maximum extraction are approached at much lower thiocyanate concentrations.

Where the ligand is the anion of a monobasic acid which can distribute between water and an organic solvent, the apparent distribution coefficient d becomes pH dependent. Provided the acid does not ionize or associate in the organic phase, it can readily be shown that

$$\log \frac{\lambda - d}{d} = \mathrm{pH} - \mathrm{p}K_a \tag{2}$$

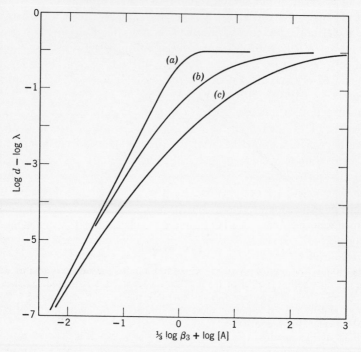

Fig. 10.2. Variation with ligand concentration (in the aqueous phase) of the apparent distribution for a 1:3 metal complex. It is assumed that three complexes MA, MA_2, and MA_3 are formed but only the latter is extractable. Curves (a), (b), and (c) are for ratios of successive formation constants, K_1/K_2 and K_2/K_3 of 0 (i.e., [MA] and [MA_2] are negligible), 10, and 100.

where λ and d have the same significance as in equation (1) and pK_a is the dissociation constant of the acid in water. Equation (2) applies, for example, to the partition of dithizone between carbon tetrachloride and water. The equation is that of a sigmoid curve resembling the titration of a weak acid with a strong base. One consequence of it, which can be seen by inserting $d = 1$, is that the pH at which the distribution between the two phases is equal depends on the value of λ, which, in turn, might be expected to reflect the solubility of the acid in the organic solvent. This has been confirmed for dithizone in a wide range of solvents.[31]

The important quantities governing distribution equilibria, then, are the pH of the solution, the stability constant of the metal chelate, and its relative solubility in the organic phase.[32]

Many *inner complexes*, in which a metal ion is surrounded by enough anionic ligands to neutralize its positive charge and fill all its coordination sites, are readily extracted from aqueous solution into organic solvents.

It can be seen, by combining equations (1) and (2), that if n monovalent ligand ions are involved in the complex, the distribution coefficient of the metal in the presence of excess of the reagent will be a function of the nth power of the hydrogen ion concentration. The range between 1% and 99% extraction when the aqueous phase is shaken with an equal volume of organic solvent is covered by $4/n$ units of pH. Thus, by suitable pH adjustment it becomes possible to select conditions favoring the extraction of an *inner complex* into an organic solvent or ensuring retention of the metal ion in the aqueous phase. This, in turn, frequently permits the separation of one or more metals from a mixture.

These considerations apply to complexes formed by many familiar reagents such as dithizone, cupferron, dimethylglyoxime, and diethyldithiocarbamate. Examples include the separation of Pb and Bi by dithizone extraction at pH 3.0 into carbon tetrachloride,[33] and the extraction of zinc by dithizone from a citrate-buffered pH 8.3 solution, using chloroform.[34] Zinc can be removed from cadmium dithizonate in carbon tetrachloride by back-washing with $1N$ sodium hydroxide.

With ligands that are di- or trianions the same relations hold in pH regions at least one pH unit less than the lowest pK_a. Relations are less simple at higher pH values and the slope of the percent extraction/pH curve falls off. Conversely, where the complexing species has basic as well as acidic groups, for example 8-hydroxyquinoline, the slope of the percent extraction/pH curve increases in more acidic solutions. In some cases, including 8-hydroxyquinoline, reaction between certain metals and ligands may be slow, so that equilibrium is reached very slowly. Moreover, basic and water-soluble complexes may be formed. These factors increase the difficulties of treating quantitatively the distribution behavior in some systems.

10.7 Metal Complexes with Organic Ligands

Qualitatively, it is to be expected that if metal ions are effectively surrounded by hydrophobic ligands which are able to bring about charge neutralization, distribution will strongly favor organic solvents without

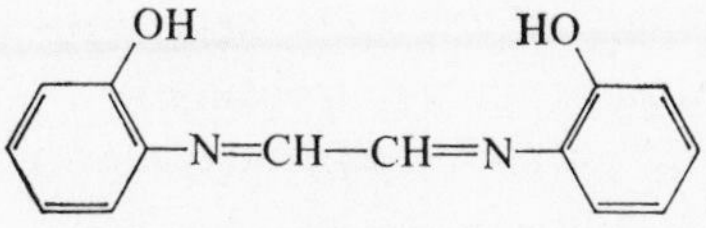

CXXI

much regard for the nature of the solvent itself. This is also true of the nature of the metal ion. Glyoxal-bis-(2-hydroxyanil) (CXXI), as its dianion, forms a 1:1 complex with calcium ion that presumably involves bonding to the metal through the oxygen and the nitrogen atoms which are disposed tetrahedrally around it. The complex is extractable into chloroform, where its intense red color provides a sensitive method (down to 1 ppm) for calcium.[35] Under the same conditions, magnesium does not interfere very much because it prefers octahedral coordination, and the extra water molecules around the metal ion inhibit extraction. No aluminium complex is extracted, because neither the mono nor the bis complex is uncharged.

Few colorimetric reagents bonding only through nitrogen atoms find analytical applications, except in ion pair formation, if extraction into organic solvents is desired. This is because, in general, they are unable to satisfy the requirement of neutralizing the charge on the cation when a metal complex is formed. Exceptions such as phenyl-α-pyridyl ketoxime ((CIII), R = phenyl), which binds metals through a pair of neutral nitrogen atoms, achieve solvent solubility by losing protons from the metal complex—in this case from the oxime —OH—so that this reagent behaves as if it were an anion, to give a neutral complex. Phenyl-α-pyridyl ketoxime has been proposed as an analytical reagent for iron and palladium,[36] while methyl α-pyridyl ketoxime has been suggested for Cu(I) and Fe(II).[37] Pyridine 2-aldoxime, itself, forms intensely colored chelates with many transition metal ions.[38] 4-(2-Pyridylazo)-1-naphthol, in the neutral form (CXXII), does not form stable complexes, but loss of the proton from the phenolic OH group leads to an anion, probably (CXXIII), which give stable solvent-extractable complexes with metal ions.[39]

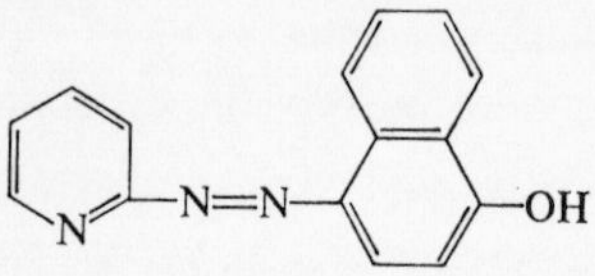

CXXII 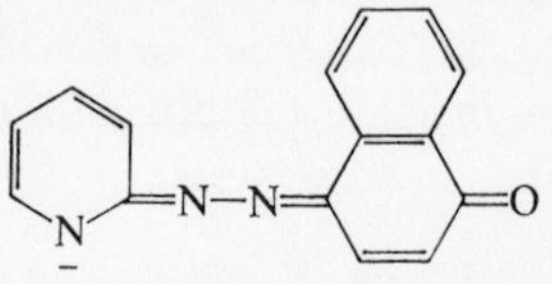   CXXIII

In some cases, salt formation with aliphatic acids is sufficient to confer extractability, so that copper propionate is extracted into chloroform as the dimer, while caesium and transition metals can be extracted as their salts of higher members of the fatty acid series. Similarly, caesium tetraphenylborate extracts into nitrobenzene. The complex $HFeR_4$ (analogous to $HFeCl_4$) where R is a carboxylate anion, is formed by iron (III) and is also extractable.

In basic solution, lithium forms an ether-extractable chelate with dipivaloylmethane.[40]

The highly polar character of morin (CXXIV) explains why some of its metal complexes can be extracted into oxygen-containing solvents such as cyclohexanol and amyl alcohol.   This behavior is similar to that shown by neutral molecules of boric acid, phosphoric acid, phosphomolybdic acid, and perchromic acid which, because of their high content of —OH,

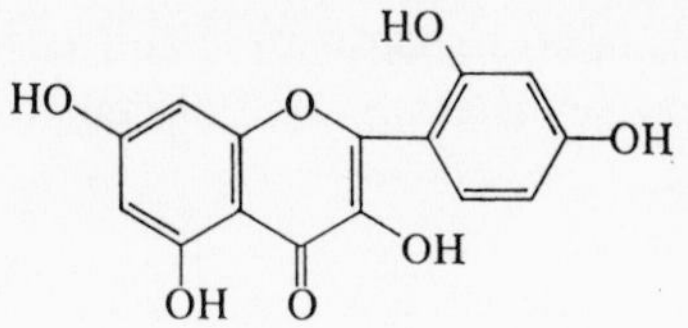

CXXIV

R → O, and R═O groups, also extract into ethyl ether and comparable solvents.

COMPLEXES WITH DIOXIMES

The strong hydrogen bonding of the —OH groups in the planar bis(dimethylglyoxime)-nickel (II) complex makes it relatively difficult to coordinate water molecules and explains its ready extractability into chloroform.   In the corresponding, but nonplanar, cobalt (II) complex the —OH groups are available for bonding to solvent water molecules, preventing extraction into chloroform and making possible the separation of Ni from Co. Thus, although the vicinal-dioximes, such as dimethylglyoxime, are well known as precipitants, they are also useful for colorimetric determination of traces of nickel, palladium, and rhenium.

The behavior of dimethylglyoxime with nickel is interesting because it can apparently be used for complexes of the same metal in different valence states.   The uncharged red bis(dimethylglyoxime) complex of nickel (II) can be extracted into chloroform.   (Co(II), Fe(II), and Cu(II) form similar complexes which are, however, water soluble, although the copper complex can be extracted into chloroform.)   If, on the other hand, dimethylglyoxime is added to an alkaline solution of a nickel salt that has been treated with an oxidizing agent, such as iodine, bromine, or potassium persulfate, the solution becomes wine-red in color ($\lambda_{max} = 445$ mμ) because of the formation of a dimethylglyoxime complex in which nickel is present in a higher-valent state (which may be Ni(III) or Ni(IV)). This water-soluble complex is not very stable, and its structure is unknown.

The Ni(II) complexes of other dioximes can also be extracted into chloroform: The wavelengths of maximum absorption lie in the sequence α-furildioxime (435 mμ) ≫ heptoxime (cycloheptanedionedioxime) > dimethylglyoxime, as expected from substituent effects.   The sensitivity for nickel is high, being around 0.1 ppm with nioxime (cyclohexane-1,2-dionedioxime), but the specificity is poor.   Palladium (II) can be estimated in the same way, furildioxime being a more sensitive reagent than dimethyl-glyoxime.[41] Complexes with 4-methylnioxime[42] and furildioxime[43] enable sensitive colorimetric estimation of low concentrations of rhenium, but the chemistry involved in unknown. The soluble yellow tris complex of 1,2,3-cyclohexanetrione trioxime with cobalt (III) has been suggested for the spectrophotometric determination of cobalt.[44]

Complexes with Acetylacetone and Thenoyltrifluoroacetone

Although the monoanion of acetylacetone, $CH_3COCH_2COCH_3$ (formed by removal of one of the enolizable protons) reacts with many metal ions to give neutral complexes, the comparable complexes of the substituted acetylacetone, α-thenoyltrifluoroacetone, (CXXV), are much

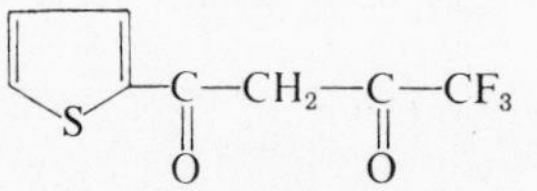

CXXV

more readily extracted into benzene (because of the thiophene moiety). Also, because of its strongly electronegative groups, thenoyltrifluoroacetone is a fairly strong acid, and its metal complexes can be extracted from solutions having quite low pH values.

Stability constants of these complexes increase with the valence of the metal ion and with increasing atomic number in any column in the periodic table. Complexes of transition metals and those with filled d shells are more stable than those of "inert-gas" type. This reagent has found many applications. Examples include the separation of Pu from U;[45] Be from Cu, Fe, Al, Sc, Y, Ca, and Zn;[46] Bi from ^{228}Pa; Ac from Th; Th from Pa, U, and Ac;[47] Zr from Hf;[48] and Ac from Ra.[49] These complexes involve six-membered ring formation, as in (CXXVI).

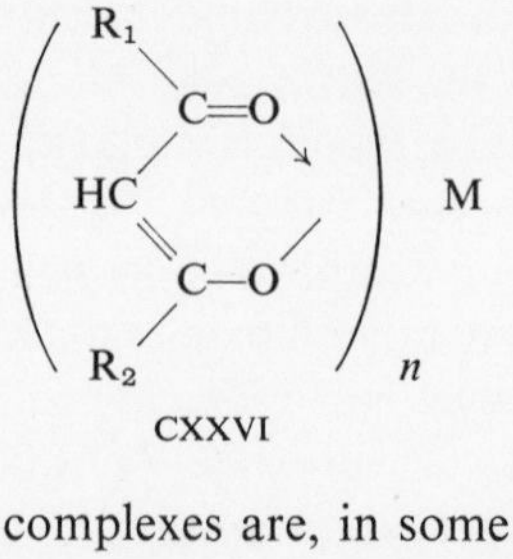

CXXVI

Thenoyltrifluoroacetone complexes are, in some cases, colored, so that TTA has been used both as an extractant and as the colorimetric reagent to determine chromium,[50] uranium,[51] and iron[52] in the organic phase.

For a recent review of extractions using thenoyltrifluoroacetone, see reference 53, and for a study of solvent extraction of metal β-diketonates, see reference 54.

COMPLEXES WITH CUPFERRON

Nitrosophenylhydroxylamine (CXXVII), in the form of an aqueous solution of its ammonium salt, cupferron, reacts with many metal ions to give insoluble or sparingly soluble metal complexes which are, however, readily extracted into chloroform, ethyl ether, ethyl acetate, methyl isobutyl

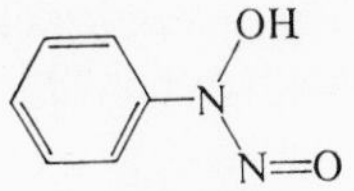

CXXVII

ketone, o-dichlorobenzene, and benzene.[55] Their extractabilities vary with pH in a manner roughly paralleling their solubilities. With chloro-form as solvent, ease of extraction follows the sequence

Fe(III), Ga, Sb(III), Ti(IV), Sn(IV), Zr, V(V), U(IV), Mo(VI) > Bi,

Cu(II), Th > Pb(II), Zn(II), Co(II), Ni(II) > Mn(II) > Mg

The first group can be extracted quantitatively as their cupferrates from 4–6N H$_2$SO$_4$, using chloroform. Extraction of the Al complex requires a pH around 3.5–4.0. The difference in stability of these complexes can be ascribed to the inert gas (Ne) electronic configuration of Al^{3+} which makes it less readily deformable than Fe^{3+}, so that in its tris(cupferron) chelate Al bonds much less strongly than Fe to the nitroso group.

Cupferron extraction has been used to purify Pa from mineral con-centrates.[56]

The appreciable solubilities of the cupferron complexes of La, Th, and U(VI) is probably due in part to increased coordination numbers resulting

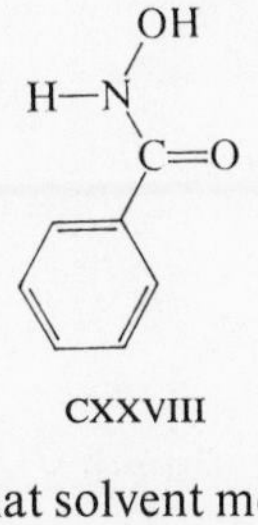

CXXVIII

from the larger ionic radii, so that solvent molecules can bond to the metals. This would explain why iso-amyl alcohol, but not chloroform, is a suitable extractant for the cupferrates of tungsten and tantalum.

Benzohydroxamic acid (CXXVIII) and other hydroxamic acids form metal complexes by chelation of the metal ion between the two oxygen atoms of the monoanion to give a five-membered ring. As would be expected, these ligands are very similar to cupferron in their complexing behavior so that benzohydroxamic acid has been suggested as a colorimetric reagent for uranium (VI)[57] and vanadium.[58] However, the reagent is very sensitive to oxidation by peroxides in solvents used for extraction,[59] and, in fact, bleaching of the color of the complexes, because of oxidation, has been suggested as a spectrophotometric method for hydrogen peroxide.[60]

This reagent is a member of the more general class (CXXIX) that has been used in inorganic analysis. When R_2 is a hydrogen atom and R_1

$$R_1-\underset{\underset{O}{\|}}{C}-\underset{\underset{OH}{|}}{N}-R_2$$

CXXIX

is an alkyl, aryl, furyl, or thienyl radical, such a reagent is a weaker acid and is more soluble in water, and its complexes are much less soluble in chloroform, than when R_2 is an aryl radical. The solubility of the latter complexes, for example of metals such as V(V), U(VI), and Fe(III), in chloroform makes their solvent extraction possible. In general, the latter group of reagents are the more useful analytically. Thus, the two substances for which R_1 = thienyl and R_2 = phenyl and p-tolyl, respectively, are the basis of extraction methods reported to be highly selective for vanadium (V).[61]

Replacement of the nitroso group of cupferron by benzoyl and cinnamoyl groups gives N-benzoyl-N-phenylhydroxylamine ((CXXIX), R_1 = R_2 = phenyl), and N-cinnamoyl-N-phenylhydroxylamine ((CXXIX), R_1 = styryl, R_2 = phenyl). The first of these has applications in gravimetric analysis, because of the insolubility of its metal complexes. In 5–9M hydrochloric acid it forms complexes only with V, Sn, Ti, and Zr,[62] and of these only the vanadium complex is extracted into chloroform. This makes possible a specific method for vanadium in chrome ores. N-Cinnamoyl-N-phenylhydroxylamine behaves similarly, but is much more sensitive.[63] In less acid solutions N-benzoyl-N-phenylhydroxylamine forms solvent-extractable complexes with other cations. For example, at pH 3.5 the orange-red uranyl (VI) complex is extracted by chloroform.[64]

COMPLEXES WITH NITROSOPHENOLS AND DERIVATIVES

The nitroso group, $-N{=}O$, is potentially capable of coordination through the oxygen, atom, $-N{=}O{\rightarrow}$, as in cupferron, or through the nitrogen atom, $-N{=}O$. According to Feigl,[65] the metal binding by α-

nitroso-β-naphthol is of the latter type, to give the five-membered chelate rings (CXXX) instead of the six-membered rings (CXXXI).

CXXX   CXXXI

α-Nitroso-β-naphthol (pK 7.70) and β-nitroso-α-naphthol (pK 7.22) are much weaker acids than nitrosophenylhydroxylamine (pK 4.15), so that their use in complex formation (as monoanions) requires solutions that are much less acid than for cupferron. The slowness of formation of the tris(α-nitroso-β-naphthol) complex of cobalt (III) and its very slow dissociation by strong acids can be attributed to the low-spin d^6 electronic configuration of Co(III) in the complex (Chapter 5). The importance of ligand-field stabilization in Co(III) complexes would be expected to favor binding through the nitrogen rather than the oxygen atom. Similar behavior is shown by the Fe(II) and Pd complexes (d^6 and d^8, respectively). Because high-spin d^6 complexes are labile, this suggests the ferrous complex is spin paired, in which case nitrogen should again be the donor atom. It is possible, however, that in complex formation some metals may use the nitrogen, and others the oxygen, of the nitroso group.

Variations in the solubilities and extraction behavior of the metal complexes of nitrosophenols, including nitrosonaphthols, probably have a different origin. In the tris complexes of o-nitrosophenol, o-nitrosocresol, and α-nitroso-β-naphthol with Co(III) and Fe(III), all coordination sites around the metal ions are occupied by the organic ligands, to give the preferred octahedral structures which, as expected from the nature of the constituents, are insoluble in water and extractable into petroleum ether. The bonding requirements of four-coordinate Pd(II) are fulfilled by two molecules of ligand, and here again the complex is petroleum ether soluble. On the other hand, the water solubility of the bis (o-nitrosophenol) complexes of Fe(II), Ni(II), and Cu(II) is due to the fact that these metals have octahedral or distorted octahedral symmetry in their complexes. Only four of the coordination sites are filled by nitrosophenol molecules, to give the uncharged bis complexes, so that two solvent molecules can also bind to the metal. This explains, also, why these complexes are extractable into ethyl ether but are insoluble in petroleum ether.

Some improvement in water solubility is obtained by insertion of a carboxyl group (to give 3-nitrososalicylic acid) or an ether group, as in 2-nitroso-5-methoxyphenol (nitrosoresorcinol monomethyl ether)[66] without, at the same time, preventing the extraction of the Co(III) complex into petroleum ether.   A carboxylic (but not, say, a sulfonic) acid group can be used in this way because in weak acid its ionization is repressed. Complexes of nitroso-R-salt (1-nitroso-2-hydroxy-naphthalene-3,6-disulfonic acid, as sodium salt) are anionic and hence are not extracted into organic solvents.   3-Nitrososalicylic acid has been used to determine Co(III) in the presence of Ni(II) by using petroleum ether extraction;[67] the noninterference by Fe(III) is probably due to its formation of water-soluble complexes by reaction with the salicylic acid moiety rather than with the nitrosophenol portion.

Annelation of a benzene ring onto the 3,4 position of o-nitrosophenol to give α-nitroso-β-naphthol, or the 5,6 position to give β-nitroso-α-naphthol, exerts the expected effects by decreasing the watersolubility of the metal complexes and increasing their ease of extraction into nonpolar organic solvents.

The same general remarks apply to isonitrosoacetone (CXXXII), and many of its derivatives in their metal-complexing tendencies to form chelate rings as in (CXXXIII).   The ligands are monoanions, and the metal

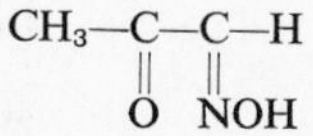

$$CH_3-\underset{\underset{O}{\|}}{C}-\underset{\underset{NOH}{\|}}{C}-H$$

CXXXII

$$\left(\begin{array}{c} R_1-C{=}O \\ | \\ R_2-C{=}N \\ \downarrow \\ O \end{array} \right)_n M$$

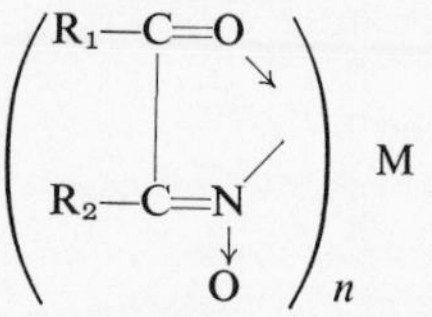

CXXXIII

is bound through an oxygen and a nitrogen atom in a five-membered ring. Their complexes with Fe(II) are blue, and they are extractable into organic solvents.   The behavior of α-benzilmonoxime in the same way confirms that enolization of the carbonyl group is not involved.   Many other metal ions form colored (water-insoluble) precipitates, soluble in chloroform, with these reagents, including the tris Co(III), and the bis Ni(II), Cu(II), Zn, Cd, and Hg(II) complexes.

COMPLEXES BONDING THROUGH SULFUR ATOMS

Diethyldithiocarbamic acid is unstable in solution,[68] but its sodium salt (CXXXIV) is frequently used as a colorimetric reagent for copper (II), with which it forms a bis complex by bonding through the sulfur atoms. This reagent is much less selective for copper than is 2,9-dimethyl-1,10-

phenanthroline, but it is much more sensitive and can detect levels of copper concentration down to 0.01 ppm. The complexes this reagent forms with copper and many heavy metals are almost insoluble in water. They can, however, be extracted into chloroform, carbon tetrachloride, and other solvents.[69] Many of the complexes, including those of Bi, Cr(VI), Co, Cu, Fe(II), Fe(III), Mo(VI), Ni, Sn(II), Sn(IV), and U(VI), are colored.

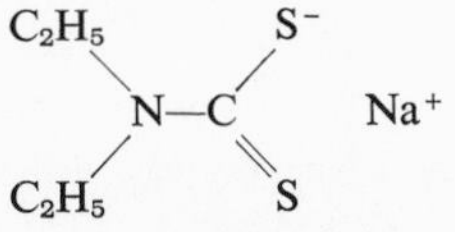

CXXXIV

The instability of the reagent limits its usefulness to solutions above about pH 6, while its poor selectivity requires the use of masking substances in its analytical applications.   For example, reaction with Cd, Co(III), Ni, Pb, Tl(I), Zn, Fe(III), In, and Mn(III) can be prevented by the addition of EDTA, and similarly addition of cyanide ion masks Ag, Co(III), Cu(II), Hg(II), Pd, Zn, and Fe(III), but neither of these reagents affects Bi, Tl(III), Sb(III), Te(IV), As(III), Se(IV), Sn(IV), or V(V). Further selection can be achieved by carrying out extractions at controlled pH values. For example, the tetrakis complex with Te(IV) is extracted into CCl_4 from pH 8.5–8.7 buffer in the presence of EDTA, phosphate, and cyanide ions as masking agents.   The reagent finds application in the removal, by chloroform or similar extraction, of elements such as Fe, Co, Ni, Cu, and Zn from Al, Be, and Mg.

To obtain dithiocarbamic acids that are more stable in acid solutions, pyrrolidine and dibenzyl analogs have been prepared.   The latter is an improved reagent for copper because it can be used in $1N$ mineral acid, so that Fe, Co, and Ni do not cause much interference.   Diethylammonium diethyldithiocarbamate is also acid stable and in 1–10N sulfuric acid forms complexes with As(III), Cu, Hg, and Bi that can be extracted by chloroform.[70]   In line with theoretical expectations, the metals most

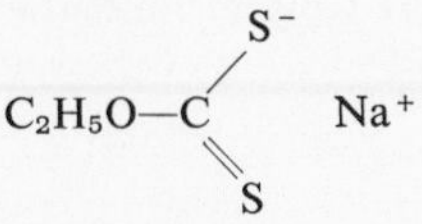

CXXXV 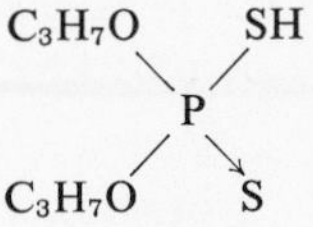   CXXXVI

readily extracted with this group of reagents are those with the greatest affinity for binding to sulfur atoms.   Potassium ethyl xanthate (CXXXV) has also been used as a reagent for copper, but it has proved less convenient than the corresponding diethyldithiocarbamate.

The central carbon atom of the xanthates has been replaced by phosphorus to give a compound such as *o,o'*-diisopropyl hydrogen phosphorodithioate (CXXXVI), which, as the zinc salt, has been proposed[71] as a reagent for copper. It is similar to zinc dibenzyldithiocarbamate in characteristics but some metals, notably mercury and zinc, cause less interference.

Toluene-3,4-dithiol ("dithiol") (CXXXVII), gives sparingly soluble complexes with Sn(II), W(VI), and Mo(VI), which are extractable into

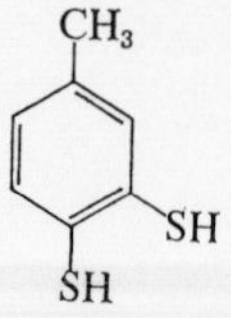

CH₃ on benzene ring with SH, SH substituents

CXXXVII

polar and nonpolar organic solvents: These properties are understandable from the discussion in Chapter 9. Such a reaction is unlikely to be specific; colored complexes are also formed with Bi, Pb, Sb(III), Cu, Ni, Co (all in acid solution), Fe, Tl, Mn, V, and Ru (in alkaline, aqueous pyridine solution). The yellow-green tris molybdenum complex can be extracted from solution with amyl acetate: If $3.7N$ hydrochloric acid is used, tungsten (VI) is left in the aqueous phase.[72] Reduction of the acidity of the solution then leads to the extraction of the blue-green tungsten (VI) complex. Tin (II) can also be estimated as a yellow complex in organic solvents, but more commonly its dithiol complex is dispersed in the aqueous phase, using a detergent, as a magenta-red suspension. The proneness of solid dithiol to aerial oxidation is overcome by storing it as the zinc complex until it is dissolved in acid or alkali. Alternatively, the mercapto groups can be protected by formation of the diacetyl derivative, which is decomposed as required by boiling with potassium hydroxide solution.

The related substance, quinoxaline-2,3-dithiol (CXXXVIII), has been suggested for the colorimetric determination of nickel,[73] and for the de-

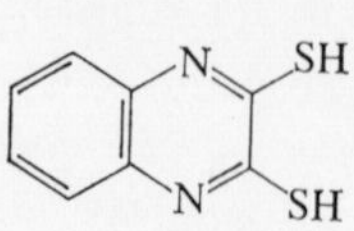

quinoxaline ring structure with N, N and SH, SH substituents

CXXXVIII

termination of cobalt and nickel in the same solution.[74] The reagent and its metal complexes are sparingly soluble in water, but can be extracted into organic solvents. 2-Mercaptobenzothiazole (CXXXIX) has been suggested[75] as a suitable reagent for the extraction of cadmium ion, using chloroform.

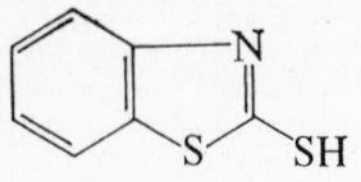

CXXXIX

COMPLEXES BONDING THROUGH SULFUR AND NITROGEN

N,N'-Bis(allylthiocarbamoyl)-hydrazine forms sparingly water-soluble metal complexes of the type (CVIII) with Cu, Ni, Zn, Pb, and Bi, in which the metal is bonded to sulfur and nitrogen atoms. Extraction of the bright orange-red bismuth complex into chloroform (in the presence of potassium cyanide to mask copper) has been suggested as a colorimetric method.[76]

With dithizone (diphenylthiocarbazone, $pK = 5.25$) (CXL), which forms highly colored complexes with many metal ions, the sequence for extraction into carbon tetrachloride is[77]

Hg(II), Pd(II), Pt(II), Te(IV) > Ag(I), Hg(I),

Au(III) > Cu(I) > Cu(II) > Bi > In(III) > Zn(II) > Fe(II),

Co(II), Ni(II) > Tl(I), Pb(II), Cd(II) > Mn(II)

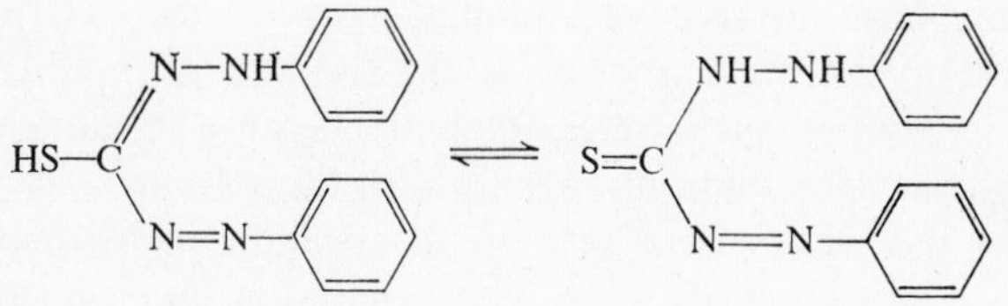

CXL

Thus the bis complex with Hg(II) can be extracted even from $6N$ sulfuric acid, whereas the corresponding Zn complex is best estimated at pH 8.3 and manganese at about pH 11. Dithizone probably exists in solution in the thiol-thione tautomeric equilibrium shown. The absorption maxima at 620 and 450 mμ for dithizone solutions in carbon tetrachloride have been assigned to the enol and keto forms, respectively.[78]

In many cases two different types of dithizonate (having widely differing pH values for half-extraction) are formed by a metal ion. The more common, "primary" forms that are the usual ones in acid solutions involve bonding through the thiolate ion.[79]

Because the bonding in dithizone complexes is through sulfur and nitrogen atoms, the metal ions forming the most stable complexes are those either of the B subgroups of the periodic table, with closed shells of 18 or 18 + 2 electrons (where the two electrons are an "inert pair"), or of the transition metals.[80]   Back-double-bonding is probably important, so that lower-valent states are favored; for example, Cu(I) > Cu(II); Tl(I) > In(III), as, also, are larger metal ions such as In(III) ≫ Ga(III); Bi(III) ≫ Sn(III); and Pb(II) > Sn(II).

In the "secondary" types of dithizone complex the metal may be bonded through two nitrogen atoms.   "Enol" forms have been suggested to involve metal-ligand bonds through two nitrogens and the sulfur atom, but atomic models show clearly the impossibility of such structures.

Diphenylcarbazone is a qualitatively similar reagent to dithizone, from which it differes only in having an oxo, instead of a thio, group.   The poorer bond-forming ability of oxygen relative to sulfur for cations with filled d shells makes it likely that the violet-to-blue complex formed by mercuric ion with diphenylcarbazone in neutral or faintly alkaline solutions is a chelate complex bonded though nitrogen atoms.   This is probably also true of the colored species formed by diphenylcarbazide (a dihydro derivative of diphenylcarbazone) with metal ions such as those of cadmium, cobalt, copper, lead, mercury, nickel, silver, and zinc. However, in some cases, for example mercury, it is likely that the reaction is with diphenylcarbazone formed by oxidation.   Insertion of p,p'-dinitro groups into diphenylcarbazide decreases its solubility in water, so that cadmium and other ions form insoluble precipitates.

The six lone pairs of electrons on sulfur and nitrogen in dithizone are insufficient to confer much water solubility because in almost all cases they would hydrogen bond only weakly with the solvent.   They explain, nevertheless, why dithizone is only slightly soluble in hydrocarbons or carbon tetrachloride but is appreciably soluble in chloroform.   In the dithizone-metal complexes, the number of lone-pair electrons is decreased, so that solubility in chloroform is diminished, whereas solubility in carbon

Thiol form
CXLI

tetrachloride is increased.   Although metal complexes are more soluble in the former than the latter, carbon tetrachloride is the more efficient extractant.   This is because of equilibria involving distribution of the free ligand between water and the organic solvent.

The reagent 1,4-diphenylthiosemicarbazide (CXLI), is structurally similar to dithizone, which it might therefore be expected to resemble in complex-forming ability. Its red-violet chloroform-extractable complex with ruthenium has been suggested as the basis of a spectrophotometric method.[81]

Dimethyl substitution of dithizone to give *o*-ditolylthiocarbazone increases selectivity for copper (II) and mercury (II).[82]

COMPLEXES WITH 8-HYDROXYQUINOLINE AND ITS DERIVATIVES

The lack of polar groups explains the extractability of metal complexes of 8-hydroxyquinoline such as (CXLII) into chloroform. This property

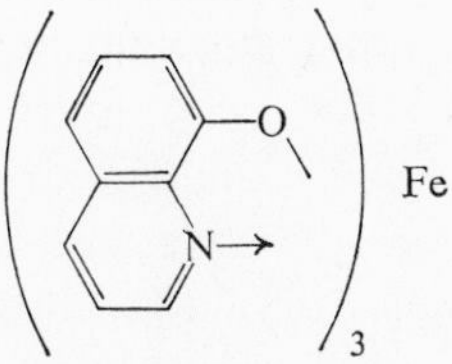

CXLII

can be used in spectrophotometric methods. Examples of metals forming complexes with this reagent include Fe(III), Al, Ga, In, Tl(III), Bi, Co, Ni, Cu(II), Th, V(V), Mo (VI), and U(VI).

The reaction can be made much more selective by using appropriate masking reagents. For example, if Al is the element sought, many interferences can be eliminated at pH 8.5–9 by adding EDTA, cyanide, and sulfite ion (the latter reducing Fe(III) to Fe(II)).[83]

Tungsten can be estimated by extraction of its 8-hydroxyquinoline complex, $WO_2(ox)_2$, from acid (pH 2) solution into chloroform.[84]

The extractability of Co, Ni, and Cu(II) depends on their tendency to form square planar complexes or tetragonal ones in which two water molecules are very weakly bonded. Ions such as Fe^{2+} and Zn^{2+} prefer octahedral coordination. In their bis(8-hydroxyquinoline) complexes this allows the coordination of two water molecules to the metal ion, thereby preventing their extraction into chloroform. (The oven-dried zinc-oxine complex is chloroform soluble.) Mg^{2+} behaves similarly. The Mn(II) complex is probably tetrahedral. The range for extraction of various metal complexes with 8-hydroxyquinoline varies from pH 1.6 to 14,[85] providing a useful method of obtaining separations of individual species.

Insertion of chloro, bromo, or iodo groups into positions 5 and 7 of 8-hydroxyquinoline increases its acidic and lowers its basic strength, so that metal complexes are extracted at lower pH values. The solubility of the reagent in water is also decreased. For steric reasons, tris complexes of 2-methyl-8-hydroxyquinoline with metals having small ionic radii cannot be formed. This property is used in separations of metals from aluminium (radius 0.51 Å), both by precipitation and by extraction of their 2-methyl-8-hydroxyquinoline complexes into chloroform: The bis complex with aluminium has a positive charge and hence is not readily extracted.

The strontium-oxine complex that extracts into chloroform is $Sr(ox)_2$ $(Hox)_2$,[86] from which two oxine molecules can probably be displaced by other ligands such as n-butylamine.[87] For a recent study of solvent extraction of oxinates see reference 88.

6-Hydroxy-1,7-phenanthroline (CXLIII), which has been suggested as a colorimetric reagent for iron,[89] belongs with this group of complexing species because it is an 8-hydroxyquinoline molecule to which a pyridine molecule has been annelated.

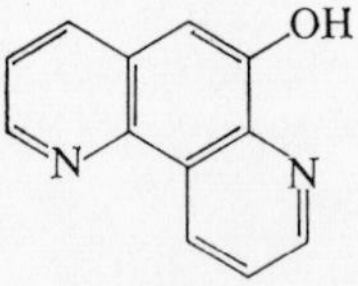

CXLIII

NEWER COMPLEXES BONDING THROUGH NITROGEN AND OXYGEN

Many of the more recently developed indicators for complexometric titration, discussed in Chapter 6, find applications also as chromogenic reagents for metals, often with extraction into suitable organic solvents. Two of the more important groups in this class are the derivatives of o,o'-dihydroxyazobenzene (CXLIV) and 1-(2-pyridylazo)-2-phenol (CXLV). Examples in the first group include the eriochrome dyes. In

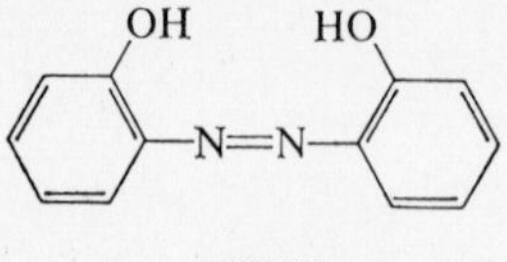

CXLIV

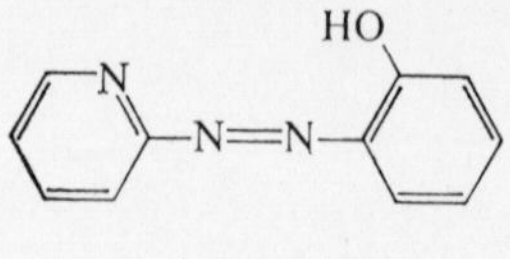

CXLV

general, these ligands are sulfonated so that their metal complexes are water soluble but are not readily extracted by organic solvents. In monoazo compounds, two such hydroxyl groups, or else one o-hydroxyl group and one o'-carboxyl group, are the minimum structural features necessary if they are to form useful 1:1 complexes with magnesium and calcium.[90]

1-(2-Pyridylazo)-2-naphthol (PAN) is representative of the second group. Bonding of a metal to the pyridine nitrogen, one of the azo nitrogens and the phenolic oxygen gives rise to two five-membered chelate rings. Coordination of two such molecules to a bivalent metal ion would lead to an uncharged octahedral complex lacking hydrophilic groups and hence to insolubility in water. Metal ions complexing with PAN belong to the same group as for oxine but, for stereochemical reasons discussed earlier (see section on *8-hydroxyquinoline*), differences are to be expected in the solvent extractability of the respective complexes. Spectrophotometric methods for microgram amounts of metal ions, using PAN and extraction into immiscible solvents, have been proposed for uranium (VI),[91] indium,[92] vanadium (V),[93] cobalt (III),[94] palladium,[95] zinc and cadmium,[96] and iron (III), manganese, mercury (II), gallium, and yttrium.[97] The desired selectivity was achieved mainly by pH control and choice of solvents. A recent study has shown that (in aqueous solutions), with metal ions, PAN is a more sensitive reagent than any of its analogs that were tested.[98] (For a solvent extraction study of transition metal complexes with PAN, see reference 99). One of the better known of these is 4-(2-pyridylazo)-resorcinol which, as its water-soluble sodium salt, finds application for the colorimetric estimation of cobalt, lead, and uranium.[100]

Glyoxal bis(*o*-hydroxyanil) (CXLVI) also belongs in this general group of reagents. Its application as a colorimetric reagent for calcium, with which it forms a chloroform-extractable 1:1 complex,[101] makes use of the

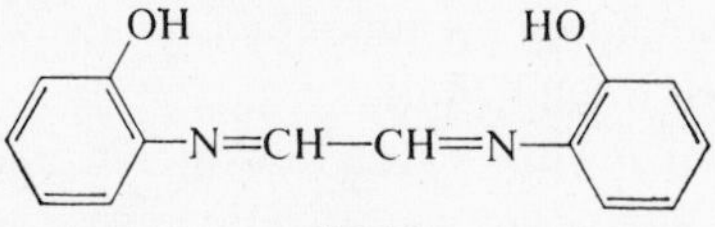

CXLVI

tendency of calcium towards partial covalent-bond formation. Tetradentate chelation involves bonding to the tertiary nitrogen atoms, a reaction favoring calcium much more than strontium or barium. Magnesium would be expected to interfere but, under the strongly alkaline conditions of the test, it is precipitated as the hydroxide.

10.8 Extraction through Ion Pair Formation

The property of extractability into an organic solvent can often be conferred on a charged complex if a suitable ion of opposite charge is added to the system to given an ion association product. Thus, the strongly colored red-violet complex of unknown identity, formed by sexivalent chromium with diphenylcarbazide, or by Cr(II) with diphenylcarbazone, is a water-soluble cation: It can be extracted into organic solvents such as isoamyl alcohol or chloroform in the presence of sufficient concentrations of acetate, chloride, or perchlorate, or of a long-chain alkyl sulfate (Teepol).[102]

Similarly, anions can be extracted in the presence of suitable cations. Thus perrhenates can be extracted into chloroform as their tetraphenylarsonium (or phosphonium) salts.[103]   Pertechnetates and permanganates behave similarly.   So, too, the corresponding ion pairs of anions such as chloro and thiocyanato complexes of Bi, Cd, Ir(IV),[104] Zn, and Sn(IV) can be extracted into chloroform.   These, and the similar ion pairs with $AuCl_4^-$,[105] find applications in spectrophotometric methods.

The blue triphenylmethylarsonium tetrathiocyanato cobalt (II) ion pair, which extracts into chloroform, has been suggested as an indicator in the back-titration of EDTA with cobalt[106]; its use offers an advantage when aqueous solutions are highly colored. The use of tricaprylmethylammonium thiocyanate dissolved in benzene as a liquid ion exchanger for the selective extraction of cobalt (II) thiocyanate[107] depends on similar ion pair formation in the organic phase.   The triphenylmethylarsonium cation also finds application as the counter-ion in the extraction of the red bis dithio-oxalate anionic nickel complex into acetophenone and chloroform in a colorimetric method for nickel.[108]   Extraction into benzene or toluene of the triphenylisopropyl phosphonium-gold thiocyanate ion pair has been suggested as an "almost specific" test for gold.[109]

A blue vanadyl (IV) thiocyanate complex is extracted by chloroform from solutions containing V(IV) or V(V) and thiocyanate ions if pyridine is present.[110]   Corresponding pyridine thiocyanate complexes are formed by Cu(II), Co, Ni, Fe(II), and Mn.[111]

In many cases involving the extraction of ion pairs formed by large cations and anions, it is apparent that solvation, in the sense of coordination of polar solvent molecules, is unnecessary. This is often true, also, of small anions, so that, for example, tetraphenylstibonium fluoride is extracted into carbon tetrachloride.

Amines, especially tertiary, readily extract anionic U(VI) complexes into organic solvents.[112]   Thus, U(VI) is quantitatively extracted from $7M$ HCl by triisooctylamine: Nb, Ru, and Zr also extract.[113]   Similarly, Fe(III) is strongly extracted by primary amines, while Th(IV) is extractable in the presence of primary and straight-chain secondary amines. Vanadium (V), but not V(IV) or Fe(II), is also extractable.

Coordination of two molecules of quinoline by silver (I) ion renders silver perchlorate extractable as $[Ag(C_9H_9N)_2]^+ClO_4^-$.[114]   Silver can be extracted into hexone from aqueous solution as the ion association product of its di-*n*-butylamine complex and stearate or salicylate ion; the presence of anthranilic acid diacetic acid as masking agent makes the reaction highly selective,[115] and the extracted silver can be determined colorimetrically using pyrogallol red.[116] Similarly, anionic complexes of many heavy metals with cyanide, azide, and thiocyanate ions form solvent-extractable ion pairs with tributylammonium ion.[117] An analytical method for amines has been suggested, based on their extraction with the thiocyanatocobalt complex.[118]

The chloroantimonate ion $SbCl_6^-$ forms a benzene-extractable, red-violet ion pair with the cation of rhodamine B (tetraethylrhodamine) (CXLVII).[119] The nature of the rhodamine B molecule explains why the

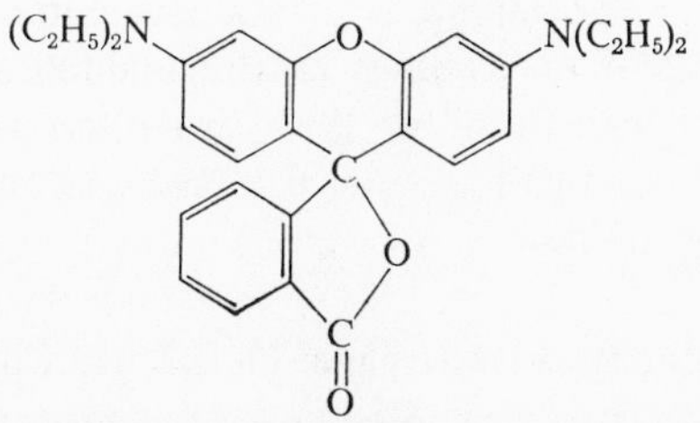

CXLVII

ion pair is soluble in benzene and toluene but not in carbon tetrachloride, while solvent coordination explains the extractability into chloroform, amyl alcohol, and isopropyl ether. Chloroantimonate ion also gives similar ion pairs with methyl violet,[120] brilliant green,[121] and anthraquinone-1-azo-4-dimethylaniline.[122] Rhodamine B also reacts in about $6M$ hydrochloric acid to form similar salts, extracting into benzene, with chloroanions, MCl_4^-, of Ga,[123] Au(III),[124] Tl(III),[125] and Fe(III), as well as benzene-insoluble tungstate. The red gallium complex can also be determined by its fluorescence. Under the same conditions, rhodamine B, itself, is virtually not extracted by benzene.

The use of a quaternary amine enables the extraction of an anionic chelate complex of uranium with 8-hydroxyquinoline.[126]

Long-chain tertiary amines such as methyldioctylamine can be used to extract chloride and sulfate ions into chloroform,[127] in which solvent the amine exists in molecular aggregates. Methyldioctylamine in trichloroethylene extracts many of the first row transition elements as chloro anions from hydrochloric acid solution.[128] Similarly, chloride ion and the bis(2,2'-biquinolinyl) copper (I) ion are extracted together into amyl alcohol;[129] the distribution coefficient is 1680/1. Niobium and tantalum in hydrochloric acid solution can be separated by solvent extraction with methyldioctylamine in xylene.[130]   Alternatively, from acid fluoride solutions, tantalum is preferentially extracted by ketones[131] or tributyl phosphate.[132]

For reviews of the extraction of metals by amines see reference 133. Because, qualitatively, the extractability of complexes from chloride-containing solutions does not vary much with the amine used, the series of papers by Nakagawa[133] can be used as a guide in designing extractions for particular situations.

For information on the extraction using quaternary amines of anions including bromide, chloride, nitrate and thiocyanate, and chloro complexes of Co, Fe(III), Hg, Mo(VI), Ta, Ti(III), and Zn, see reference 134.   A more general survey is given by Maeck, Booman, Kussy, and Rein.[135]

It is likely that this type of ion pair formation will find increasing analytical application.   For example, in view of the currently unsatisfactory conventional methods for determining alkali metal ions, it may be possible to develop suitable procedures for their extraction and concentration. Thus, cesium, in the form of its ion pair with tetraiodobismuthite, is extractable by nitrobenzene.[136]

10.9   Extraction with Organic Phosphorus Compounds

If in a neutral covalently bonded metal complex with an organic ligand all of the coordination sites around the metal are not filled by the ligand, extraction from water into nonpolar solvents is difficult.   Conversely, extraction is facilitated if the solvent contains a hydrophilic group, e.g. if it is an ether, an ester, or a higher alcohol.   Similar remarks apply to ionic species, except that here one thinks of the anions as electrostatically shielding the cation.   If this shielding is incomplete, useful extraction into organic solvents can be achieved only if the solvents contain polar groups that can be oriented and held to the metal ion by ion-dipole interaction.

Until about ten years ago, the immiscible solvents used in such extractions were characterized as having oxygen bonded to carbon.   More recently, however, oxygenated phosphorus compounds, such as di-t-butyl hydrogen phosphate (CXLIX) and tri-n-butyl phosphate, have come increasingly into use, particularly in applications to nuclear technology.   Their potentialities as extractants cover a much wider range than, say, ethers or ketones, but their behavior is qualitatively similar.

Thus the complexes ScL_3 and SrL_2, where HL is perfluoro-octanoic acid, $C_7F_{15}COOH$, are not extractable by carbon tetrachloride unless a solvent such as methyl isobutyl ketone, isopropyl ether, or di-t-butyl phosphate (DBP) is added to the system.   With SrL_2, DBP displaces water molecules to form the complex $SrL_2(DBP)_4$ which extracts into carbon tetrachloride.[137]   Similarly, ScL_3 forms extractable complexes containing 6 molecules or 3 molecules of either methyl isobutyl ketone or isopropyl ether,[137] and $ScCl_3$ can be extracted from strong hydrochloric acid solutions by tributyl phosphate.   All of these complexes have no net ionic charge, and part of the reason for the efficiency of species such as β-isopropyl tropolone (CXLVIII) and di-*n*-butyl phosphate (CXLIX) as

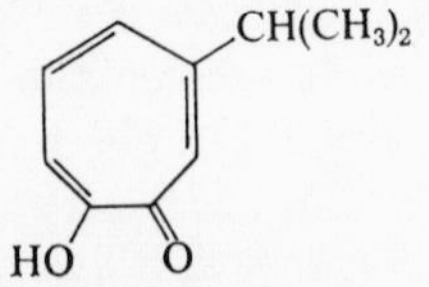

CXLVIII

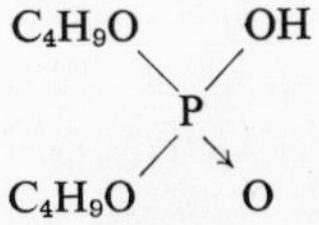

CXLIX

complexing agents for metal extraction lies in their ability to add to metal ions either as neutral molecules or as anions.

Hence these complexing species can act either as bases or as acids. Dialkyl phosphates are usually dimeric in organic solutions and often, in extracting a metal, equal amounts of organic neutral molecules and anions are coordinated.   The same is true of β-isopropyl tropolone. This may be pictured as a chelation of the metal by the organic anion, followed by further solvation by the neutral molecule.   One of the advantages of β-isopropyl tropolone is that it can be used over a wide pH range, extending to solutions of considerable acidity: It also extracts alkaline earth metal ions.[138]   In the presence of β-isopropyl tropolone (HA), uranyl ion forms the chloroform-extractable complex UO_2 $(A)_2(HA)_2$.[138]

Newer organophosphoric acid derivatives used as extractants of metal ions, with which their anions react, include monoheptadecylphosphoric acid and di-(2-ethylhexyl)-phosphoric acid.   To lower their viscosity, inert diluents such as kerosene or xylene are frequently added.   This also produces other effects, such as lowering the dielectric constant which, in turn, may cause electrolytes that would otherwise be dissociated to be present as ion pairs.   Synergistic enhancement of extraction by these reagents in the presence of tributyl phosphate, dihexyl hexylphosphonate, trioctylphosphine oxide, and similar neutral extractants, occurs with uranyl, plutonyl, and Pu(IV) solutions,[129] but not with U(IV), V(IV), Al, or Mo.   This has been interpreted as being due to a diminution in the extent to which the organophosphoric acid is dimerized or polymerized in the organic phase.[140]   For reviews of dialkylphosphoric acids as extractants, see reference 141.

Tributyl phosphate, pure or diluted with carbon tetrachloride or benzene, extracts the chloro-uranium complex $UO_2Cl_2(TBP)_2$ from hydrochloric acid solutions.   It is also the best extractant for molybdenum (as$[MoO_2Cl_2(TBP)_x]$) from hydrochloric acid solutions.[142]   In such cases the tributyl phosphate is probably coordinated through the oxygen of the $P \rightarrow O$ group to the central metal atom.   The same effect operates in the extraction of the nitrates of Ce, La, Th, and UO_2 using tri-n-butyl phosphate. The disolvates, $UO_2(NO_3)_2(TBP)_2$, and $Th(NO_3)_4(TBP)_2$ exist in the solvent phase.[143]   Similarly, $La(NO_3)_3$ is extracted from aqueous solutions as $La(NO_3)_3(TBP)_3$.   (For further examples, see reference 144.)   The bivalent plutonyl and neptunyl oxyions can also be extracted in this way. Polonium can be separated from Bi, Ra, and Pb by extraction into tributyl phosphate from HCl or H_2SO_4 solutions.

The preference of Cu(I) for a coordination number of 2 makes it likely that the Cu(I) halide complexes extracted by triphenyl phosphite into carbon tetrachloride are of the type $[(RO)_3P:CuX]_n$, in which the lone pair of electrons on the phosphorus are shared with the copper.   This behavior makes triphenyl phosphite a selective extractant for Cu(I) halides.[145]

Complexing agents such as tributyl phosphate lack a dissociable proton, so that they behave only as strongly basic solvents.   Besides their ability to coordinate to cations they extract acids, including mineral acids, from aqueous solutions with varying efficiency, the main controlling factors being the acid strength, anion size, and hydrophilic or hydrophobic nature of the anion.   Species such as $[H(H_2O)_4]^+[A(TBP)_x]^-$, where $A = ClO_4$, Cl, Br, I, exist as ion pairs in the organic phase.[146]

Perchlorates are also extractable by TBP, examples extracted from about $6M$ perchloric acid including zirconium, thorium, cerium (III), and yttrium.[147]   Plutonium (IV) is extracted as $Pu(ClO_4)_4(TBP)_2$,[148] and uranium as $UO_2(ClO_4)_2(TBP)_2$.[149]   In all these cases it is likely that TBP solvates the cation.

Modification of the tributyl phosphate molecule alters its extractive powers.   Replacement of the butyl groups by other alkyl groups has a relatively small effect, except that bulky alkyl groups can depress extraction in cases where several of the ester molecules have to be accommodated around a metal ion.   This steric effect operates in the extraction of thorium.[150]   Phenyl, haloalkyl, and other base-weakening groups sharply decrease distribution coefficients, whereas progressive replacement of alkoxy groups by alkyl groups increases both the basicity and the effectiveness as extractants.   The sequence is phosphate < phosphonate < phosphinate < phosphine oxide.   Examples of phosphonates used in this way are dibutyl butylphosphonate[151] and diisoamyl methylphosphonate.[152]   The use of phosphine oxides such as tri-n-butyl, tri-n-octyl, tri-n-phenyl, and tri-(2-ethylhexyl) as extractants in analytical chemistry has been reviewed by White and Ross.[153]

Trialkyl thionophosphates, $(RO)_3PS$, can be used as extractants, particularly of metals such as silver and mercury that bind more strongly to sulfur than to oxygen.[154] Triphenyl phosphites extract copper (I) halides.[145] In all these cases the extractant is used as a dilute solution in an inert solvent. Similarly, the dialkyl phosphorodithioic acids, $(RO)_2P(S)SH$, resemble sodium diethyldithiocarbamate in extraction behavior, but they extract metals from, and are much more stable in, strongly acid solutions.[155]

References

1. For recent reviews of solvent extraction of inorganic species, see Diamond, R. M., and D. G. Tuck, *Prog. Inorg. Chem.*, **2**, 109 (1960); Martin, F. S., and R. J. W. Holt, *Quart. Rev.*, **52**, 327 (1959); Marcus, Y., *Chem. Rev.*, **63**, 139 (1963); and for more detailed analytical applications, see Morrison, G. H., and H. Freiser, *Solvent Extraction in Analytical Chemistry*, John Wiley and Sons, New York, 1957, and *Anal. Chem.*, **32**, 37R (1960); **34**, 64R (1962). Earlier Russian literature is covered by Kuznetzov, V. I., in *Usp. Khim.*, **23**, 654 (1954); British translation *AERE Lib. Trans.* 532; *Nucl. Sci. Abstr.*, **10**, 6596 (1956).

2. Diamond, R. M., *J. Phys. Chem.*, **63**, 659 (1959).

3. Debye, P., *Z. Physik. Chem.*, **130**, 56 (1927).

4. McDevit, W. F., and F. A. Long, *Chem. Rev.*, **51**, 119 (1952).

5. Menzies, I. A., *J. Appl. Chem.*, **9**, 249 (1959).

6. Bjerrum, N., and E. Larrson, *Z. Physik. Chem.*, **127**, 358 (1927).

7. Pullin, A. D. E., and J. M. Pollock, *Trans. Faraday Soc.*, **54**, 11 (1958).

8. Caley, E. R., and H. D. Axilrod, *Anal. Chem.*, **14**, 242 (1942).

9. Mottola, H. A., and E. B. Sandell, *Anal. Chim. Acta*, **24**, 301 (1961).

10. See, for example, Stevenson, P. C., and H. G. Hicks, *Anal. Chem.*, **25**, 1517 (1953).

11. Wada, I., and R. Ishii, *Bull. Inst. Phys. Chem. Res. Tokyo*, **13**, 264 (1934).

12. Bock, R., H. Kusche, and E. Bock, *Z. Anal. Chem.*, **138**, 167 (1953).

13. Denaro, A. R., and V. J. Occleshaw, *Anal. Chim. Acta*, **13**, 239 (1955); Irving, H., and F. J. C. Rossotti, *J. Chem. Soc.*, **1955**, 1927, 1946.

14. McBryde, W. A. E., and J. H. Yoe, *Anal. Chem.*, **20**, 1094 (1948).

15. Kitahara, S., *Rept. Sci. Res. Inst. Tokyo*, **24**, 454 (1948).

16. Irving, H. M., and F. J. C. Rossotti, *Analyst*, **77**, 801 (1952).

17. For further discussion, see Poskanzer, A. M., Thesis, M.I.T., 1957; Saldick, J., *J. Phys. Chem.*, **60**, 500 (1956); Diamond, R. M., and D. G. Tuck, *Progr. Inorg. Chem.*, **2**, 109 (1960).

18. Bock, R., *Z. Anal. Chem.*, **113**, 110 (1951).

19. Fischer, W., and R. Bock, *Z. Anorg. Chem.*, **249**, 146–197 (1942).

20. Chalybeus, W., M. Zumbusch-Pfisterer, and W. Fischer, *Z. Anorg. Chem.*, **255**, 79 (1947); **255**, 277 (1948).

21. Shelton, S. M., E. D. Dilling, and J. H. McClain, *U.N. Int. Conf. on Peaceful Uses At. Energy*, **8**, 505 (1955).

22. Gluekauf, E., and H. A. C. McKay, *Nature*, **165**, 594 (1950).

23. Bock, R., and E. Bock, *Z. Anorg. Chem.*, **263**, 146 (1950).

24. Hudswell, F., and J. M. Hutcheon, *U.N. Int. Conf. on Peaceful Uses At. Energy*, **8**, 563 (1955).

25. Templeton, C. C., and J. A. Peterson, *J. Am. Chem. Soc.*, **70**, 3967 (1948).
26. Asselin, G. F., and E. W. Comings, *Ind. Eng. Chem.*, **42**, 1021–1230 (1950).
27. Hesford, E., E. E. Jackson, and H. A. C. McKay, *J. Inorg. Nucl. Chem.*, **9**, 279 (1959).
28. Rydberg, J., *Acta Chem. Scand.*, **4**, 1503 (1950).
29. Perrin, D. D., *J. Am. Chem. Soc.*, **80**, 3852 (1958).
30. Perrin, D. D., *J. Am. Chem. Soc.*, **80**, 3540 (1958).
31. Irving, H., S. J. H. Cooke, S. C. Woodger, and R. J. P. Williams, *J. Chem. Soc.*, **1949**, 1847.
32. For a more detailed analysis of solvent extraction systems, see Irving, H., F. J. C. Rossotti, and R. J. P. Williams, *J. Chem. Soc.*, **1955**, 1906; and, for dithizone, see Sandell, E. B., *Colorimetric Determination of Traces of Metals*, Interscience New York, 3rd ed., 1959, pp. 140–176.
33. Sandell, E. B., reference 32, p. 328.
34. Cholak, J., D. M. Hubbard, and R. E. Burkey, *Ind. Eng. Chem. (Anal. Ed.)*, **15**, 754 (1943).
35. Kerr, J. R. W., *Analyst*, **85**, 867 (1960).
36. Sen. B., *Anal. Chem.*, **31**, 881 (1959); Trussell, F., and H. Diehl, *Anal. Chem.*, **31**, 1978 (1959).
37. Banerjea, D., and K. K. Tripathi, *Anal. Chem.*, **32**, 1196 (1960).
38. Kirson, B., *Bull. Soc. Chim. France.* **1962**, 1032.
39. Betteridge, D., P. K. Todd, Q. Fernando, and H. Freiser, *Anal. Chem.*, **35**, 729 (1963).
40. Guter, G. A., and G. S. Hammond, *J. Am. Chem. Soc.*, **78**, 5166 (1956).
41. Menis, O., and T. C., Rains, *Anal. Chem.*, **27**, 1932 (1955).
42. Kassner, J. L., S. F. Ting, and E. L. Grove, *Talanta*, **7**, 269 (1960).
43. Meloche, V. W., R. L. Martin, and W. H. Webb, *Anal. Chem.*, **29**, 527 (1957).
44. Frierson, W. J., N. Patterson, H. Harrill, and N. Marable, *Anal. Chem.*, **33**, 1096 (1961).
45. Magnusson, L. B., J. C. Hindman, and T. J. La Chapelle, *U.S. At. Energy Comm. Rept.* ANL–4066 (1947).
46. Bolomy, R. A., and L. Wish, *J. Am. Chem. Soc.*, **72**, 4483 (1950).
47. Meinke, W. W., "Chemical Procedures used at Berkeley," *U.S. At. Energy Comm. Rept.* AECD 2738 (1949).
48. Huffman, E. H., and L. J. Beaufait, *J. Am. Chem. Soc.*, **71**, 3179 (1949).
49. Hageman, F., *J. Am. Chem. Soc.*, **72**, 768 (1950).
50. Majumdar, S. K., and A. K. De, *Anal. Chem.*, **32**, 223 (1960).
51. Khopkar, S. M., and A. K. De, *Analyst*, **85**, 376 (1960).
52. Khopkar, S. M., and A. K. De, *Anal. Chim. Acta*, **22**, 223 (1960).
53. Poskanzer, A. M., and B. M. Foreman, *J. Inorg. Nucl. Chem.*, **16**, 323 (1961).
54. Stary, J., and E. Hladky, *Anal. Chim. Acta*, **28**, 227 (1963).
55. For review, see Furman, N. H., W. B. Mason, and J. S. Pekola, *Anal. Chem.*, **21**, 1325 (1949).   See also Miller, C. C., and R. A. Chalmers, *Analyst*, **78**, 686 (1953).
56. Maddock, A. G., and G. L. Miles, *J. Chem. Soc.*, S248, S253 (1949).
57. Meloan, C. E., P. Holkeboer, and W. W. Brandt, *Anal. Chem.*, **32**, 791 (1960).
58. Wise, W. M., and W. W. Brandt, *Anal. Chem.*, **27**, 1392 (1955).
59. Meloan, C. E., and W. W. Brandt, *Anal. Chem.*, **33**, 102 (1961).
60. Meloan, C. E., M. Mauck, and C. Huffman, *Anal. Chem.*, **33**, 104 (1961).
61. Tandon, S. G., and S. C. Bhattacharyya, *Anal. Chem.*, **33**, 1267 (1961).
62. Ryan, D. E., *Analyst*, **85**, 569 (1960).

63. Priyadarshini, U., and S. G. Tandon, *Analyst*, **86**, 544 (1961).
64. Dyrssen, D., *Acta Chem. Scand.*, **10**, 353 (1956).
65. Feigl, F., *Spot Tests in Inorganic Analysis*, Elsevier Publishing Co., Amsterdam, 5th ed., 1958, p. 144.
66. Peach, S. M., *Analyst*, **81**, 371 (1956).
67. Perry, M. H., and E. J. Serfass, *Anal. Chem.*, **22**, 565 (1950).
68. Bode, H., *Z. Anal. Chem.*, **142**, 414 (1954).
69. For extractability into carbon tetrachloride, see Bode, H., *Z. Anal. Chem.*, **143**, 182 (1954); **144**, 90, 165 (1955).
70. Wyatt, P. F., *Analyst*, **80**, 368 (1955); **78**, 656 (1953); Strafford, N., P. F. Wyatt, and F. G. Kershaw, *Analyst*, **70**, 232 (1945).
71. Forster, W. A., P. Brazenall, and J. Bridge, *Analyst*, **86**, 407 (1961).
72. Bagshawe, B., and R. J. Truman, *Analyst*, **72**, 189 (1947).
73. Skoog, D. A., M. Lai, and A. Furst, *Anal. Chem.*, **30**, 365 (1958).
74. Burke, R. W., and J. H. Yoe, *Anal. Chem.*, **34**, 1378 (1962); Ayres, G. H., and R. R. Annand, *Anal. Chem.*, **35**, 33 (1963).
75. Schweitzer, G. K., and D. R. Randolph, *Anal. Chim. Acta*, **26**, 567 (1962).
76. Gupta, J., and K. P. S. Sarma, *J. Indian Chem. Soc.*, **28**, 89 (1951).
77. Based on Table 22, in Sandell, E. B., reference 32.
78. Irving, H., and J. J. Cox, *Proc. Chem. Soc.*, **1959**, 324.
79. Irving, H., and C. F. Bell, *J. Chem. Soc.*, **1954**, 4253.
80. Fischer, H., *Microchem.*, **30**, 38 (1942).
81. Hara, T., and E. B. Sandell, *Anal. Chim. Acta*, **23**, 65 (1960).
82. Takei, S., *Japan Analyst*, **6**, 630 (1957).
83. Classen, A., L. Bastings, and J. Visser, *Anal. Chim. Acta*, **10**, 373 (1954).
84. Eberle, A. R., *Anal. Chem.*, **35**, 669 (1963).
85. Gentry, C. H. R., and L. G. Sherrington, *Analyst*, **75**, 17 (1950).
86. Dyrssen, D., *Svensk Kem. Tidskr.*, **67**, 311 (1955).
87. Umland, F., and W. Hoffman, *Anal. Chim. Acta*, **17**, 234 (1957).
88. Stary, J., *Anal. Chim. Acta*, **28**, 132 (1963).
89. Duswalt, J. M., and M. G. Mellon, *Anal. Chem.*, **33**, 1782 (1961).
90. Diehl, H., and J. Ellingboe, *Anal. Chem.* **32**, 1120 (1960).
91. Shibata, S., *Anal. Chim. Acta*, **22**, 479 (1960); Gill, H. H., R. F. Rolf, and G. W. Armstrong, *Anal. Chem.*, **30**, 1778 (1958); Cheng, K. L., *Anal. Chem.*, **30**, 1027 (1958).
92. Shibata, S., *Anal. Chim. Acta*, **23**, 434 (1960).
93. Staten, F. W., and E. W. D. Huffman, *Anal. Chem.*, **31**, 2003 (1959).
94. Goldstein, G., G. L. Manning, and O. Mannis, *Anal. Chem.*, **31**, 192 (1959).
95. Busev, A. I., and L. V. Kiseleva, *Vestn. Mosk. Univ.*, **4**, 179 (1958); *Anal. Abstr.*, **6**, 2179 (1959).
96. Berger, W., and H. Elvers, *Z. Anal. Chem.*, **171**, 255 (1959).
97. Shibata, S., *Anal. Chim. Acta*, **25**, 348 (1961).
98. Hnilivkova, H., and L. Sommer, *Z. Anal. Chem.*, **177**, 425 (1960).
99. Betteridge, D., Q. Fernando, and H. Freiser, *Anal. Chem.*, **35**, 294 (1963).
100. Pollard, F. H., P. Hanson, and W. J. Geary, *Anal. Chim. Acta*, **20**, 26 (1959).
101. Goldstein, D., and C. Stark-Meyer, *Anal. Chim. Acta*, **19**, 437 (1958); Williams, K. T., and J. R. Wilson, *Anal. Chem.*, **33**, 244 (1961).
102. Powell, R., and C. G. Taylor, *Chem. Ind. (London)*, **1954**, 726.
103. Tribalat, S., *Anal. Chim. Acta*, **3**, 113 (1949); **4**, 228 (1950).
104. Neeb, R., *Z. Anal. Chem.*, **154**, 17 (1957).

105. Murphy, J. W., and H. E. Affsprung, *Anal. Chem.*, **33**, 1658 (1961).
106. Cameron, A. J., and N. A. Gibson, *Anal. Chim. Acta*, **25**, 24 (1961).
107. Wilson, A. M., and O. K. McFarland, *Anal. Chem.*, **35**, 302 (1963).
108. Cameron, A. J., and N. A. Gibson, *Anal. Chim. Acta*, **24**, 360 (1961).
109. Senise, P., and L. R. M. Pitombo, *Anal. Chim. Acta*, **26**, 89 (1962).
110. Ayres, G. H., and L. E. Scroggie, *Anal. Chim. Acta*, **26**, 470 (1962).
111. Baird, S. S., Ph.D. Diss., Univ. of Texas, 1958; *Talanta*, **7**, 237 (1961).
112. Crouse, D. J., and J. O. Denis, *U.S. At. Energy Comm.* ORNL–1859 (1955); Preuss, A., and J. Saunders, *U.S. At. Energy Comm.* RMO–2533 (1955).
113. Moore, F. L., *Anal. Chem.*, **30**, 908 (1958).
114. Antikainen, P. J., and D. Dyrssen, *Acta Chem. Scand.*, **14**, 86 (1960).
115. Betteridge, D., and T. S. West, *Anal. Chim. Acta*, **26**, 101 (1962).
116. Dagnall, R. M., and T. S. West, *Anal. Chim. Acta*, **27**, 9 (1962).
117. Ziegler, M., *Angew. Chem.*, **71**, 522 (1959); Ziegler, M., and O. Glemser, *Angew. Chem.*, **68**, 411, 620 (1956); *Z. Anal. Chem.*, **157**, 19 (1957).
118. Ashbrook, A. W., *Analyst*, **84**, 177 (1959).
119. Webster, S. H., and L. T. Fairhall, *J. Ind. Hyg. Toxicol.*, **27**, 184 (1945).
120. Jean, M., *Anal. Chim. Acta*, **4**, 360 (1950); **7**, 462 (1952); **11**, 82 (1954).
121. Lapin, L. N., and V. O. Gein, *Trudy Komis. po Analit. Khim.*, *Akad. Nauk SSSR, Inst. Geokhim. i Analit. Khim.*, **7**, 217 (1956); through *CA*, **50**, 15329 (1956).
122. Kuznetsov, V. I., *Compt. Rend. Acad. Sci. USSR*, **52**, 231 (1946).
123. Onishi, H., and E. B. Sandell, *Anal. Chim. Acta*, **13**, 159 (1955).
124. Macnulty, B. J., and L. D. Wollard, *Anal. Chim. Acta*, **13**, 154 (1955).
125. Onishi, H., *Bull. Chem. Soc. Japan*, **29**, 945 (1956); **30**, 567 (1957).
126. Clifford, W. E., E. P. Bullwinkle, L. A. McClaine, and P. Noble, *J. Am. Chem. Soc.*, **80**, 2959 (1958).
127. Smith, E. L., and J. E. Page, *J. Soc. Chem. Ind.*, **67**, 48 (1948).
128. Mahlman, H. A., G. W. Ledlicotte, and F. L. Moore, *Anal. Chem.*, **26**, 1939 (1954).
129. Hoste, J., J. Eeckhout, and J. Gillis, *Anal. Chim. Acta*, **9**, 263 (1953).
130. Ledlicotte, G. W., and F. L. Moore, *J. Am. Chem. Soc.*, **74**, 1618 (1952).
131. Werning, J. R., K. B. Higbie, J. T. Grace, B. F. Speece, and H. L. Gilbert, *Ind. Eng. Chem.*, **46**, 644 (1954).
132. Fletcher, J. M., D. F. C. Morris, and A. G. Wain, *Bull. Inst. Min. Met.*, No. 597, 487 (1956).
133. Moore, F. L., *Natl. Acad. Sci. Nucl. Sci.*, NAS–NS–3101 (1960); Nakagawa, G., *J. Chem. Soc. Japan*, **81**, 444, 446, 747, 750, 1255, 1258, 1533, 1536 (1960).
134. Wilson, A. M., L. Churchill, K. Liluk, and P. Hovsepian, *U.S. At. Energy Comm. Rept.* TID 12351 (1960); *Anal. Chem.*, **34**, 203 (1962).
135. Maeck, W. J., G. L. Booman, M. E. Kussy, and J. E. Rein, *Anal. Chem.*, **33**, 1775 (1961).
136. Kyrs, M., and S. Podesva, *Anal. Chim. Acta*, **27**, 183 (1962).
137. Dyrrsen, D., *J. Inorg. Nucl. Chem.*, **8**, 291 (1958).
138. Dyrssen, D., *Acta Chem. Scand.*, **15**, 1614 (1961); Dyrssen, D., M. Heffez, and T. Sekine, *J. Inorg. Nucl. Chem.*, **16**, 367 (1961).
139. Blake, C. A., D. E. Horner, and J. M. Schmidt, *U.S. At. Energy Comm. Unclassified Document* ORNL 2259 (1959).
140. Kennedy, J., *U.K. At. Energy Auth.*, *Document Number* AERE C/M 369 (1958).

141. Blake, C. A., C. F. Baes, and K. B. Brown, *Ind. Eng. Chem.*, **50**, 1763 (1958); Kimura, K., *Bull. Chem. Soc. Japan*, **33**, 1038 (1960); **34**, 63 (1961).
142. Nelidow, I., and R. M. Diamond, *J. Phys. Chem.*, **59**, 710 (1955).
143. Moore, F. L., *U.S. At. Energy Comm. Unclassified Document* AECD 3196 (1951).
144. Fletcher, J. M., *Progr. Nucl. Energy. Ser. III, Process Chem.*, **1**, 105 (1956); Ishimori, T., and K. Watanabe, *Bull. Chem. Soc. Japan*, **33**, 1443 (1960).
145. Handley, T. H., and J. A. Dean, *Anal. Chem.*, **33**, 1087 (1961).
146. Warf, J. C., *J. Am. Chem. Soc.*, **71**, 3257 (1949).
147. Siekierski, S., *J. Inorg. Nucl. Chem.*, **12**, 129 (1959).
148. Solovkin, A. S., A. I. Ivantsev, and E. V. Renard, *Zh. Neorg. Khim.*, **4**, 2826 (1959).
149. Hesford, E., and H. A. C. McKay, *J. Inorg. Nucl. Chem.*, **13**, 165 (1960).
150. Siddall, T. H., *J. Inorg. Nucl. Chem.*, **13**, 151 (1960).
151. Madigan, D. C., and R. W. Cattrall, *J. Inorg. Nucl. Chem.*, **21**, 334 (1961).
152. Shevchenko, V. B., V. S. Shmidt, and E. A. Nenarokomov, *Radiokhimiya*, **3**, 129 (1961).
153. White, J. C., and W. J. Ross, *Natl. Acad. Sci. Nucl. Sci.*, NAS–NS–3102 (1961).
154. Handley, T. H., and J. A. Dean, *Anal. Chem.*, **32**, 1878 (1960).
155. Handley, T. H., and J. A. Dean, *Anal. Chem.*, **34**, 1312 (1962).

CHAPTER 11

Reactions of Organic Reagents
with Inorganic Anions

In principle it is possible to discuss the chemical behavior of inorganic anions in terms of the factors applied in considering metal ions, such as the size, extent of polarization effects, and the nature of filled and vacant orbitals, together with their spatial distributions. In practice this is difficult, because the nonmetallic elements tend to combine together to form polyatomic anions, such as SO_4^{2-}, NO_3^-, and $S_2O_3^{2-}$, which can, in some cases, condense further to give polynuclear species like the polyphosphates. So too, many elements recognizably metals can form anions that have little tendency to dissociate into free metal ions and anionic species. Examples include the germanates, beryllates, borates, and aluminates. For the purpose of the present discussion, anionic complexes such as $CuCl_4^{2-}$, the dianion of Ca-EDTA, and all other species whose existence depends on mobile equilibria will be excluded, whereas others such as $Fe(CN)_6^{4-}$ that persist as entities under thermodynamically unfavorable conditions for times long enough to ensure their analytical characterization will be dealt with.

In some cases it may be necessary to separate or partially purify anionic species, e.g. by coprecipitation or ion exchange, as a preliminary to analytical estimation. Coprecipitation as a means of concentrating traces of anions finds application in examples such as collection of traces of sulfate as barium sulfate with barium chromate, of phosphate as aluminium phosphate with aluminium hydroxide, and of sulfide by zinc sulfide with zinc hydroxide. Care is needed in the use of ion exchange to remove interfering cations. Thus, ferric ion is readily removed by cation-exchange columns, but once adsorbed it acts as an anion-exchanging species and retains multivalent anions such as phosphate. Conversely, anion-exchange

236

columns are sometimes used to remove interfering anions. It is also occasionally expedient to change the oxidation state of the element or radical sought, e.g. SO_4^{2-} to S^{2-}, Br^- to BrO_3^-, and NO_3^- to NO_2^- or NH_3.

11.1   Indirect Methods for Detecting and Determining Anions

COLORIMETRIC METHODS BASED ON DIFFERENCES IN STABILITY CONSTANTS OF COMPLEXES

The simpler anions are generally determined indirectly by organic reagents. For example, fluoride ion is determined colorimetrically by the extent to which it bleaches the red complex of zirconium with alizarin-3-sulfonic acid.[1] The process is simply one of competitive formation of fluoride ions and alizarin-3-sulfonate anion for zirconium. Thorium can be used instead of zirconium,[2] and quinalizarin instead of alizarin-3-sulfonic acid. Alternatively, either of these metals is suitable as its eriochrome cyanine R complex, this reagent giving bigger color differences.[3] Aluminium has also been used as its 8-hydroxyquinoline, eriochrome cyanine R[4], and eriochrome red B[5] complexes (in methods based on fluorescence quenching). Other examples include the zirconium complexes with SPADNS[6] and purpurin-sulfonic acid,[7] and the beryllium-chrome azurol S complex.[8]

In such methods standardization of the experimental technique is essential because of the stepwise nature of the equilibria involved in the complex formation and dissociation, particularly as it relates to mono and bis complexes of the dye with the metal ion, and also of the fluoride ion with the metal ion. The methods are subject to interference by all other anions able to compete with the dye for the metal ion.

A similar principle is involved in the addition of mercuric thiocyanate to a chloride-containing solution to form undissociated mercuric chloride, the amount of thiocyanate ion displaced being obtained colorimetrically using its red complex formation with excess ferric ion. Conversely, micro amounts of chloride ion can be determined from the extent of the diminution of the color of the mercury-diphenylcarbazone complex.[9] More generally, solutions of chlorides, bromides, and iodides can be determined by mercurimetric titration in the presence of diphenylcarbazide or diphenylcarbazone to indicate the endpoint by detecting the first excess of mercury (II) ions.

Discrimination between chloride ion, on the one hand, and bromide and iodide ion, on the other, is possible by adding hydrogen peroxide which oxidizes the latter to bromine and iodine, both of which readily form colorless substitution products with 8-hydroxyquinoline, whereas chloride ion persists unchanged.   Chloride ion can also be confirmed by volatilization as chromyl chloride, the distillate being tested for chromium with diphenylcarbazide.

In the same way, fluoride ion can be determined by measuring the extent to which it discharges the colors of ferric thiocyanate and ferric acetylacetone complexes.

METHODS DEPENDING ON PRECIPITATION OR DIFFERENCES IN SOLUBILITY OF COMPLEXES AND SALTS OF INORGANIC CATIONS

Colorimetric.   Sulfate concentrations in solution have been determined by measuring by ultraviolet spectrophotometry the unused excess of 4-amino-4'-chlorodiphenyl added as a precipitant,[10] and also by similar measurements to obtain the benzidine content of benzidine sulfate precipitates.[11]   More usually, the benzidine in the precipitate or remaining in the solution is oxidized[12] or diazotized and coupled with a suitable phenol[13] or amine.[14]

The greater insolubility of thorium sulfate leads to the quantitative release of an equivalent number of amaranth dye molecules when the solid thorium "lake" with this dye is shaken in a sulfate solution.[15]

Barium sulfate is less soluble than barium rhodizonate; hence a test for sulfate ion uses its ability to diminish the red-brown color of freshly prepared barium rhodizonate by combining competitively with the barium ion.[16]   Conversely, because lead rhodizonate is less soluble than lead sulfate, the blue-violet color of the former appears when the latter is moistened with sodium rhodizonate solution.[17]   Solubility differences are again exploited in the reaction of neutral alkali sulfates on warming with barium carbonate, to give barium sulfate and alkali carbonate which gives the red alkaline color with phenolphthalein:[18]

$$BaCO_3 + Na_2SO_4 \rightarrow BaSO_4 + Na_2CO_3$$

Sulfide and thiosulfate ions, shaken with solid silver thiocyanate, liberate thiocyanate ion, which can be determined as the colored ferric complex.[19]

Chapter 9 described the determination of fluoride, chloride, and sulfate in solution, based on the colorimetric measurement of the chloranilic (or bromanilic) acid liberated when a suspension of its appropriate slightly soluble metal salt was shaken with the test material.   Similarly the brown, sparingly soluble, zirconium complex with *p*-dimethylaminoazophenylarsonic acid forms colorless ZrF_6^{2-} ions and liberates the red acid.   So, too, chloride ion can be estimated by shaking with solid silver chromate or silver orthophosphate and determining the displaced chromate and phosphate ions.

A double displacement technique is involved in a procedure suggested for determining sulfide ion.[20] A known (excess) amount of cadmium sulfate precipitates the sulfide ion as cadmium sulfide. Addition of sodium diethyldithiocarbamate forms the corresponding cadmium complex with unreacted cadmium, which is then extracted into chloroform prior to shaking with copper sulfate, so that the final colorimetric measurement is made on a chloroform solution of copper diethyldithiocarbamate.

Titrimetric. Sulfate ion can be determined by direct titration with barium chloride using tetrahydroxyquinone,[21] alizarin red S,[22] and thoron[23] as indicators: Formation of their colored barium complexes cannot occur until precipitation of barium sulfate is complete. The same principle applies to the use of lead nitrate as titrant, with eosin,[24] erythrosin,[25] and dithizone[26] as indicator. Dithizone has also been used as an indicator in the titration of an alkaline sulfide solution in acetone with lead acetate. The method can also be used for sulfate by reducing the latter to sulfide.[27]

Precipitation with excess reagent, followed by back-titration, is used, for example, in the determination of sulfate with barium ion, the excess barium being titrated with EDTA using eriochrome black T as indicator.[28] Many variations are possible, such as the addition of excess EDTA and back-titration with magnesium chloride, using solochrome black,[29] or the separation of the precipitate, followed by dissolution in excess EDTA and titration with a standard solution of a suitable metal ion.[30] Diethylenetriaminepentaacetic acid, which forms a more stable complex with barium than EDTA does, has been used instead of EDTA.[31] The method has also been applied to the rapid determination of sulfur in steel by dissolving the sample in hydrochloric acid, oxidizing to the ferric state and then removing ferric iron by amyl acetate extraction.[32] The determination of sulfate ion in the almost pure aqueous hydrochloric acid presents no difficulties.

A method combining precipitation, oxidation reduction, and photometric effects has been described. Sulfate is precipitated with lead nitrate, and the excess lead is titrated with potassium dichromate which, at the endpoint, oxidizes the chemiluminescent indicator siloxene.[33]

Sulfide concentrations can be determined by precipitation of sulfide with excess copper (II) perchlorate, followed by back-titration with EDTA, using murexide as indicator.[34]

Indirect methods are also involved in the precipitation of fluoride as CaF_2 by the addition of excess calcium ion, followed by EDTA titration,[35] and in similar procedures for sulfate[36] and chromate[37] ions with Ba^{2+}.

Ferrocyanide can be precipitated by zinc, and the excess zinc determined by EDTA titration.[38]   Alternatively, the precipitate may be collected, dissolved in acid, and titrated.   Examples include phosphate[39] and arsenate,[40] precipitated as the magnesium ammonium salts, the magnesium being titrated, finally, against EDTA.   Pyrophosphate ion, precipitated as the manganous salt, has been dissolved in excess EDTA and then titrated with standard zinc solution.[41]

Cyanide ion can be determined by treating with excess Ni^{2+} to form $Ni(CN)_4^{2-}$, and titrating the remaining Ni^{2+} with EDTA.[42]

11.2   Methods Based on Precipitation with Organic Cations, Including Extraction into Organic Solvents

Large anions such as SO_4^{2-} are likely to form their least soluble salts with large cations.   The use of the dication of benzidine, $H_2NC_6H_4C_6H_4NH_2$, as a precipitant for sulfate and molybdate in weakly acid solutions is an example.   It also gives precipitates with phosphate and tungstate, for which it can be used as a reagent, but specificity for sulfate can be achieved by using an ion-exchange procedure.[43]   (Alternatively, if sulfate is the only anion present in a solution, passage through the hydrogen form of a cation-exchange resin gives sulfuric acid, which can be determined by titration with standard alkali.)   Belcher and coworkers[44] have found that the less water-soluble bases, 4-chloro-4'-aminodiphenyl and 4,4'-diamino-tolane, are much better for this purpose.   Large complex cations such as octa-ammino-μ-amino-μ-nitrodicobalt (III) in aqueous acetone[45] and hexa-amminocobalt (III) bromide in aqueous ethanol, methanol, or ace-tone[46] are also useful precipitants of sulfate ion.   Tris(ethylenediamine) nickel (II) ion precipitates thiosulfate ion as $[Ni(en)_3]S_2O_3$.

Tetraphenylarsonium ion forms insoluble salts with many anions, including perchlorate, periodate, permanganate, perrhenate, fluoride, bromide, iodide, iodate, thiocyanate, chromate, molybdate, and tungstate: This reaction has been used in analytical methods.[47]   For example, perchlorate in sea water has been determined following precipitation as tetraphenylarsonium perchlorate, using the corresponding perrhenate as collector.[48]

Formation of phosphomolybdate as a means of detecting orthophosphate has been improved by the introduction of o-dianisidine molybdate, which makes it easier to weigh the precipitate while at the same time providing a chromophoric group for spectrophotometric estimation.[49]   The in-solubility of quinoline phosphomolybdate has also been used in gravi-metric micro[50] and semi-micro[51] determinations of phosphate.   8-Hydroxyquinoline can also be used in this way.[52]   In all these cases the important factor appears to be the large size of the cation which, on ion pair formation, has a large hydrophobic portion projecting into the aqueous solution.

In strongly acid solutions, α-benzoinoxime forms insoluble precipitates with molybdate and tungstate ions and, less completely, with chromate, vanadate, niobate, and tantalate. These anions also yield precipitates in acetic acid solutions with 8-hydroxyquinoline. The natures of these precipitates are unknown but the oxime complexes, formed as they are in weakly acid solutions, may simply be bis complexes of cations such as MoO_2^{2+} and $VO(OH)^{2+}$. It may be significant that, under the conditions where the benzoinoxime complexes are precipitated, the reacting anions are all probably at least partially condensed to polyanions. The vanadium complex with oxine is extractable into chloroform.

The insolubility of the mixed copper-aniline-thiocyanate complex serves as a sensitive test for thiocyanate ion.[53] The corresponding pyridine complex, extracted into chloroform and its absorbance measured at 410 mμ, is used for quantitative determination of 0.5 to 30 ppm thiocyanate concentrations.[54] At higher concentrations, the same reagent determines thiocyanate gravimetrically.[55] Similar chloroform-extractable compounds are formed between copper (II), pyridine, and a series of anions including cyanate, cyanide, peroxydisulfate, bromide, and iodide. Differences in the colors of the solutions have been suggested as being useful in qualitative analysis.[56]

However, the predictability of solubilities of complexes is not good, except for the generalization that insolubility is most likely to be found with large cations and large anions. In particular, the relative solubilities of sulfates, perchlorates, and nitrates with any given cation vary considerably, although usually the nitrates are the most soluble. Di(cyclohexyl) thallium (III) sulfate, perchlorate, and acetate are, however, soluble, but the nitrate and a number of other salts are not, so that this reagent has been suggested as a precipitant for nitrate ion.[57] Slightly soluble nitrates are also formed by cinchonamine, di-1-naphthyldimethylamine and N-diethylbenzohydrylamine.

Many endiminotriazoles form sparingly soluble nitrates; the one most commonly used as a reagent for nitrate ion is nitron (1,4-diphenyl-endanilo-dihydrotriazole) which, for steric reasons, is believed to exist as the

CL

zwitterion, (CL).[58]   Many other anions give precipitates, including nitrite, chlorate, perchlorate, iodide, thiocyanate, persulfate, ferricyanide, ferrocyanide, chromate, molybdate, tungstate, and permanganate, but not sulfate.[59]   Nitron has been suggested for the gravimetric determination of perrhenate,[60] perchlorate,[61] chlorate,[62] and fluoride as fluoborate or fluophosphate.[63]   Fluoborate can also be weighed as its hexadecyltrimethylammonium ion.[64]   Borate ion can be determined by reaction with fluoride ion to form fluoborate which extracts as a colored ion pair with methylene blue (tetramethylthionin) into 1,2-dichloroethane.[65] Similar ion pairs are formed by methylene blue with perchlorate, thiocyanate, and trichloroacetate ions: The complex with perchlorate ion is soluble in chloroform.   Other chlorinated solvents and thionin derivatives can also be used to extract BF_4^-.[66]

11.3   Methods Depending on Oxidation or Reduction

Colorimetric methods are extensively used in the detection and estimation of inorganic anions.   In a few cases, such as permanganate and chromate, the concentration of the ion can be obtained directly by spectrophotometry.   Much more commonly, however, oxidative or reductive reactions are involved.

Oxidation of brucine,[67] reduced strychnine,[68] diphenylamine,[69] diphenylaminesulfonic acid,[70] diphenylbenzidine,[71] hydroquinonesulfonic acid,[72] β-methylumbelliferone,[73] pentachlorophenol,[74] pyrogallol, and pyrogallolsulfonic acid[75] in acid solution has been suggested as the basis of a number of colorimetric methods for nitrate ion.   Careful control of the experimental conditions is essential, and nitrite ion interferes.   Alternatively, to achieve greater selectivity nitrate ion is often determined by reducing it to nitrite ion or ammonia, but the reduction is seldom quantitative.

Conversely, nitrite can be determined by oxidation to nitrate using chloramine T.   The excess of the latter is found by titration of the iodine liberated when potassium iodide is added.   (For discussion on the use of chloramine T as a titrimetric agent, in which it resembles sodium hypochlorite, see reference 76.)

A qualitative test for nitrite ion is its oxidation of thiourea to thiocyanate ion which can be detected by the red color obtained on adding ferric ion to an acid solution.   The same color reaction can be used as a test for cyanide ion which forms thiocyanate ion on warming with sulfur.

The very considerable stabilization of the copper (I) state by cyanide ion makes copper (II) a powerful oxidizing agent when cyanide ion is present in the solution, so that it oxidizes benzidine to "benzidine blue."

This reaction can also provide a test for thiocyanate ion by using oxidizing agent like potassium permanganate which convert thiocyanate to cyanide ions. Under the same conditions, chlorides, bromides, and iodides also give the "benzidine blue" reaction.

Similar enhancement of oxidizing power by complex formation is shown in the reactions of ferricyanide with orange IV (tropaeolin) and benzidine. If zinc ion is added so as to precipitate ferrocyanide ion as it is formed, and hence to keep the oxidation-reduction potential low, the rates of oxidation of orange IV and benzidine are greatly speeded up. Ferricyanide ion can also be determined by oxidative titration with ascorbic acid.[77]

Determination of cyanide ion by oxidative degradation of pyridine, followed by polymethine dye formation, is discussed in Chapter 12. Thiocyanate can be oxidatively titrated with potassium iodate in 3.5–4N HCl, and the endpoint detected with amaranth dye.[78]

Colorimetric phosphate determinations are based mainly on the formation and reduction of molybdophosphoric acid by hydrazine sulfate to blue polymeric complexes, which can then be extracted into oxygen-containing organic solvents. Conversely, the molybdophosphoric acid can be extracted and then reduced by shaking with a reductant such as chlorostannous acid. In all such heteropoly acids the molybdic acid portions are much stronger oxidizing agents than they are in the uncomplexed state, either as an acid or as an anion. When benzidine is used as reducing agent it is oxidized to "benzidine blue" at the same time as the heteropoly acid is reduced to "molybdenum blue." If a 1:4 mixture of n-butanol and chloroform is used, molybdophosphoric acid is selectively extracted from solutions containing arsenate, silicate, and germanate ions.[79]

Silicates can similarly be determined, either directly by the yellow color of molybdosilicic acid, or by reduction to molybdenum blue using hydroxyl-

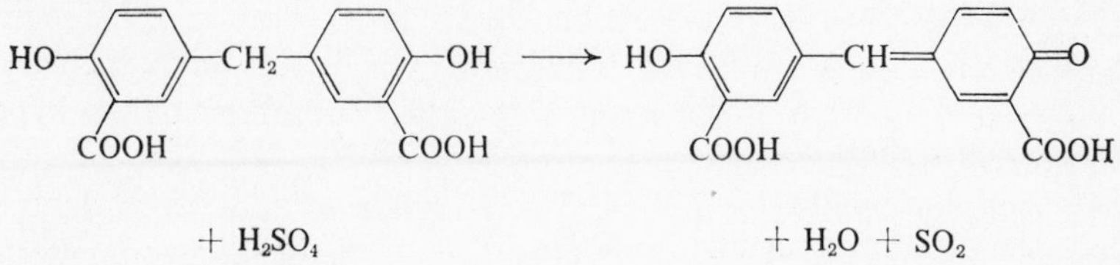

$$+ H_2SO_4 \qquad\qquad + H_2O + SO_2$$

CLI   CLII

amine, benzidine, hydroquinone, 1-amino-2-naphthol-4-sulfonic acid, chlorostannous acid, or some other suitable reducing agent.[80] Arsenates behave similarly.

The oxidizing and dehydrating effects of concentrated sulfuric acid can be used for its detection by warming with methylenedisalicyclic acid (CLI), when intensely red formaurindicarboxylic acid (CLII) is formed.[81] Alternatively, *m*- or *p*-hydroxybenzaldehyde can be used.

In neutral or weakly acetic acid solutions, persulfate ion oxidizes benzidine to "benzidine blue." The reaction is also given by chromate, permanganate, ferricyanide, and hypochlorite ions, and, in more alkaline solutions, by cations such as Pb(IV), Tl(III), Au(III), and Ce(IV) that have oxidizing properties. 2,7-Diaminofluorene and 2,7-diaminodiphenylene oxide are also oxidized by such species. Similarly, chromates and dichromates give a blue color with α-naphthylamine. Tetramethyldiaminodiphenylmethane (Arnold's base) (CLXV) is oxidized to a blue material by permanganate and chromate ions.

Unlike sulfite ion, selenite ion, SeO_3^{2-}, shows oxidizing ability. For example, like many other oxidants, selenite and selenate ions oxidize asymmetric diphenylhydrazine in acid solution to form the violet quinonoid species, (CLIII).[82]

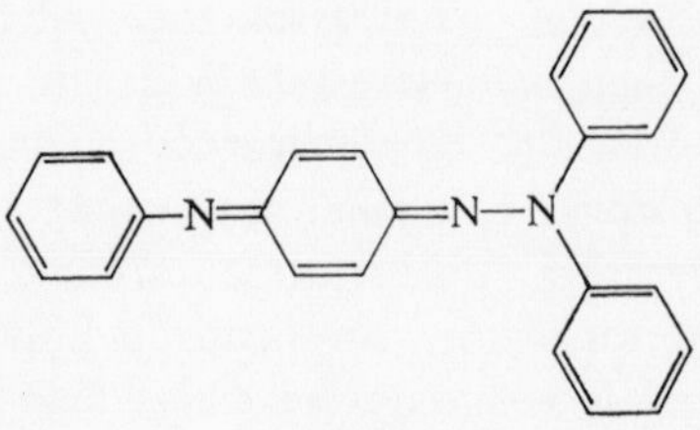

CLIII

Sulfites can be determined colorimetrically by the extent to which fuchsin is converted to a colorless bisulfite addition compound,[83] or, in the range 0.01 to 1 ppm, by reduction of iodine in starch-iodine complex to iodide.[84]

In the same way, neutral solutions of malachite green are decolorized by sulfite ion, which destroys the quinonoid structure of the dye. Mono- and polysulfides react in the same way. The reducing action of sulfur dioxide and sulfites is the basis of tests in which the dye astrazone pink FG[85] and tetramethyldiaminodiphenylmethane[86] are bleached and in which the green photooxidation product of 2-benzylpyridine is converted to a red substance.[87]

Oxidation of Co(II) azide complexes, which are violet, to yellow Co(III) azide complexes by simultaneous autoxidation of bisulfite ion,[88] and subsequent reaction of Co(III) with *o*-tolidine, has been suggested as a test for sulfite ion.[89]

Sulfide has been determined by its quantitative oxidation to sulfur using ferricyanide in an ammoniacal buffer, pH 9.4, with ferrous dimethylglyoxime as indicator,[90] and, in more alkaline solutions, with sodium nitroprusside as indicator.[91]

Thiosulfate ion is oxidized by ferric ion to give tetrathionate ion: This has been made the basis of volumetric methods using methylene blue-fuchsin[92] and meconic acid[93] as indicators. Similarly, thiosulfate has been oxidized with excess vanadic acid which was back-titrated with ferrous ammonium sulfate, using diphenylbenzidine as indicator.[94]

Hyposulfites can be detected by their powerful reducing action on alcoholic solutions of o- or p-dinitrobenzene, which in alkaline (ammoniacal) solution are converted to the (violet or red, respectively) colored anions of the aci-form of nitrosonitrobenzene (e.g. CLIV).[95]   Interference

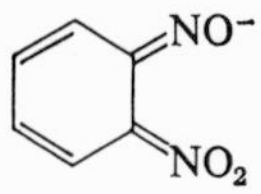

CLIV

by sulfide ion can be prevented by prior removal as lead sulfide.   Other methods of determination of hyposulfite (dithionite) ion that are based on its reducing action include measurement of the extent of color diminution of standard solutions of indigo carmine as indicator.

Selenite ion has been detected colorimetrically by the oxidation of pyrrole to "pyrrole blue,"[96] and of asymmetric diphenylhydrazine to the violet quinone-anildiphenylhydrazone.[97]

Reduction of selenites and selenates to selenium by reducing agents such as tetraethylthiuram disulfide,[98] ascorbic acid,[99] glucose,[100] and thiourea[101] has been used in gravimetric methods for selenium.

Chlorate (in concentrated hydrochloric acid solutions) and hypochlorite (in dilute hydrochloric acid solutions) oxidize benzidine to an intensely yellow-colored substance which is probably meriquinoid.   (Compare the reaction of chlorine, Chapter 12.)   Colorimetric methods based on this reaction apply in the concentration range 0–1 ppm.[102]

Similarly, bromate in trace amounts gives color reactions by oxidizing strychnine, methyl orange, indigo carmine, oxalic acid-fluorescein, oxalic acid-leucofluorescein, manganous sulfate-benzidine, p,p'-dihydroxytriphenylmethane and 3-aminophenoxazine-2-one. The red-brown color with o-arsanilic acid has been made the basis of a quantitative method.[103]

In acid solutions iodate oxidizes pyrogallol to reddish-brown purgallin.[104]

Traces of permanganate ion can be detected by its oxidizing action on the cellulose of filter paper, leading to precipitation of brown, hydrated manganese dioxide. (Chromates do not react.)

Ferricyanide ion in neutral solution is quite a strong oxidizing agent, especially if zinc, mercury, or lead salts are present to ensure precipitation of ferrocyanide ion, and hence to keep the oxidation-reduction potential low. Under these conditions, ferricyanide ion readily gives a positive test with benzidine (formation of a blue meriquinoid compound), phenolphthalin (oxidation to the red phenolphthalein anion) and tetramethyldiaminodiphenylmethane (oxidation to the blue cation of a diphenylmethane dye). These reactions are given by a number of other oxidizing agents.

The platinichloride ion, $PtCl_6^{2-}$, is reduced to platinum in boiling neutral formate solutions.

11.4   Diazotization Reactions

Coupling of diazotized sulfanilic acid with 1-naphthylamine affords a sensitive colorimetric method for nitrite. The diazotization should be carried out in a cool, strongly acid solution, but the coupling should be done in weak acid.[105] Interfering substances include urea, aliphatic amines, strong oxidants and reductants (all of which react with nitrite), Cu^{2+} (which catalyzes the decomposition of the diazonium salt), and chloroplatinite, Fe(III), Au(III), and metavanadate ions (all of which form precipitates with 1-naphthylamine). Alternatively, the ultraviolet absorption of diazotized sulfanilic acid (at 270 mμ) can be determined directly.[106] Sulfanilamide can be used instead of sulfanilic acid, with N-(1-naphthyl)-ethylenediamine as the base.[107] Other reagents that have been investigated for use in this way are listed in reference 108. Recently, 4-aminoazobenzene and 1-naphthylamine have been recommended.[109] The reaction can be used as a test for nitrate ion by converting it to nitrosyl chloride (using concentrated sulfuric acid and sodium chloride) which becomes hydrolyzed to nitrous acid.

If 1,8-naphthalenediamine is used as the reagent, diazotization leads to self-coupling to form insoluble, orange-red 1,8-aziminonaphthalene (CLV). Selenite interferes in this reaction, probably giving the corresponding piazoselenol.

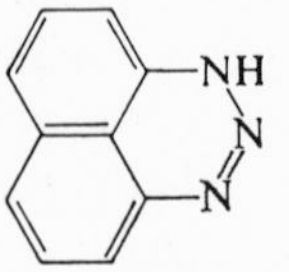

CLV

The diazotization reaction has also been applied as the basis of a spectrophotometric method for sulfate ion which is precipitated with benzidine. The benzidine is diazotized and coupled with N-(1-naphthyl) ethylenediamine.[110] Reaction with sodium β-naphthoquinone-4-sulfonate[111] and p-dimethylaminobenzaldehyde[112] has also been used.

Molybdates in acid solution oxidize phenylhydrazine to a diazonium salt which then couples with excess base and molybdate to give a red product.

11.5 Nitration Reactions

Nitrate ion can also be determined colorimetrically on the basis of nitration reactions. Phenol-2,4-disulfonic acid forms yellow 6-nitrophenol-2,4-disulfonic acid, the reaction being carried out in highly acid solution followed by development of the color in alkaline solution.[113] Nitrite, chloride, and organic matter interfere. Chromotropic acid in concentrated sulfuric acid is a much more sensitive reagent.[114] 2,4-Xylenol[115] has also been used extensively. 1,5-Naphtholsulfonic acid,[116] sulfosalicylic acid,[117] 2,6-xylenol,[118] and 3,4-xylenol[119] have also been suggested as reagents. The xylenols have the advantage that the product can be distilled or extracted into an organic solvent such as toluene. A method for determining nitrate has been suggested that depends on the nitration of 2,6-xylenol to 4-nitro-2,6-xylenol, followed by polarographic reduction.[120]

11.6 Heterocyclic Synthesis

Selenites oxidize iodide ion to iodine, which can be estimated in the usual way. An alternative method is based on the formation of a piazselenol such as (CLVI) from a suitable diamine. This reaction, due to Hinsberg,[121] has been developed using 3,3'-diaminobenzidine which, left

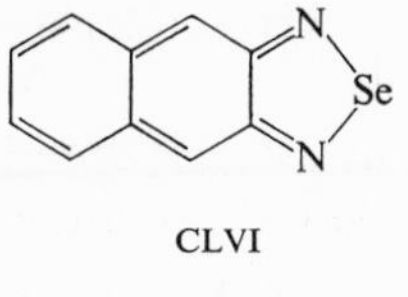

CLVI 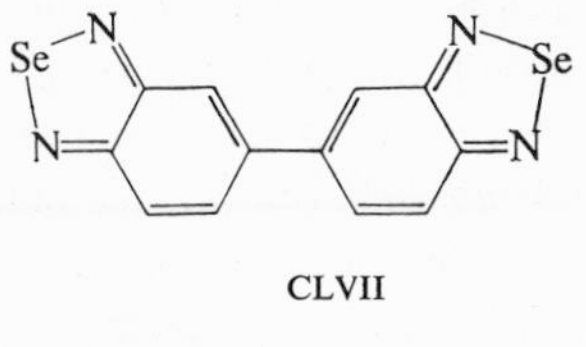   CLVII

with selenous acid in 0.1 M hydrochloric acid during 50 minutes, forms the yellow piazselenol (CLVII).[122] At pH 5, the latter can be extracted by toluene.[123] It is only sparingly soluble in water (2.5 μg Se per ml). Tellurium does not give this reaction. Oxidizing and complexing species interfere, but most of the products are not extracted by toluene. 2,3-

Diaminonaphthalene is used in this way for the direct gravimetric determination of selenium in milligram amounts, spectrophotometrically at the microgram level in toluene, and fluorometrically at the submicrogram level, also in toluene.[124] For the gravimetric method, adequate masking (at pH 2) is achieved with sodium fluoride, sodium oxalate, and EDTA, and for the spectrophotometric method the solution is also passed through a cation-exchange column.   Interference by cations, particularly copper (II), is prevented; in fact, the method can be used to determine selenium in copper.   Other reagents used in piazselenol formation as colorimetric reagents for selenium include 4-dimethylamino-1,2-phenylenediamine and 4-methylthio-1,2-phenylenediamine,[125] which give red and blue-purple colors with selenium in strong acid.

Formation of the piazselenol proceeds through an intermediate o-quinonediimine.[126]

In alkaline solutions sulfide ion reacts with the mercury (II)-diphenylcarbazide complex to give an intense red color.[127]   Dithizone synthesis may possibly be involved in the reaction, which is claimed to be specific for sulfides.

11.7   Complex Formation with Organic Ligands

Boric acid is a weak monobasic acid ($pK_a = 9.20$) so that its solutions cannot be titrated accurately with standard alkali.   However, in the presence of suitable polyhydroxy compounds such as glucose, glycerol, and (analytically more convenient) mannitol, the borate anion is stabilized by chelate complex formation in which some or all of its surrounding water molecules are replaced by hydroxyl groups of the organic ligand. This stabilization increases the strength of boric acid about 10,000-fold, so that it can then be titrated with standard alkali, using phenolphthalein.

Steric limitations are very critical in this reaction.   Thus, 1,2- and 1,3-diols are suitable if they are cis but not trans; and pyrocatechol, but not resorcinol or p-quinol, also reacts.   This reaction is useful in distinguishing cis and trans isomers in series like the inositols.

An interesting variation of this reaction is its use to determine boric acid by measuring the effect of the latter on the optical rotation of a tartaric acid solution.[128] This borotartrate complex ion also forms an insoluble barium salt, so that the use of barium chloranilate and tartaric acid has been suggested as a means of determining boron spectrophotometrically, based on the amount of chloranilate ion liberated.[129]   The same type of complex formation, using glycerol, prevents interference by boron in the gravimetric determination of silicon by dehydration of silicic acid,[130] and, using mannitol, in a fluorometric method for silicate ion, based on reaction of the latter with benzoin.[13]

Germanium, like boron, can form complexes with suitable polyvalent alcohols. The resulting compounds of germanic acid with, for example, glycerol or mannitol, are strong monobasic acids.

At levels of boron below about 0.01% colorimetric procedures are preferable. Interference by most species can be avoided by prior separation of boron as methyl borate or by passage of borate-containing solutions through a cation-exchange column. (The voltatile methyl or ethyl borate, formed when sulfuric acid, boric acid, and the appropriate alcohol are warmed together, is the basis of the flame test for borates.) In strong sulfuric acid solutions, boric acid coordinates with polyhydroxyanthraquinones to form colored chelates that serve for its colorimetric determination. Examples include quinalizarin (CLVIII)[132] and carminic acid (CLIX).[133]

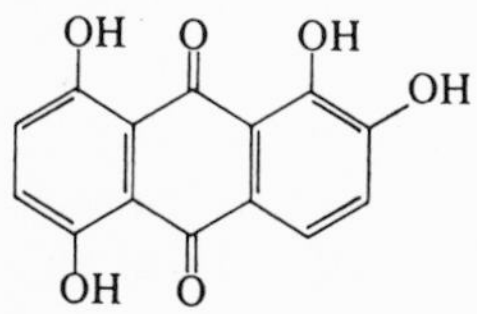

CLVIII 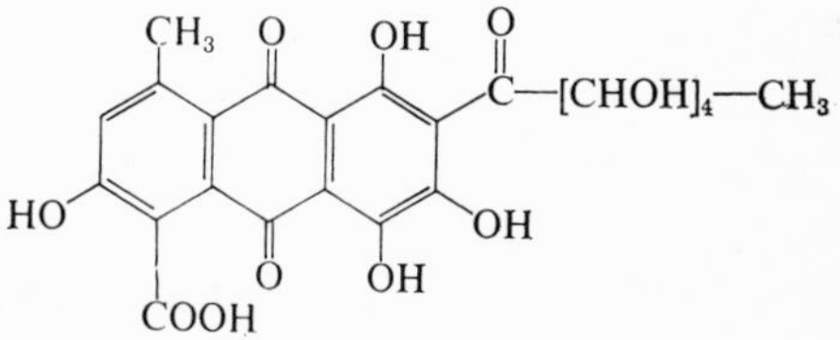   CLIX

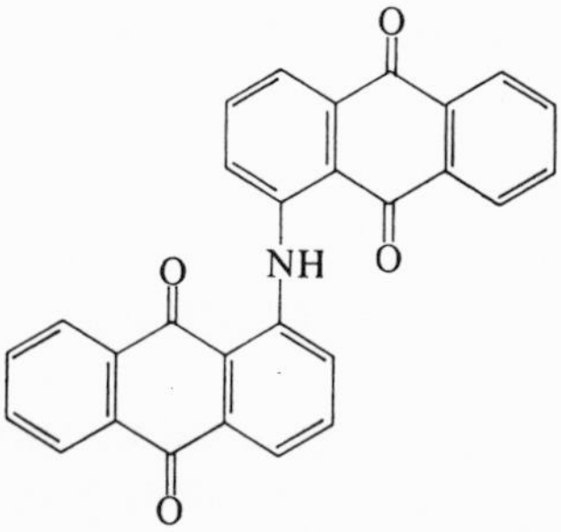

CLX

The methods using quinalizarin are rapid and accurate, but the spectral change between quinalizarin and its boron complex is rather small. A much bigger difference, from red to blue, is found with carminic acid (520 mμ and 585 mμ respectively). An imino analog of 1-hydroxyanthraquinone, 1,1-dianthrimide (CLX), is also used as a reagent for boric acid under the same conditions, also in the range 0–1 ppm.[134] Similar reagents that have been proposed include alizarin red S and purpurin.

In all cases, chelation probably involved the CO group and the hydroxyl (or imino, in (LC)) groups that are in a peri position with respect to it.[135] *p*-Nitrobenzeneazochromotropic acid (chromotrope 2B) in sulfuric acid also serves as a spot test for boric acid.[136]

The reaction between boric acid and an alcoholic solution of curcumin (CLXI) (a constituent of turmeric) in dilute oxalic and hydrochloric acid provides a very sensitive color test—yellow to rose-red—which can be used for determinations of from 0.1 to 10 μg of boron.[137] The nature of the reaction is unknown, but it may be a borate-catalyzed rearrangement of curcumin to rosocyanine.

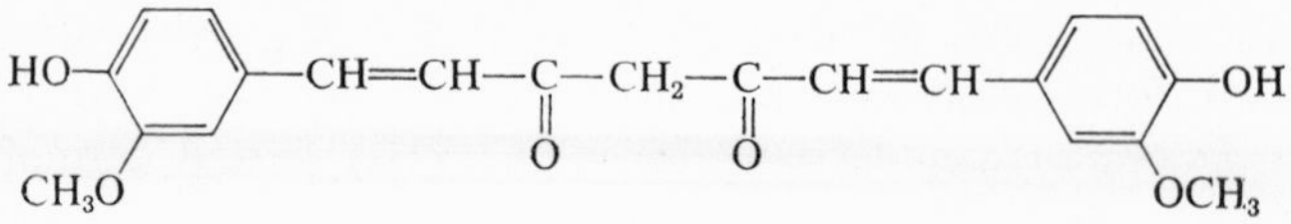

CLXI

In alkaline solution, sulfide ion reacts with the nitrosocyanide or "nitro-prusside" ion [ON $\rightarrow$ Fe(CN$_5$)]$^{2-}$ to form an intense violet-colored compound. The reaction is due to the conversion of the nitrosyl radical into the thionitro-group, NOS, as in (CLXII). Similarly, caustic alkalies give rise to a nitro group, and sulfites form (CLXIII), so that the qualitative test for sulfites consists of the formation of a red color with zinc

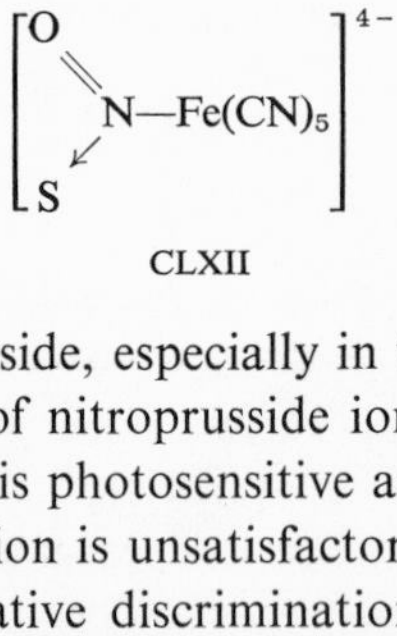

CLXII 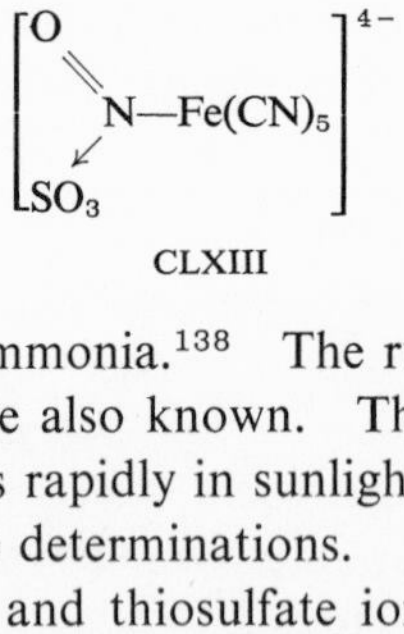   CLXIII

nitroprusside, especially in the presence of ammonia.[138] The ruthenium analogs of nitroprusside ion and (CLXII) are also known. The species (CLXII) is photosensitive and the color fades rapidly in sunlight, so that the reaction is unsatisfactory for quantitative determinations.

Qualitative discrimination between sulfite and thiosulfate ions in admixture is possible after addition of formaldehyde or some other aldehyde to the neutral solution. Sulfite, but not thiosulfate, forms an aldehyde addition compound, with production of hydroxyl ions so that the solution becomes alkaline.

An unexpected and highly specific test for fluoride ion has been developed using the red cerous complex of alizarin complexan (alizarin fluorine blue) (CLXIV).

In this complex the metal ion is coordinated to the amino nitrogen, the two carboxylate anions, and the adjoining phenolic OH, the remaining two sites round the metal ion being occupied by water molecules. Displacement of one of these water molecules by a fluoride ion to form a cerous fluoride complex tends to withdraw electrons from the aromatic nucleus and causes the loss of the proton from the 1-hydroxyl group in the alizarin molecule, producing a characteristic blue-purple color that can detect fluoride ion down to 0.1 ppm.[139,140]   The color is close to that of the fully ionized ligand, observed at pH $\geq$ 13.   The method can be rendered more sensitive (down to 0.002 ppm) by using extraction into amyl alcohol

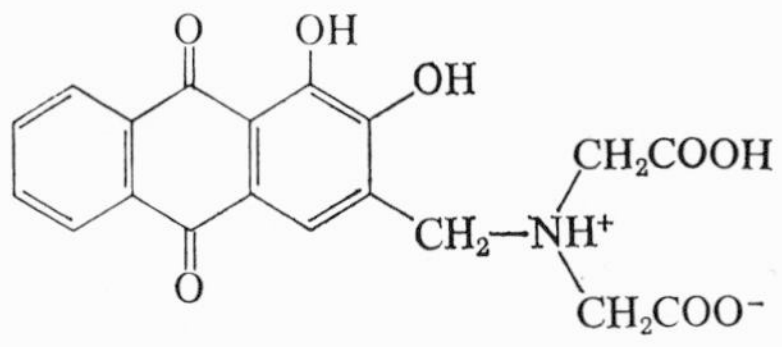

CLXIV

containing tributylamine: Only the fluoro complex is extracted. The amine is needed as its cation to neutralize the charge on the complex. Although Ce, La, Pr, Sm, Sc, Y, Gd, Dy, Er, and Hb all form red chelates with (CLXIV), only Ce, La, and Pr give the blue complex with fluoride ion. The fact that the reaction is given by fluoride but not by other anions is attributed to the unusually strong electrophilic properties of this atom. Other di(carboxymethyl)aminomethyl-hydroxyanthraquinones give the same reaction.[140]

11.8   Other Indirect Reactions

Catalytic effects can be used as qualitative tests for a number of anions. The reaction between chloramine T and the aromatic base, tetramethyl-diaminodiphenylmethane (CLXV), to yield a quinonoid compound proceeds very slowly in weakly (acetic) acid solutions unless iodide ion or iodine is present, in which case rapid oxidation occurs.   The catalysis is

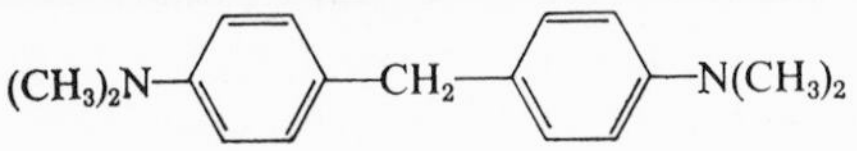

CLXV

due to the reaction between hypochlorite ion (formed by hydrolysis of chloramine T) and iodide ion to yield iodine which oxidizes (CLXV) with regeneration of iodide ion.[141]

Sulfide, thiosulfate and thiocyanate ions can be detected by their acceleration of the reaction between sodium azide and iodine to yield sodium iodide and nitrogen.

In basic solutions cyanide ion catalyzes the condensation of benzaldehyde to give benzoin by a reaction involving intermediate formation of the cyanohydrin, mandelonitrile. Cyanide ion can also be detected by a demasking reaction based on the liberation, in (ammoniacal) alkaline solutions, of dimethylglyoxime from the bis(dimethylglyoxime) complex of palladium (II) if cyanide ion is present to compete for the metal ion. Addition of nickel ion then precipitates the red nickel dimethylglyoxime complex.[142]

An analogous demasking reaction provides a test for ferrocyanide ion. Addition of a soluble mercuric salt to an alkaline solution containing α,α'-bipyridine leads to the dissociation of any ferrocyanide ions that are present, because of the formation of the very stable mercuric cyanide complex, so that ferrous ions are liberated and form the red α,α'-bipyridine complex.[143]

Cyanate ion can be detected by its reaction with hydroxylamine to form a salt which is in isomeric equilibrium with hydroxyurea (compare ammonium cyanate and urea). But, because hydroxyurea is an amidohydroxamic acid, it gives a violet water-soluble tris complex with ferric ion is weakly acid solutions.[144]

Fluoride ion can be detected by distillation as SiF_4 or H_2SiF_6 by heating with sulfuric acid in the presence of silica, with subsequent hydrolysis and conversion to silicomolybdic acid which gives a positive test with benzidine.

References

1. Bumstead, H. E., and J. C. Wells, *Anal. Chem.*, **24**, 1595 (1952).
2. Icken, J. M., and M. B. Blank, *Anal. Chem.*, **25**, 1741 (1953).
3. Megregian, S., *Anal. Chem.*, **26**, 1161 (1954).
4. Richter, F., *Chem. Tech. (Berlin)*, **1**, 84 (1949).
5. Powell, W. A., and J. H. Saylor, *Anal. Chem.*, **25**, 960 (1953).
6. Wharton, H. W., *Anal. Chem.*, **34**, 1296 (1962).
7. Wakimoto, S., *Nippon Kagaku Zasshi*, **77**, 1489 (1956).
8. Silverman, L., and M. E. Shideler, *Anal. Chem.*, **31**, 152 (1959).
9. Kemula, W., A. Hulanicki, and A. Janowski, *Talanta*, **7**, 69 (1960).
10. Jones, A. S., and D. S. Letham, *Analyst*, **81**, 15 (1956).
11. Andersen, L., *Acta Chem. Scand.*, **7**, 689 (1953).
12. For example, Hubbard, R. S., *J. Biol. Chem.*, **128**, 537 (1939).
13. Kahn, B. S., and S. L. Lieboff, *J. Biol. Chem.*, **80**, 623 (1928); Lentonoff, T. V., and J. G. Reinhold, *J. Biol. Chem.*, **114**, 147 (1936).
14. Klein, B., *Ind. Eng. Chem. (Anal. Ed.)*, **16**, 536 (1944).
15. Lambert, J. L., S. K. Yasuda, and M. P. Grotheer, *Anal. Chem.*, **27**, 800 (1955).
16. Gutzeit, G., *Helv. Chim. Acta*, **12**, 736 (1929).
17. Feigl, F., and H. A. Suter, *Ind. Eng. Chem. (Anal. Ed.)*, **14**, 840 (1942).

18. Feigl, F., *Rec. Trav. Chim.*, **58**, 471 (1939).
19. Utsumi, S., *Nippon Kagaku Zasshi*, **74**, 358 (1953).
20. Vasak, V., and V. Machalek, *Chem. Listy*, **47**, 850 (1953).
21. *Standard Methods for the Examination of Water, Sewage, and Industrial Wastes*, 10th ed., American Public Health Association, New York, 1955, pp. 196–200.
22. Fritz, J. S., and M. Q. Freeland, *Anal. Chem.*, **26**, 1593 (1954).
23. Fritz, J. S., S. S. Yamamura, and M. J. Richard, *Anal. Chem.*, **29**, 158 (1957).
24. Ricci, J. E., *Ind. Eng. Chem. (Anal. Ed.)*, **8**, 130 (1936).
25. Burg, W. V., *Ind. Eng. Chem. (Anal. Ed.)*, **11**, 28 (1939).
26. Archer, E. E., *Analyst*, **82**, 208 (1957); Kirsten, W. J., K. A. Hansson, and S. K. Nilsson, *Anal. Chim. Acta*, **28**, 101 (1963).
27. Archer, E. E., *Analyst*, **81**, 181 (1956).
28. Munger, J. R., R. W. Nippler, and R. S. Ingols, *Anal. Chem.*, **22**, 1455 (1950).
29. Belcher, R., D. Gibbons, and T. S. West, *Chem. Ind. (London)*, **1954**, 127.
30. Sporek, K. F., *Anal. Chem.*, **30**, 1032 (1958).
31. Wanninen, E., *Suomen Kem*, **B29**, 184 (1956).
32. Belcher, R., D. Gibbons, and T. S. West, *Analyst*, **80**, 751 (1955).
33. Kenny, F., R. B. Kurtz, I. Beck, and I. Lukosevicius, *Anal. Chem.*, **29**, 543 (1957).
34. Kivalo, P., *Anal. Chem.*, **27**, 1809 (1955).
35. Belcher, R., and S. J. Clark, *Anal. Chim. Acta*, **8**, 222 (1953).
36. Anderegg, G., H. Flaschka, R. Sallman, and G. Schwarzenbach, *Helv. Chim. Acta*, **37**, 113 (1953).
37. Isagai, K., and N. Takeshita, *Japan Analyst*, **4**, 222 (1955).
38. Hol, P. J., and G. C. H. Leendertse, *Chem. Weekblad*, **48**, 181 (1952).
39. Flaschka, H., and A. Holasek, *Mikrochem. Microchim. Acta*, **39**, 101 (1952).
40. Malinek, M., and B. Rehak, *Chem. Listy*, **49**, 765 (1955).
41. Nielsch, W., and L. Giefer, *Z. Anal. Chem.*, **146**, 323 (1955).
42. Huditz, F., and H. Flaschka, *Z. Anal. Chem.*, **136**, 185 (1952).
43. Gottschalk, G., and R. Dehmel, *Z. Anal. Chem.*, **155**, 251 (1957).
44. Belcher, R., M. Kapel, and A. J. Nutten, *Anal. Chim. Acta*, **8**, 122, 146 (1953); Belcher, R., A. J. Nutten, and W. I. Stephen, *J. Chem. Soc.*, **1953**, 1334.
45. Belcher, R., and D. Gibbons, *J. Chem. Soc.*, **1952**, 4216.
46. Mahr, C., and K. Kraus, *Z. Anal. Chem.*, **128**, 477.
47. Willard, H. H., and G. M. Smith, *Ind. Eng. Chem. (Anal. Ed.)*, **11**, 186, 269 (1939).
48. Greenhalgh, R., and J. P. Riley, *J. Marine Biol. Assoc. U.K.*, **41**, 175 (1961).
49. Robinson, J. W., and P. W. West, *Microchem. J.*, **1**, 93 (1957).
50. Wilson, H. N., *Analyst*, **76**, 65 (1951).
51. Fennell, T. R. F. W., and J. R. Webb, *Talanta*, **2**, 105 (1959).
52. Brabson, J. A., and O. W. Edwards, *Anal. Chem.*, **28**, 1485 (1956).
53. Kreshkov, A. P., S. S. Vilborg, and K. I. Filippova, *J. Anal. Chem. USSR*, **8**, 225 (1953).
54. Kruse, J. M., and M. G. Mellon, *Anal. Chem.*, **25**, 446 (1953).
55. Spacu, G., *Bull. Soc. Stiinte Cluj*, **1**, 302 (1922); through *CA*, **17**, 1772 (1923).
56. Ayres, G. H., and S. S. Baird, *Anal. Chim. Acta*, **23**, 446 (1960).
57. Hartmann, H., and G. Bäthge, *Angew. Chem.*, **65**, 107 (1953).
58. Schönberg, A., *J. Chem. Soc.*, **1938**, 824.
59. Heck, J. E., H. Hunt, and M. G. Mellon, *Analyst*, **59**, 18 (1934).
60. Geilmann, W., and A. Voigt, *Z. Anorg. Allgem. Chem.*, **193**, 311 (1930).

61. Vürtheim, A., *Rec. Trav. Chim.*, **46**, 97 (1927).
62. Cope, W. C., and J. Barab, *J. Am. Chem. Soc.*, **29**, 504 (1917).
63. Elving, P. J., C. A. Horton, and H. H. Willard, "Analytical Chemistry of Fluorine and Fluorine-Containing Compounds," in Simons, J. H., *Fluorine Chemistry*, Academic Press, New York, 1954, Vol. 2, Chapter 3.
64. Schaack, H. J., and W. Wagner, *Z. Anal. Chem.*, **146**, 326 (1955).
65. Ducret, L., *Anal. Chim. Acta*, **17**, 213 (1957).
66. Pasztor, L., and J. D. Bode, *Anal. Chim. Acta*, **24**, 467 (1961).
67. Noll, C. A., *Ind. Eng. Chem. (Anal. Ed.)*, **17**, 426 (1945); Wolf, B., *Ind. Eng. Chem. (Anal. Ed.)*, **16**, 121 (1944).
68. Machida, Y., *Bull. Chem. Soc. Japan*, **24**, 254 (1951); Gritsuyta, S. D., *Zh. Anal. Khim.*, **5**, 286 (1950).
69. Isodoro, R., *Boll. Lab. Chim. Provinciali (Bologna)*, **2**, 16 (1951).
70. Kolthoff, I. M., and G. E. Naponen, *J. Am. Chem. Soc.*, **55**, 1448 (1933).
71. Pfeilsticker, K., *Z. Anal. Chem.*, **89**, 1 (1932)
72. Bini, G., *Atti Accad. Lincei*, **11**, 593 (1930).
73. Vasil'ev, A. S., and M. M. Dukhinova, *Zavodsk. Lab.*, **10**, 35 (1941).
74. Cholak, J., and R. McNary, *J. Ind. Hyg. Toxicol.*, **25**, 354 (1943).
75. De Nardo, L. U., *Compt. Rend.*, **188**, 563 (1929).
76. Bishop, E., and V. J. Jennings, *Talanta*, **1**, 197 (1958).
77. Erdey, L., G. Svehla, and L. Koltai, *Anal. Chim. Acta*, **27**, 498 (1962).
78. Hammock, E. W., D. Beavon, and E. H. Swift, *Anal. Chem.*, **21**, 970 (1949).
79. Wadelin, C., and M. G. Mellon, *Anal. Chem.*, **25**, 1668 (1953).
80. Boltz, D. F., and M. G. Mellon, *Ind. Eng. Chem. (Anal. Ed.)*, **19**, 873 (1947); Case, O. P., *ibid.*, **16**, 309 (1944).
81. Feigl, F., *Spot Tests in Inorganic Analysis*, Elsevier, Amsterdam, 5th ed., 1958, p. 317.
82. Feigl, F., and V. Demant, *Mikrochim. Acta*, **1**, 322 (1937).
83. Atkin, S., *Anal. Chem.*, **22**, 947 (1950); Stang, A. M., J. E. Zatek, and E. D. Robson, *Am. Ind. Hyg. Assoc. Quart.*, **12**, 5 (1951).
84. Katz, M., *Anal. Chem.*, **22**, 1040 (1950).
85. Liddell, H. F., *Analyst*, **80**, 901 (1955).
86. McConnaughey, P. W. (to the Mine Safety Appliance Co.), U.S. Pat. 2,736,638 (Feb. 28, 1956).
87. Freytag, H., *Ber.*, **67B**, 1477 (1934).
88. Compare Feigl, F., and E. Frankel, *Ber.*, **65**, 545 (1932) for the oxidation of Ni(II) oxide to hydrated Ni(IV) oxide by simultaneous autoxidation of sulfur dioxide.
89. Senise, P., *Mikrochim. Acta*, **1957**, 640.
90. Charlot, G., *Bull. Soc. Chim. Franç*, **6**, 1447 (1939).
91. Kiboku, M., *Japan Analyst*, **6**, 491 (1957).
92. Jellinek, K., and L. Winogradoff, *Z. Anorg. Chem.*, **129**, 15 (1925).
93. Kolthoff, I. M., and O. Tomicek, *Pharm. Weekblad*, **61**, 1205 (1925).
94. Gowda, H. S., K. B. Rao, and G. G. Rao, *Anal. Chim. Acta*, **12**, 506 (1955).
95. Kuhn, R., and F. Weygand, *Ber.*, **69**, 1969 (1936).
96. Berg, R., and M. Teitelbaum, *Mikrochem.*, **15**, 32 (1934); Suzuki, M., *Nippon Kagaku Zasshi*, **5B**, 323 (1953).
97. Reference 81, p. 347.
98. Michal, J., and J. Zyka, *Chem. Listy*, **48**, 1338 (1954).
99. Simon, V., and V. Grim, *Chem. Listy*, **48**, 1774 (1954).

100. Fidler, J., *Chem. Listy*, **46**, 221 (1952).
101. Deshmukh, G. S., and K. M. Sankaranarayanan, *J. Sci. Res. Banaras Hindu Univ.*, **3**, 5 (1952–1953); through *CA*, **48**, 6320c (1954).
102. Horvorka, V., and Z. Holzbecher, *Coll. Czech. Chem. Comm.*, **14**, 490 (1949); Klut, H., *Kl. Mitt, Ver. Wasserversag. Abwasserbeseitig*, **3**, 184 (1927).
103. Macdonald, J. C., and J. H. Yoe, *Anal. Chim. Acta*, **28**, 383 (1963).
104. Gotlib, A. L., *J. Appl. Chem. (USSR)*, **11**, 135 (1938); through *CA*, **32**, 4469 (1938).
105. Rider, B. F., and M. G. Mellon, *Ind. Eng. Chem. (Anal. Ed.)*, **18**, 96 (1946); Barnes, H., and A. R. Folkard, *Analyst*, **76**, 599 (1951).
106. Pappenhagen, J. M., and M. G. Mellon, *Anal. Chem.*, **25**, 341 (1953).
107. Barnes, H., and A. R. Folkard, *Analyst*, **76**, 599 (1951).
108. Boltz, D. F. (ed.) *Colorimetric Determination of Non-Metals*, Interscience, New York, 1958, p. 131.
109. Sawicki, E., and J. L. Noe, *Anal. Chim. Acta*, **25**, 166 (1961).
110. Klein, B., *Ind. Eng. Chem. (Anal. Ed.)*, **16**, 536 (1944).
111. Letonoff, T. V., and J. G. Reinhold, *Am. J. Med. Sci.*, **188**, 142 (1934); *J. Biol. Chem.*, **114**, 147 (1936).
112. St. Lorant, I., *Biochem. Z.*, **289**, 425 (1937).
113. Taras, M. J., *Anal. Chem.*, **22**, 1020 (1950); de Carvalho, A., *Anais Asoc. Brasil. Quim.*, **9**, 106 (1950).
114. West, P. W., and G. L. Lyles, *Anal. Chim. Acta*, **23**, 227 (1960).
115. Barnes, H., *Analyst*, **75**, 388 (1950); Jones, G. B., and R. E. Underdown, *Anal. Chem.*, **25**, 806 (1953).
116. Murty, G. V. L. N., *Proc. Indian Acad. Sci.*, **14A**, 43 (1941).
117. Vasil'eva, L. A., *Trans. Kirov Inst. Chem. Tech. Kazan*, **8**, 48 (1940).
118. Hartley, A. M., and R. I. Asai, *J. Am. Water Works Assoc.*, **52**, 255 (1960).
119. Holler, A. C., and R. V. Huch, *Anal. Chem.*, **21**, 1385 (1949).
120. Hartley, A. M., and D. J. Curran, *Anal. Chem.*, **35**, 686 (1963).
121. Hinsberg, O., *Ber.*, **52**, 21 (1919).
122. Hoste, J., and J. Gillis, *Anal. Chim. Acta*, **12**, 158 (1955).
123. Cheng, K. L., *Anal. Chem.*, **28**, 1738 (1956).
124. Parker, C. A., and L. G. Harvey, *Analyst*, **87**, 558 (1962); Lott, P. F., *Chem. Eng. News*, March 18, 1963, p. 45.
125. Sawicki, E., *Anal. Chem.*, **29**, 1376 (1957); Demeyere, D., and J. Hoste, *Anal. Chim. Acta*, **27**, 288 (1962).
126. Efros, L. S., *J. Gen. Chem. USSR*, **27**, 1064 (1957).
127. Kreshkov, A. P., and L. P. Senetskaya, *Tr. Mosk. Khim.-Tekhnol. Inst.*, **22**, 108 (1956).
128. Kodama, K., and H. Shiio, *Anal. Chem.*, **34**, 106 (1962).
129. Srivastava, R. D., P. A. Van Buren, and H. Gesser, *Anal. Chem.*, **34**, 209 (1962).
130. Pasztor, L. C., *Anal. Chem.*, **33**, 1270 (1961).
131. Elliott, G., and J. A. Radley, *Anal. Chem.*, **33**, 1623 (1961).
132. Martin, G., and M. Maes, *Bull. Soc. Chim. Biol.*, **34**, 1178 (1952); MacDougall, D., and D. A. Briggs, *Anal. Chem.*, **24**, 566 (1952); Ripley-Duggan, B. A., *Analyst*, **78**, 183 (1953).
133. Hatcher, J. T., and L. V. Wilcox, *Anal. Chem.*, **22**, 567 (1950).
134. Ellis, G. H., E. G. Zook, and O. Brandish, *Anal. Chem.*, **21**, 1345 (1949); Brewster, P. A., *Anal. Chem.*, **23**, 1809 (1951); Codell, M., and G. Norwitz, *Anal. Chem.*, **25**, 1446 (1953).

135. Dimroth, O., and T. Faust, *Ber.*, **54**, 3020 (1921).
136. Komarowsky, A. S., and N. S. Polnektoff, *Mikrochem.*, **14**, 317 (1933–1934).
137. Dible, W. T., E. T. Truog, and R. C. Berger, *Anal. Chem.*, **26**, 418 (1954).
138. Eegriwe, E., *Z. Anal. Chem.*, **65**, 182 (1924).
139. Belcher, R., M. A. Leonard, and T. S. West, *J. Chem. Soc.*, 3577 (1959).
140. Leonard, M. A., and T. S. West, *J. Chem. Soc.*, **1960**, 4477.
141. Feigl, F., and E. Jungreis, *Z. Anal. Chem.*, **161**, 87 (1958).
142. Feigl, F., and H. E. Feigl, *Anal. Chim. Acta*, **3**, 300 (1949).
143. Feigl, F., and A. Caldas, *Anal. Chim. Acta*, **13**, 526 (1955).
144. Davidson, D., *J. Chem. Ed.*, **17**, 84 (1940).

CHAPTER 12

Procedures for Detecting and Determining Inorganic Neutral Molecules

One of the most important properties of nonmetallic elements from the point of view of chemical analysis is their ability to form species that can be separated by volatilization, diffusion, or distillation. This is true also of many of the metalloids and some of the metals. Examples of the latter include chromyl, ruthenium, and osmium chlorides, and the following yield volatile bromides which distil from sulfuric acid solutions: As(III), As(V), Sb(III), Sb(V), Se(IV), Se(VI), Ge, Hg(I), Hg(II), Re, Sn(II), Sn(IV), and, to a much smaller extent, B, Te(IV), Te(VI), Mo, Bi, P, and Au. In the group of elements

B	C	N	O	F
	Si	P	S	Cl
	Ge	As	Se	Br
			Te	I

volatile species include: for B, $B(OCH_3)_3$, BF_3; for C, CO, CO_2; for Si, SiF_4; for Ge, $GeBr_4$; for N, NH_3, NO, NOCl; for P, PH_3, PCl_3; for As, $AsCl_3$, $AsBr_3$, AsH_3; for S, SO_2, SO_3, H_2S; for Se, H_2Se, $SeCl_2$, $SeOCl_2$, $SeBr_4$, $SeCl_4$, $SeOBr_2$; for Te, H_2Te, $TeCl_2$, $TeBr_4$, $TeCl_4$, $TeOBr_2$, $TeOCl_2$; for F, F_2, H_2F_2, SiF_4, H_2SiF_6; for Cl, Cl_2, HCl; for Br, Br_2, HBr, CNBr; for I, I_2 and HI. Application of this property greatly reduces the stringency of the requirement that a reagent should be highly selective.

Where bromine or chlorine is used as an oxidant, any unused excess can be removed by adding sulfosalicyclic acid, which readily undergoes substitution by free halogens.

Many neutral molecules react as their corresponding cations or anions, for example SO_2 as HSO_3^- and SO_3^{2-}, NO_2 as NO_2^- and NO_3^-, and HCl as Cl^-. Hence they are dealt with in other chapters.

257

12.1   Direct Spectrophotometry

In a limited number of cases the substance can be determined by direct spectrophotometry.

Elemental sulfur, at levels from 0 to 40 ppm, has been estimated by its ultraviolet absorption in ethanolic solutions or in n-hexane.[1]

Iodine, in nonpolar solvents such as carbon tetrachloride or carbon disulfide, is purple in color and has a spectrum similar to iodine in the vapor state. The distribution between organic solvent and water favors the former, so that the color is useful for estimating iodine and as an indicator in iodometric titrations. In the presence of hydroxylic solvents such as water or ethanol, iodine is solvated to a brown complex which absorbs more intensely in the ultraviolet. It also forms with iodide ion yellow-to-brown polyiodide complexes that are detectable at concentrations down to about $10^{-4}M$; more intense iodine-iodide complexes are formed with amylose (blue), amylopectin (red-purple), glycogen (brown), and some other starches.[2] Modified starches high in amylose ("linear starch") are available for use in iodometric titrations. Chlorine and bromine can also be detected by their reaction with iodide ion in starch-iodide paper, to liberate iodine, which then gives the blue starch-iodine color. Many other oxidizing agents including hydrogen peroxide, nitrite, and permanganate ions react in the same way.

In aqueous solution, iodine forms a blue addition compound with α-naphtholflavone, with quenching of fluorescence. The reaction is more sensitive than the starch-iodine reaction.[3] Under the same conditions, bromine forms an orange-red compound, but chlorine does not react.

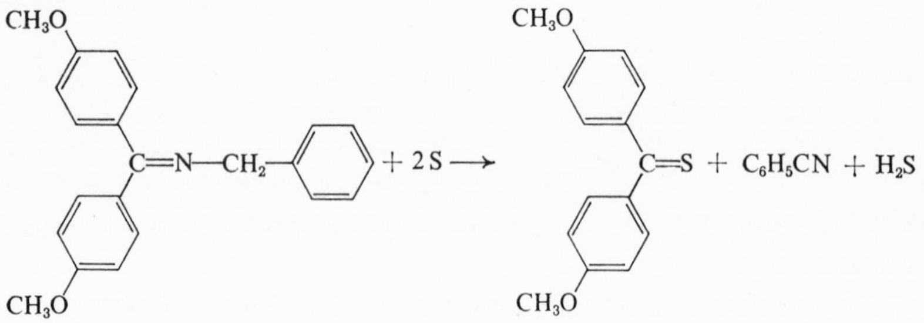

CLXVI

Addition of dilute sodium hydroxide to a solution of sulfur in pyridine gives a series of colors which serve to detect 10 or more ppm of sulfur.[4] A direct spectrophotometric method for free sulfur has been devised,[5] based on the reaction (CLXVI) of sulfur when heated with Schoenberg reagent, N-(4,4'-dimethoxybenzohydrylidene)benzylamine, to give a blue thioketone (4,4'-dianisylthioketone) that is soluble in benzene.   Addition of a small crystal of mercuric chloride can be used as a confirmatory qualitative test: The thioketone slowly bonds to the mercury through the sulfur atom, producing a red complex.

Qualitative tests for traces of water include the formation of an orange color with a 1% solution of dipicrylamine in anhydrous dioxane,[6] and of a brown color with a 3% solution of lead tetraacetate in anhydrous benzene.[7]

Selenium and tellurium are most commonly determined as their sols. Osmium and ruthenium tetraoxides can be determined by direct spectro-photometry of solutions in organic solvents.

12.2   Oxidation Reactions

In general, however, neutral inorganic species are detected and estimated either by conversion to suitable ionic forms or by their chemical reactions, which often produce changes in the color or fluorescence of organic molecules.

The oxidizing power of chlorine, bromine, and iodine in acid solution is the basis of the sensitive colorimetric methods using o-tolidine (CLXVII), which is oxidized to the p-quinoneimide (CLXVIII), and then condenses further to give a meriquinoid molecular compound which is an intense yellow for chlorine[8] and blue-green for iodine.[9]   The method is sensitive at the 1-ppm level, but many oxidizing agents, including nitrite, Fe(III), Mn(III), osmium tetroxide, vanadate, and tungstate, interfere.   Benzidine behaves similarly and can be used instead of o-tolidine but is less stable.

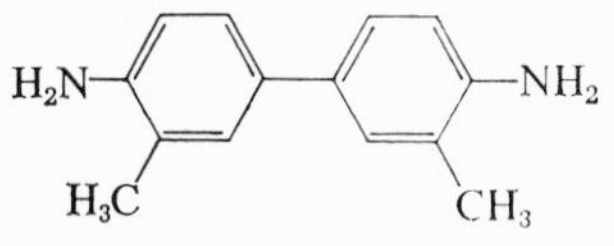

CLXVII 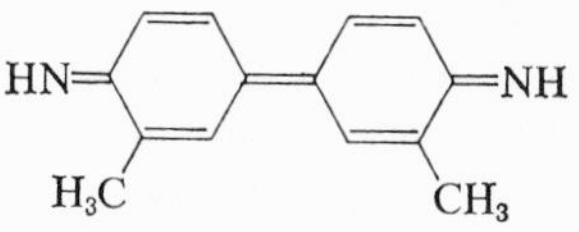   CLXVIII

The same reaction is the basis of a method for estimating gold after oxidizing it to chloroauric acid.[10]   Solid antimony (V) oxide likewise oxidizes a sulfuric acid solution of N,N'-diphenylbenzidine, giving an intense blue color.   Many aromatic bases, including aniline, are oxidized to colored products by chlorine and bromine.

Similarly, 4,4'-bis-dimethylaminothiobenzophenone (CLXIX), is oxi-dized in benzene solution by chlorine, bromine, or iodine to the disulfide (CLXX), with a color change from yellow to blue.[11]   Nitrous acid and some metal ions also react, but not hydrogen peroxide or persulfates.

Conversely, leuco-malachite green and *o*-dianisidine, which in weakly acidic solutions are oxidized by Au(III) to colored compounds,[12] could also probably be used as reagents for chlorine and bromine. Chlorine dioxide in low concentrations can be determined by its oxidation of 1-amino-8-naphthol-3,6-disulfonic acid.[13]

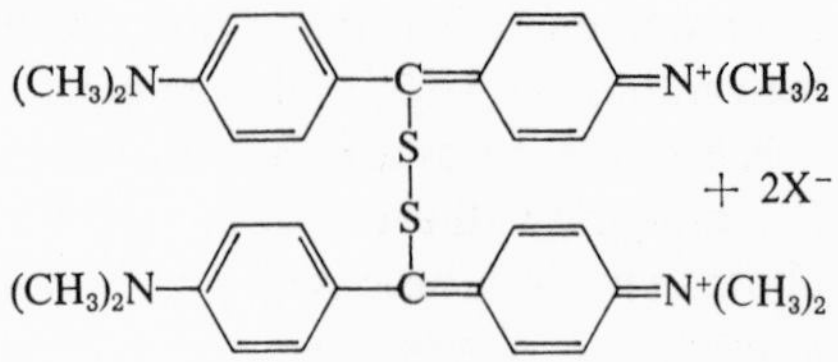

CLXX

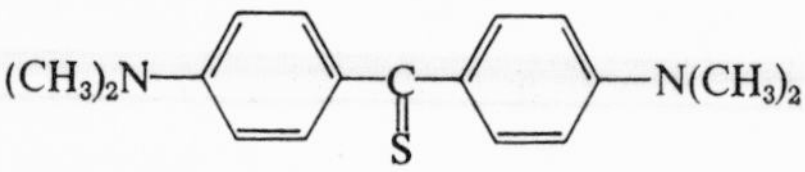

CLXIX

Similarly, oxidative removal of the azo group of methyl orange (CLXXI) by chlorine or bromine, to give colorless *p*-halodimethylaniline and phenol-*p*-sulfonic acid, has been used for the quantitative colorimetric determination of chlorine[14] and bromine. The reaction is more selective than with

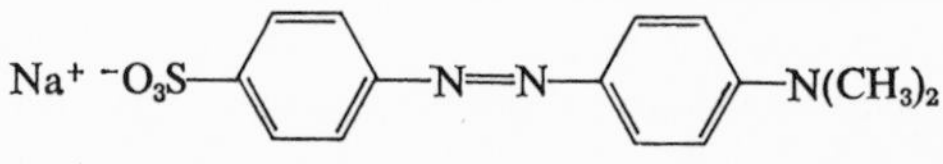

CLXXI

o-tolidine, although comparable in sensitivity, because iron (III) and chloramine do not interfere.

Much better selectivity in methods for chlorine and bromine is obtained by using reactions based on their prior conversion to the corresponding cyanogen halide, $KCN + Cl_2 \rightarrow KCl + CNCl$. In König's reaction, cyanogen chloride or cyanogen bromide oxidizes pyridine to glutaconic aldehyde, which condenses with an aromatic amine such as benzidine to give an intensely colored compound, Ar—N=CH—CH=CH—CH=CH—NH—Ar, which is a polymethine dye. The sensitivity of the method is greater than 1 ppm but varies with the amine used.[15] The method is also applicable to the determination of cyanide ion and to thiocyanate ion, which forms cyanogen chloride by reaction with chloramine T.[16]

Although the usual methods for determining ammonia are based either on the Nessler reaction or on distillation and acid titration, several color reactions can also be used for low concentrations. For example, in sodium hydroxide solutions, ammonia reacts with *p*-nitrobenzenediazonium chloride (Riegler's solution) to give a red compound, $O_2NC_6H_4N$= $NONH_4$, which is the ammonium salt of *p*-nitrophenylnitrosamine.

A colorimetric method, based on an observation made originally by Berthelot in 1859 and comparable in senstivity with the Nessler reaction, depends on the formation of a stable, soluble, blue indophenol dye when sodium phenate is added to an ammonium solution that has been treated with chlorine water.[17]   Variations of this method include the use of thymol and sodium hypobromite, and extraction into ethyl ether or xylene. Reaction probably proceeds through chloroamine (NH_2Cl) which, with phenol, gives quinonechloroamine. The latter, in turn, couples with another phenol molecule to give the indophenol.

Ammonia in air can be determined by the ninhydrin reaction in which two molecules of triketohydrindene hydrate condense with a molecule of ammonia to give the blue-colored species (CLXXII).[18]

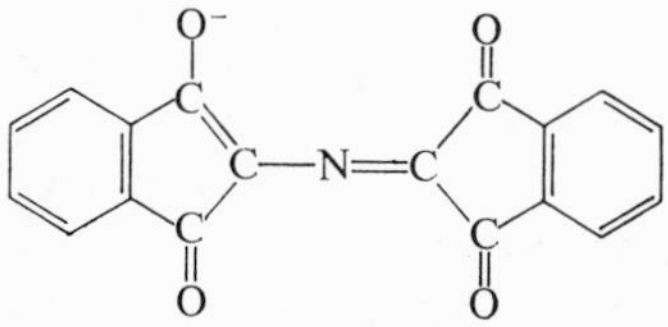

CLXXII

Similarly, a condensation is involved in a test for hydrazine in which reaction with salicylaldehyde forms colorless, insoluble, yellow-fluorescent salicylaldazine (CLXXIII).[19]   Its insolubility in water is probably due to internal hydrogen bonding.   From its relation to glyoxal bis(*o*-hydroxyanil), from which it differs by having the —CH= and —N=

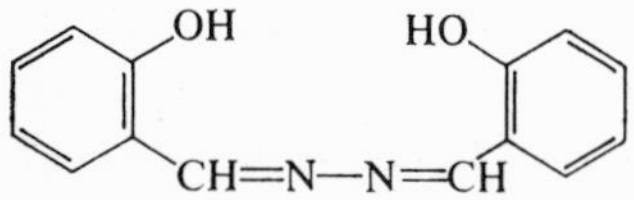

CLXXIII

groups interchanged, (CLXXIII) would be expected to form colored, chloroform-extractable metal complexes that could be used to confirm this test. Hydroxylamine forms a soluble aldoxime with salicylaldehyde, which shows metal-binding properties.[20] Two molecules of *p*-dimethylaminobenzaldehyde condense through their aldehyde groups with one molecule of hydrazine in the same way, to give a soluble aldazine which, in acids, has a red quinonoidal cation.

Synthesis of dimethylglyoxime from diacetylmonoxime and hydroxyl-amine, followed by formation of its red nickel salt, serves as a test for hydroxylamine.[19] In mixtures of hydroxylamine and a large excess of hydrazine, most of the latter can be precipitated with salicylaldehyde before testing the solution for hydroxylamine. Hydroxylamine condenses with formaldehyde, and the product is converted to formhydroxamic acid by hydrogen peroxide or persulfate ion. This substance, in weakly acid solutions, gives a red tris complex with ferric ion.[21] The reducing properties of hydrazine and hydroxylamine are used in color tests with dinitrobenzenes. Again, in the absence of hydrazine, salicylaldehyde and cupric ion can be used to detect hydroxylamine, with which they form the copper chelate of salicylaldoxime. Hydroxylamine, in alkaline solution, adds onto 8-hydroxyquinoline to form 5-amino-8-hydroxyquinoline which, in the presence of air, is oxidized and condensed with another molecule of 8-hydroxyquinoline to form the acid-base indicator, indo-oxine.

The color produced when sodium anthraquinone sulfonate is oxidized by oxygen has been made the basis of methods for estimating oxygen.[22]

The ability of oxygen dissolved in water to oxidize ferrous ethylenedi-amine sulfate to the ferric state, which can then be determined by EDTA, using salicyclic acid as indicator, has been suggested as an analytical method for determining oxygen.[23]

Oxidation of N-phenyl-2-naphthylamine in o-dichlorobenzene is the basis of a quantitative colorimetric method for ozone.[24] Small quantities of ozone can also be determined by their (oxidative) effect on the fluorescence color and intensity of luminol, fluorescein, and fuchsine on silica gel,[25] and by the decolorization of indigo carmine (because of splitting of a double bond in the dye) under the same conditions.[26] Sodium diphenylaminesulfonate has been suggested as an analytical reagent for ozone, which oxidizes it to a blue product.[27] Ozone can also be determined by the oxidation of phenolphthalin in alkaline solution to regenerate the red phenolphthalein anion (from which it is prepared by reduction with zinc).[28] Other oxidizing agents such as ferricyanide ion and hydrogen peroxide (in the presence of Cu(II) which leads to free radical formation) behave similarly.

The chemiluminescence produced when luminol (3-aminophthal-hydrazide) is oxidized by hydrogen peroxide in the presence of haemin[29] —a sensitive qualitative test for hydrogen peroxide—also proceeds by a free radical mechanism.

The determination of small amounts of water by the Karl Fischer reagent, prepared by the action of sulfur dioxide upon iodine dissolved in pyridine and methanol (or, better, ethylene-glycol monomethyl ether)[30] depends on the oxidation of the sulfur dioxide by the iodine in the presence of water. The reaction gives pyridinium iodide and an intermediate pyridine-sulfur trioxide complex which rearranges, reacting with the methanol to form the methyl ester of pyridine-N-sulfonic acid. The endpoint of the titration is best determined electrometrically. Oxidizing agents such as chromates, dichromates, cupric and ferric salts, and peroxides, as well as reducing agents such as thiosulfates, stannous salts, and sulfides, interfere.[31]

The formation of methylene blue (CLXXIV) from p-amino-N,N-dimethylaniline in an acid ferric chloride solution serves for the detection

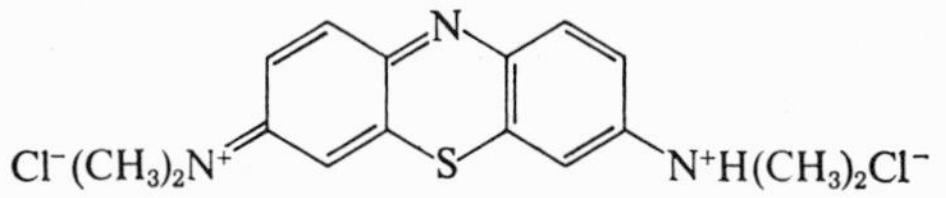

$$Cl^- (CH_3)_2N^+ \quad \text{[phenothiazine ring]} \quad N^+H(CH_3)_2Cl^-$$

CLXXIV

and estimation of hydrogen sulfide down to about 0.01 ppm.[32] The reaction involves the oxidative deamination of one molecule of the amine, followed by its condensation with a second molecule and subsequent ring closure through the sulfur atom. The pK_a value of methylene blue is 3.8, so that its color is pH dependent. It is also destroyed rapidly in sunlight. Modified reagents have also been used, so that the end product has been an iododerivative of methylene blue[33] and Bindschedler's green.[34] Mercaptans interfere in the reaction.

12.3 Substitution Reactions

An alternative approach in estimating free bromine is to allow it to brominate a suitable organic dye such as phenol red,[35] bisulfite-reduced fuchsin, rosaniline,[36] or, less satisfactorily, fluorescein,[37] and measure the change spectrophotometrically. An advantage in using phenol red is that the brominated end products (bromophenol red and bromo-phenol blue) are pH indicators differing in pK value and color change from phenol red. By measuring the optical density (580 mμ) at pH 5.0–5.4, good discrimination is possible between the blue color of the product and the yellow color of phenol red. The method can also be used for bromide ion by prior oxidation to bromine with sodium hypochlorite at pH 8.8. The reaction between rosaniline and bromine in acid solution gives an insoluble red tetra- or pentabromo derivative that can, however, be extracted into benzyl alcohol.

Fluorescein has been used in a method for determining iodine, based on the diminution of fluorescence when it is partially converted to the nonfluorescent diiodo derivative.[38]   This reaction is used as a spot test. Filter paper moistened with (yellow) fluorescein turns red in bromine vapor because of conversion to eosin, whereas with iodine the red-yellow erythrosine is formed.   In the presence of potassium bromide, chlorine can also be detected by the liberation of bromine.

Alternatively, the reaction of free bromine with *m*-phenylenediamine to give 2,4,6-tribromo-*m*-phenylenediamine, which is only slightly soluble in water (but readily soluble in ethanol) can be used as a qualitative test for bromine and bromides.

12.4   Indirect Reactions

Iodine can be estimated indirectly by reaction with hydroxylamine to give nitrous acid which is determined by diazotizing sulfanilic acid with it, the latter, in turn, coupling with α-naphthylamine to give a red dye.[39]

The pseudo-halogen dicyanogen $(CN)_2$ reacts with water in a manner analogous to the halogens to give HCN and HCNO, so that its detection is by the same methods as for cyanide ion.

Sulfur can be determined, down to about 2 ppm, by allowing its solution in acetone to react with cyanide ion to form thiocyanate, which is then converted to the red ferric complex.[40]   Tetrathionate ion also reacts with cyanide to form thiocyanate, and a similar spectrophotometric method for tetrathionate based on the production of ferric thiocyanate has been described.[41]   Higher polythionates also give this reaction.   When sulfur is heated with molten benzoin, benzil and hydrogen sulfide are produced: the latter can be detected by lead acetate paper as a black stain.   This test is specific for sulfur.[42]

Carbon disulfide can be detected and determined by synthesizing from it (using diethylamine) diethyldithiocarbamate ion which, in turn, is converted to the yellow copper complex for spectrophotometric measurement.[43]

The Schiff reaction for the determination of sulfur dioxide by its reaction with pararosaniline and formaldehyde depends on the synthesis from the colorless trianilinium chloromethane (obtained by adding HCl to pararosaniline), by sulfur dioxide and formaldehyde, of a pararosaniline methyl sulfonic acid that is purple in color.   The colored substance that corresponds to neutral pararosaniline is observed because its pK_a value is much too low for its colorless anilinium-like salt to be produced under the experimental conditions.   The reaction can be made quantitative.[44]

Whereas most aldehydes combine with ammonia to give aldehyde-ammonias, formaldehyde forms hexamethylenetetramine which is only weakly basic.   This makes possible a titrimetric procedure for ammonium ion, based on the addition of excess of neutral formaldehyde to the ammonium salt solution, followed by alkaline titration against phenol phthalein. No permanent color change is observed until all of the ammonia has been converted into hexamethylenetetramine.[45]

Precipitation of the metal hydroxides from magnesium and aluminium ethoxides can be used as a qualitative test for traces of water. Hydrolysis of acetyl pyridinium chloride to pyridinium chloride and acetic acid has also been used for determining water,[46] and succinyl chloride[47] and cinnamoyl chloride[48] find similar application. Hydrolysis of acid anhydrides in the presence of acids as catalysts has been used to a limited extent in determination of water content, mainly in acetic acid.[49] The methanesulfonic acid-catalyzed hydrolysis of 2,2-dimethoxypropane, to give acetone and two molecules of methanol, has also been suggested as a method for determining water, based on infrared absorption measurements at 5.87 microns of the acetone produced.[50] Addition of materials containing water to a solution of dipicrylamine in anhydrous dioxan (an aprotic solvent) allows dipicrylamine to ionize as an acid, the color difference between the (orange) anion and the (light yellow) neutral molecule providing a simple qualitative test for water.[51] For further methods, references, and discussion, see reference 52.

The yellow to orange-red color when tannin and silver nitrate are added to a dilute solution of ammonia is due to the formation of a colloidal silver dispersion, the tannin acting as both a reductant and a protective colloid.

Catalytic effects can sometimes be used in the detection of neutral species. Elemental selenium can be tested for on the basis of its powerful catalytic action on the reduction of methylene blue, fuchsine, picric acid, dipicrylamine, and cacotheline by sulfide ion,[53] the effective catalyst being selenosulfide ions resulting from solution of selenium in alkali sulfide solutions. Selenite ion is also detected in this way because, under these conditions, it is reduced to selenium. Reaction is stopped if potassium cyanide is added, because potassium selenocyanide KCNSe is formed.

Discrimination between elementary sulfur and selenium is possible when they are dissolved in sulfite solution to give thiosulfate and selenosulfate, respectively. Addition of formaldehyde leaves the former unchanged, but the latter disproportionates to form an aldehyde-bisulfite addition compound, with precipitation of selenium.

Some of the neutral metals, including aluminium, lead, tin, and zinc, can be detected by their addition to a strongly alkaline, alcoholic solution of o-dinitrobenzene. The nascent hydrogen produced in the reaction between hydroxyl ions and the metal is able to reduce the nitro compound with the production of a nitrol-nitro acid, the anion of which is intensely violet colored.[54]

This test is also given by other strong reducing agents, including hydroxylamine, hydrazine, sulfides, stannites, hyposulfites and the sodium sulfoxylate-formaldehyde addition product. p-Dinitrobenzene can also be used in this test.

References

1. Heatley, N. G., and E. J. Page, Anal. Chem., 24, 1854 (1952).
2. Rundle, R. E., and D. French, J. Am. Chem. Soc., 65, 558 (1943); Swanson, M. A., J. Biol. Chem., 172, 825 (1948).
3. Reith, J. F., Pharm. Weekblad, 66, 1097 (1929).
4. Sommer, H., Ind. Eng. Chem. (Anal. Ed.) 12, 368 (1940).
5. Ory, H. A., V. L. Warren, and H. B. Williams, Analyst, 82, 189 (1957).
6. Caldas, A., Chemist-Analyst, 43, 100 (1954).
7. Pesez, M., Bull. Soc. Chim. France, 15, 1108 (1948).
8. Marks, H. C., and R. R. Joiner, Anal. Chem., 20, 1197 (1948).
9. Lange, N. A., and L. A. Ward, J. Am. Chem. Soc., 47, 1000 (1925).
10. Clabaugh, W. S., J. Res Natl. Bur. Std., 36, 119 (1946).
11. Feigl, F., D. Goldstein, and R. A. Rosell, Z. Anal. Chem., 158, 421 (1957).
12. Kul'berg, L. M., Zavodsk. Lab., 5, 170 (1936); Block, W. D., and O. H. Buchanan, J. Biol. Chem., 136, 379 (1940).
13. Post, M. A., and W. A. Moore, Anal. Chem., 31, 1872 (1959).
14. Gad, G., and E. Priegnitz, Gesundh.-Ingr., 68, 174 (1947); Taras, M., Anal. Chem., 19, 342 (1947).
15. For experimental details, which must be carefully standardized, see Asmus, E., and H. Garschagen, Z. Anal. Chem., 136, 269 (1952); Milton, R. F., Nature, 164, 448 (1949); Norris, P. K., and H. A. Grant, Analyst, 76, 492 (1951); Nusbaum, I., and P. Skupenko, Anal. Chem., 23, 1881 (1951); Van Pinxteren, J. A. C., Analyst, 77, 367 (1952); Pharm. Weekblad., 88, 489 (1953).
16. Epstein, J., Anal. Chem., 19, 272 (1947); Asmus, E., and H. Garschagen, Z. Anal. Chem., 138, 414 (1953).
17. Bolleter, W. T., C. J. Bushman, and P. W. Tidwell, Anal. Chem., 33, 592 (1961).
18. Williams, D. D., and R. R. Miller, Anal. Chem., 34, 225 (1962).
19. Feigl, F., Rec. Trav. Chim., 58, 471 (1939).
20. Ephraim, F., Ber., 63, 1928 (1930).
21. Guagnini, O. A., and E. E. Vonesch, Mikrochim. Acta, 1954, 211.
22. See, for example, Séris, G., P. Vernotte, M. Klein, and A. M. Clavé, Chim. Anal., 42, 200 (1960).
23. Roskam, R. T., and D. de Langen, Anal. Chim. Acta, 28, 78 (1963).
24. Allison, A. R., A. D. Delman, A. E. Ruff, and B. B. Simms, U.S. Pat. 2,849,291 (Aug. 26, 1958).
25. Peregud, E. A., and E. M. Stepanenko, Zh. Anal. Khim., 15, 96 (1960).
26. Mokhov, L. A., and V. P. Dzedzichek, Zavodsk. Lab., 25, 1304 (1959).
27. Bovee, H. H., and R. J. Robinson, Anal. Chem., 33, 1115 (1961).
28. Haagen-Smit, A. J., and M. J. Brunelle, J. Air Pollution, 1, 51 (1958).
29. Langenbeck, W., and U. Ruge, Ber., 70, 267 (1937).
30. Peters, E. D., and J. L. Jungnickel, Anal. Chem., 27, 450 (1955).
31. For further details, see Mitchell, J., and D. M. Smith, Aquametry, Interscience, New York, 1948.

32. Sands, A. E., M. A. Grafius, H. W. Wainwright, and M. W. Wilson, *U.S. Bur. Mines. Rept. Invest., No.* 4547 (1949); *Standard Methods for the Examination of Water, Sewage and Industrial Wastes,* Am. Public Health Assoc., New York, 10th ed., 1955, pp. 273–279.
33. Kuhlberg, L. M., *Kurzes Lehrbuch der Analytischen Chemie,* Leipzig, 11th ed., Vol. 1, 1920.
34. Wright, R. H., M. A. Schoening, and A. M. Hayward, *Tappi,* **34,** 289 (1951).
35. Stenger, V. A., and I. M. Kolthoff, *J. Am. Chem. Soc.,* **57,** 831 (1935); Houghton, G. U., *J. Soc. Chem. Ind. (London),* **65,** 277 (1946).
36. Hunter, G., and A. A. Goldspink, *Analyst,* **79,** 467 (1954).
37. Van der Meulen, J. H., *Chem. Weekblad,* **36,** 702 (1939); Pinching, G. D., and R. G. Bates, *J. Res. Natl. Bur. Std.,* **37,** 311 (1946).
38. Harley, V., *Ann. Pharm. Franç.,* **5,** 81 (1947).
39. Endres, G., and L. Kaufman, *Z. Physiol. Chem.,* **243,** 144 (1936).
40. Bartlett, J. K., and D. A. Skoog, *Anal. Chem.,* **26,** 1008 (1954).
41. Nietzel, O. A., and M. A. De Sesa, *Anal. Chem.,* **27,** 1839 (1955).
42. Feigl, F., and C. Stark, *Anal. Chem.,* **27,** 1838 (1955).
43. Dick, T. A., *J. Soc. Chem. Ind. (London),* **66,** 253 (1947); Lowen, W. K., *Anal. Chem.,* **23,** 1846 (1951).
44. Naumann, R. V., P. W. West, F. Tron, and G. C. Gaeke, *Anal. Chem.,* **32,** 1307 (1960).
45. Kolthoff, I. M., *Pharm. Weekblad,* **58,** 1463 (1921).
46. Smith, D. M., and W. M. D. Bryant, *J. Am. Chem. Soc.,* **57,** 841 (1935).
47. Belcher, R., J. H. Thompson, and T. S. West, *Anal. Chim. Acta,* **19,** 148 (1958).
48. Lindner, J., *Mikrochem. Mikrochim. Acta,* **32,** 133 (1944).
49. Greathouse, L. H., H. J. Janssen, and C. H. Haydel, *Anal. Chem.,* **28,** 357 (1956).
50. Critchfield, F. E., and E. T. Bishop, *Anal. Chem.,* **33,** 1034 (1961).
51. Caldas, A., *Chemist-Analyst,* **43,** 100 (1954).
52. *Treatise on Analytical Chemistry,* Kolthoff, I. M., and P. J. Elving (eds.), Interscience, New York, Part II, Vol. 1, 1961, pp. 69–197.
53. Feigl, F., and P. W. West, *Anal. Chem.,* **19,** 351 (1947).
54. Kuhn, R., and F. Weygand, *Ber.,* **69,** 1969 (1936).

CHAPTER 13

Analytical Properties of the Elements

In devising a procedure for estimating any inorganic species, it is necessary to take account of all other constituents likely to be present in the sample being analyzed. This is because, as we have seen, reactions of organic reagents with inorganic species are, with few exceptions, nonspecific. To help in deciding some of the differences that can be exploited to ensure greater selectivity, some of the more analytically important properties of inorganic substances are given in this chapter. These brief summaries omit such chemical topics as the boron hydrides, the ferrocenes, structures of silicates, and carbonyl complexes, which seem to be unlikely to provide reactions useful in analytical procedures for the elements concerned.

Except for hydrogen, carbon, and the inert gases (which have been omitted), the rare earth elements (grouped under lanthanum), and higher members of the actinide series (grouped under americium), all elements are listed alphabetically.

Where mention is made of analytical reactions, without references being given, further details can be found in reference 1.

It is hoped that the information given in this chapter will serve as a useful guide even in cases where definite information is lacking. For example, Pb(II) forms a blue precipitate of unknown composition in

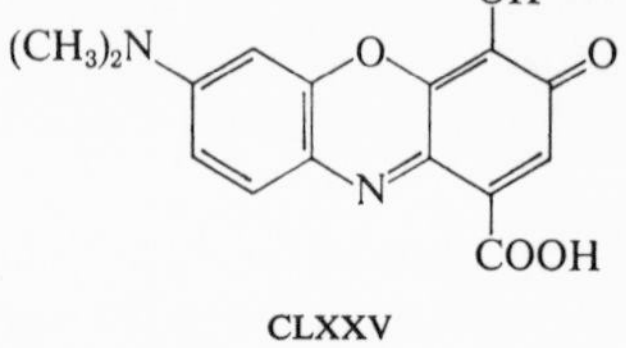

CLXXV

neutral or ammoniacal solution with gallocyanine (CLXXV). Two types of chelate complex may be possible. One of these would involve the bonding of the metal to the nitrogen and to a carboxylic oxygen. Alternatively, the phenolic oxygen and the neighboring oxygen might be concerned. From the properties discussed under *lead*, the former seems much the more likely. (Compare, also, the insoluble complex lead forms with quinaldinic acid.)

Actinium

The intensely radioactive Ac^{3+} ion has the electronic configuration of the inert gas radon. Except that it is more basic, Ac^{3+} is closely similar to La^{3+} in chemical properties. They also have almost identical radii. The greater basic strength of Ac^{3+} shows up in its stronger absorption on cation-exchange resins and in its poorer extraction from nitric acid solutions by tributyl phosphate.

Aluminium

The high charge, the small radius, and the inert gas (Ne) electronic configuration of Al^{3+} determine its chemical properties. Al^{3+} is strongly hydrated in aqueous solution, probably as the ion $[Al(H_2O)_6]^{3+}$ which, in neutral or weakly acid solutions, undergoes extensive hydrolysis and readily precipitates hydrated Al_2O_3. The insolubility of its hydroxide in neutral ammoniacal solution, and its phosphate at pH 5–5.5, serve to separate Al from Mg, Ca, Sr, and Ba. When only small amounts of Al are present, Zr(IV) or Fe(III) hydroxides, and Fe(III) phosphate, respectively, can be used as collectors. In alkaline solutions aluminates, perhaps $[Al(OH)_4]^-$, are produced.

Aluminium complexes can be tetrahedral or octahedral. The former are usually either monoanions, for example $AlBr_4^-$, or, more commonly, neutral species from the addition of donors such as ammonia, amines, ethers, alcohols, ketones, phosphines, or thioethers to AlX_3. The small anion F^- gives the very stable octahedral complex AlF_6^{3-}. However, the chloro complex, $AlCl_4^-$, is unimportant in aqueous solution, even in $12M$ HCl,[2] so that, whereas in $9M$ HCl anionic complexes of many metals are adsorbed onto columns of anion-exchange resins, Al passes through.[3]

In complex formation to give octahedral Al complexes, anionic oxygen-containing bidentate ligands are much preferred to neutral amines and other polarizable ligands so that stable tris complexes are formed by β-diketones, pyrocatechol and dicarboxylic acids. The nonformation (for steric reasons) of a tris(8-hydroxyquinaldine) complex with Al, and the weakness of its complexing ability with diethyldithiocarbamate, enable these reagents to be used to extract many interfering cations from Al solutions. Similarly, 8-hydroxyquinoline, but not 1,10-phenanthroline, yields analytically useful complexes for Al. The more commonly used colorimetric reagents for Al, such as aurintricarboxylate ion (aluminon), eriochrome cyanine R, and alizarinsulfonic acid, all depend on bonding of the Al to carboxylic, phenolic, or quinonoid oxygens.

Americium and Higher Members of the Actinide Series

The oxidation states of ions in this series, and the absorption spectra of the ions themselves, are due to the presence of the incomplete $5f$-electron shell, so that the series has a striking similarity to the lanthanide (rare earth) series, in which the $4f$-electron shell is incomplete. The higher valences seen in Np and Pu arise from the comparable energies of the $5f$ and $6d$ orbitals in these atoms, but in the other members of the series the promotion of more than one $5f$ electron in this way to take part in bonding is much more difficult because of the greater nuclear changes and decreasing ionic radii. In aqueous solution, Am, Cm, and higher members are very stable in the trivalent state. The ability of berkelium to exist as Bk(IV) arises in the following way: Bk(III) has eight electrons spread over the seven $5f$ orbitals, so that the energy needed to promote one of these electrons to a $6d$ orbital, leaving seven electrons in the $5f$ orbitals, is partly offset by the resulting gain in exchange energy which arises from the special stability of the half-filled f-electron shell. (Compare the five $3d$ electrons in Fe^{3+} and the seven $4f$ electrons in Tb^{4+}.) A similar explanation would account for the possible existence of Cf(V), and also for the fact that f–f transitions in the f^7 atoms gadolinium and curium require more energy, and hence lie at shorter wavelengths, than other members of the series.

The intense radioactivity of most of these elements presents difficulties in elucidating their chemistry, partly manipulative and partly arising from self-irradiation. The trivalent cations can be coprecipitated with LaF_3, $La(OH)_3$, CeF_3, and $LaK(SO_4)_2$, and americium can then be separated by persulfate oxidation to Am(VI), followed by extraction from $6M$ HNO_3 by hexone, or from $1M$ HNO_3 + saturated NH_4NO_3 by diethyl ether.

In general, separation of the trivalent actinides is based on cation exchange followed by fractional elution, on anion exchange, and on liquid-liquid exchanges. For example, the neutral tris thenoyltrifluoroacetone complexes of Np(III) and Pu(III) are extracted from moderately acid solution with xylene, whereas the complex with Am(III) is extracted at pH 4 or in less acid solutions.[4] Similarly, Am(III) can be extracted into 30% tributyl phosphate from low-acid, aluminium nitrate-salted solutions.

Cm(III), but not Am(III), is extracted from $16M$ HNO_3 by tributyl phosphate. A cation-exchange column adsorbs Am(III) from $0.05M$ HCl, which can then be eluted with ammonium α-hydroxyisobutyrate.[5] Conversely, Am(III) in $20M$ lithium chloride forms an anionic complex which can be adsorbed on an anion-exchange resin and then eluted with $8M$ HNO_3.[6]

The quantitative prediction of these properties is handicapped for two reasons. There is an almost complete lack of stability constant data; in addition, the necessary ligand-field treatment (similar to that for the transition metal ions) has not been developed for the actinide and lanthanide series. This, in turn, presupposes some knowledge of the stereochemistry of these cations in their complexes. By analogy with the transition metal ions, stability constants might be expected to increase from Np(III) to Pu(III) or Am(III), passing through a minimum at Cm(III) and increasing to another maximum at Mv(III) or No(III). Published stability constants for EDTA chelates increase from Pu(III) ($10^{16.0}$), through Am(III) ($10^{18.2}$) and Cm($10^{18.4}$) to Cf($10^{19.1}$), showing no minimum, but this may be a consequence of the low ligand-field strength of the EDTA anion. Qualitatively, chelating agents known to complex the actinides are mainly those binding through oxygen atoms, such as citrate, tartrate, lactate, glycolate, α-hydroxyisobutyrate, thenoyltrifluoroacetone and EDTA, all of which also have weak ligand fields.

Colorimetric reagents for these cations have not been developed. Methods of determination are based mainly on radiochemical techniques and on the rather weak color of some of the metal ions themselves.

Antimony

Antimony is more basic than arsenic, although Sb_2O_3 dissolves in alkaline solutions to form antimonate (V) ion. Because of the "inert-pair" character of its $5s^2$ electrons, Sb is usually trivalent. Salts, mostly of the antimonyl ion SbO^+, but also of Sb^{3+}, are known.

The electronic configuration of Sb ($[Kr]4d^{10}5s^25p^3$) favors covalent bonding, so that Sb_2S_3 precipitates from acid solutions on passage of hydrogen sulfide. (If only small concentrations of Sb(III) are present, copper sulfide can be used as a collector.) However, Sb^{3+} readily forms complexes with oxygen-containing ligands to give anions such as $[Sb(SO_4)_2]^-$, $[Sb(C_2O_4)_2]^-$, and $[Sb(OH)_2C_4H_4O_6]^-$ (antimonyl tartrate ion), and (in neutral or slightly acid solutions) neutral molecules such as (CLXXVI).

The sparing solubility of the antimony-pyrogallol complex is probably the result of polynuclear complex formation, arising from the ability of the hydroxyl group not bonded as in (CLXXVI) to coordinate to another antimony atom. (Structures that involve the linking of the three oxygen atoms of pyrogallol to the same antimony atom are sterically impossible.) Bismuth forms similar neutral species.

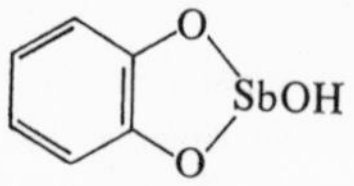

CLXXVI

In the presence of a strong oxidizing agent such as Ce(IV), in very strong hydrochloric acid, Sb(V) forms an anionic complex which is strongly adsorbed by anion-exchange resins, permitting separations from metals such as Pb. This chloroantimonate ion forms water-insoluble, organic-solvent-extractable ion pairs with large bases such as methyl violet, rhodamine B, brilliant green, and anthraquinone-1-azo-4-dimethylaniline. The iodoantimonite ion reacts similarly with pyridinium and triphenyl-methylarsonium ions. These ion pairs are used in colorimetric determinations.

The neutral antimony (V) chloro complex is extractable by oxygen-containing solvents from strong hydrochloric acid (for example, isopropyl ether from $6.5–8.5M$ HCl). Under the same conditions Sb(III) is only slightly extracted. The Sb(V) and Sb(III) bromo complexes in $4.5M$ HBr resemble the chloro complexes in their extraction behavior. On the other hand, Sb(III) is quantitatively extracted from $6.9M$ HI by ethyl ether as a strongly yellow-colored iodoantimonite ion. SbI_3 can also be extracted by benzene from $5M$ H_2SO_4 containing about $0.01M$ iodide and a reducing agent.

Arsenic

Arsenic has valencies of III and V, but III is more stable. Bonding is covalent, as is shown by reduction of arsenic compounds by zinc in hydrochloric or sulfuric acid to give the gas arsine, AsH_3; this reaction serves as the basis of the Gutzeit method for arsenic. Similarly, $AsCl_3$ is covalent and can be either extracted by carbon tetrachloride or distilled from strong hydrochloric acid solutions in the presence of reducing agents. $AsBr_3$ is largely extracted from $4.5M$ HBr by ethyl ether; it can be distilled from concentrated HBr. $AsBr_5$ is also volatile. It is doubtful if the ion As^{3+} exists in aqueous solution.

Arsenic bonds strongly to sulfur, so that As_2S_3 and As_2S_5 can be precipitated by hydrogen sulfide from acid solutions of As(III) and As(V).

So, too, it forms strong complexes in mineral acid with diethylammonium diethyldithiocarbamate and with potassium ethyl xanthate. These complexes are extractable into chloroform. In the arsenic trioxide molecule, As_4O_6, the oxygen atoms are tetrahedrally disposed around the arsenic atoms. Solution in water gives the weak acid, arsenious acid, and arsenites, which are readily oxidized. Arsenic pentoxide, prepared indirectly, is an oxidizing agent and is very soluble in water to give arsenic acid.

There does not at present appear to be a good organic reagent for arsenic, the usual methods of determination being based on the arsenic mirror and the molybdenum blue methods. (The latter method involves the formation of a heteropoly molybdiarsenate which, on reduction with hydrazine sulfate or stannous chloride, gives a strongly colored, blue complex.) Traces of arsenic can be "collected" from solution using ferric hydroxide or, in acid solution, by reduction to the element on solid mercurous chloride.

Astatine

The longest-lived isotope of astatine has a half life of only 8.3 hours, so that knowledge of its chemistry is based entirely on tracer studies. Its properties appear to resemble iodine and to be very similar to those expected by extrapolation from the halogens.

Barium

See *calcium*.

Beryllium

The small size of Be^{2+} enables it to fit into the cavity left inside four molecules of water when they are hydrogen bonded to form a tetrahedral unit. Strong ion-dipole interactions thus hold together the hydrated beryllium ion, which readily loses one or more protons to form polynuclear complexes with oxo (Be—O—Be) and hydroxo (Be—OH—Be) bridges. Beryllium hydroxide is precipitated on addition of ammonia (aluminium or ferric salts can be used as collectors) but in alkaline solutions anionic beryllate species are produced.

Because of its small size, and hence its high charge-to-radius ratio, Be^{2+} has a much greater tendency to form at least partially covalent bonds than Mg^{2+}, Ca^{2+}, Sr^{2+}, or Ba^{2+}. This covalent bonding requires unpairing of the two $2s$ electrons to give linear sp hybrid orbitals and a coordination number of 2. The preferred coordination number is 4, however, and it is achieved either by polymerization through μ bridging or by accepting electrons from electron donors to give structures approximating to tetrahedral. The bis(acetylacetone) beryllium complex is an example of the latter, and the anhydrous beryllium halides $(BeX_2)_n$, (X = F, Cl, Br) are examples of the former.

Oxygen is a stronger donor to beryllium than is nitrogen, so that most of the reagents used in colorimetric and fluorimetric methods for Be are typified by morin, substituted hydroxyanthraquinone, and aurintricarboxylic acid ("aluminon"). Similarly, the acetylacetone chelate is stable and extractable by benzene, but there is much less complex-forming tendency with reagents such as cupferron and 8-hydroxyquinoline. Nevertheless, 8-hydroxyquinaldine forms a chloroform-soluble bis complex with Be which can be used to determine Be in the presence of Al, and a number of reagents having the —N=N—(o-aryl)OH group, including thoron and p-nitrobenzene-azoorcinol, have also been proposed for colorimetric determinations of Be. Selectivity of the analytical procedures can be improved by prior separation of Be, either as the hydroxide or, at pH 4.4, as the phosphate (using ferric or aluminium phosphates as collectors).

Bismuth

Bismuth forms two series of trivalent salts, derived from the ions BiO^+ and Bi^{3+}. Of these, the bismuthyl salts are generally insoluble in water, and Bi^{3+} has a strong tendency to covalent-bond formation with polarizable ligands such as those containing sulfur and nitrogen. The $6s^2$ inert pair of electrons greatly reduces any stabilization by back-double-bonding, so that complex formation by a ligand such as cyanide ion is less strong than it is with, say, cuprous ion. Typical reagents for bismuth are dithizone, cupferron, and diethyldithiocarbamate. Thus, Bi is extractable by dithizone in CCl_4 from neutral solutions containing citrate, by cupferron in chloroform from $0.1M$ nitric acid, and by diethyldithiocarbamate in CCl_4 at pH 11–12. Thiourea and thiocyanate ion also form colored complexes, in acid solution, with Bi. Oxygen-containing ligands, such as citrate and tartrate ions and EDTA, complex only weakly with Bi and can be used as masking reagents.

The oxide, Bi_2O_3, and hydroxide, $Bi(OH)_3$, of bismuth are basic, whereas the corresponding derivatives of As(III) and Sb(III) are amphoteric. This greater basicity leads to less tendency to anionic complex formation and to lower extractability into organic solvents. Nevertheless, both effects are still important. For example, BiI_3 is extracted by benzene from a bismuth solution $5M$ in H_2SO_4 and $0.01M$ in iodide ion. Yellow to orange iodobismuthous acid, $HBiI_4$, is extracted from acid solutions by oxygen-containing solvents such as amyl alcohol, or its brucine salt can be extracted into chloroform. Chloride and fluoride ions interefere in in these reactions by competitive formation of chloro and fluoro complexes. Similarly, Bi forms anionic complexes in HCl solutions which can be adsorbed on anion-exchange resins.

In dilute mineral acid solutions, Bi^{3+} can be precipitated as the phosphate or the sulfide. (The latter can be "collected" with copper sulfide or possibly cadmium sulfide.) Alternatively, $Bi(OH)_3$ can be precipitated at pH 9 with ammonia, and collected on aluminium or ferric hydroxides.

Boron

Boron compounds have predominantly covalent bonds and resemble similar compounds of other nonmetals, notably silicon, in their properties and reactions. Monomeric, three-covalent boron compounds involve sp^2 hybridization to give planar structures which, in the halides, are partially stabilized by further bonding from filled p_π orbitals on the halogens into the vacant p_π orbital of boron. This π bonding follows the sequence $BF_3 \gg BCl_3 > BBr_3$. The electron deficiency of BX_3 compounds makes them strong electron acceptors, so that such substances as amines, phosphines, ethers, and sulfides are able to coordinate to the boron atom, with the formation of tetrahedral 1:1 complexes. Coordination is strongest with BBr_3 and least with BF_3, as expected if π-bonding differences are more important than steric or electronegativity effects.

Boron shows a great affinity for oxygen, forming boron oxides, boric acid, and borates, which can have cyclic or linear polynuclear structures because of oxo (B—O—B) bridging. Borate esters, $B(OR)_3$, of the lower alcohols are volatile and are used in separating boron from other elements. The tetraphenylborate ion finds application in gravimetric determinations of alkali metal ions. Boron forms stable tetrahedral complexes with

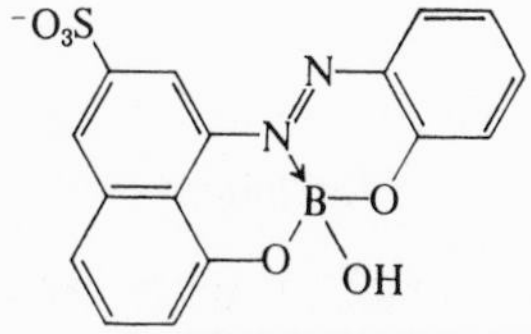

CLXXVII

organic oxyanions. Examples include the bis complexes with salicylate ion and pyrocatechol. As discussed in Chapter 11, complex formation with oxygen-containing ligands is important in the titration and the colorimetric determination of boric acid and borate ion. The reagent, azomethine H, that has been suggested for use in the colorimetric determination of boron[7] exploits both the strong bonding of boron to oxygen and the donor property of nitrogen atoms to form the yellow chelate complex (CLXXVII).

Bromine

Bromine completes its outermost octet of electrons by accepting one electron to give either a covalently bonded bromine or a bromide ion. Even when its compounds are nominally ionic, bromine forms bonds having greater covalent character than similar ones involving chlorine: This is because the greater size of Br^- makes it more readily polarizable. In bromides of metal ions which have a filled, or almost-filled, d shell, the vacant d orbitals of bromine are also more readily accessible for back-bonding. Pairs of electrons on bromine have a strong donor character. These two properties account for the tendency of bromine to act as a "bridge" in polynuclear complex formation, leading to the insolubility of many bromides, particularly those of d-filled, univalent cations that form two-coordinate complexes, such as Cu, Ag, Au, Hg, Tl, BiO, and SbO. Platinum (II) and palladium (II) bromides are also insoluble. The only important oxyanions of bromine are BrO^- and BrO_3^-. The former is obtained when bromine is dissolved in water. It is unstable, rapidly disproportionating into bromate and bromide ions. Oxidizing agents, such as hypochlorite ion in weak acid, oxidize bromide ion to bromate.

Estimations of bromine species commonly involve gravimetric determination as silver bromide, the insolubility of which also serves as the basis of most of the titrimetric methods. Some titration procedures depend on the nondissociation of mercuric bromide, using an indicator to detect the abrupt change in mercuric ion concentration at the endpoint. Colorimetric procedures, based on the effects of substitution of bromine with organic molecules, or its oxidizing power, are discussed in Chapters 11 and 12.

Cadmium

The bivalent cadmium ion Cd^{2+} is more basic than Zn^{2+}, to which it shows many similarities. However, Cd shows little tendency to form cadmate ions. The main differences between Cd and Zn arise from the greater radius of Cd^{2+}, so that it forms the weaker ionic, but the more stable covalent, complexes. Its electronic configuration, $[Kr]4d^{10}$, accounts for the "softness" of Cd^{2+} and its preference for ligands such as amines, cyanide, and sulfide ions, so that $Cd(OH)_2$, which is insoluble in solutions of alkalies, dissolves in strong ammonia to form an ammine complex.   Oxygen-containing anions such as citrate and tartrate bind Cd relatively weakly, so that dithizone (or di-β-naphthylthiocarbazone) in CCl_4 (or $CHCl_3$), which forms complexes through nitrogen and sulfur atoms, extracts Cd from alkaline solutions containing such species.   The Cd can be reextracted into the aqueous phase using $0.01M$ HCl.   The Cd complex of diethyldithiocarbamate can be extracted from alkaline solutions, and so, too, $CHCl_3$ extracts the Cd complex of 2-mercaptobenzothiazole from ammoniacal solution.   Conversely, Cd does not form a strong complex with cupferron, where bonding through oxygen would be involved.

The Cd halide complexes are considerably more stable than the corresponding zinc ones, and stability increases in the sequence $F < Cl < Br < I$. Cd halides are soluble in oxygen-containing solvents.   For example, an iodide complex of Cd is extracted from $6.9M$ HI by ethyl ether.   There is no ligand-field stabilization of cadmium complexes, which, when the ligand is an anion, tend to be tetrahedral, as in $CdBr_4^{2-}$, but otherwise are usually octahedral.   Thiocyanatocadmic acid is less readily extracted than the corresponding zinc complex, so that Zn can be separated from Cd in $0.6M$ HCl containing ammonium thiocyanate by extraction with amyl alcohol-ethyl ether.

The covalent character of its bonding enables cadmium sulfide to be precipitated in weakly acid solutions, and, if necessary, Cu, Hg(II), or Zn sulfides can be used as collectors.

Caesium

See *sodium*.

Calcium, Strontium, Barium, and Radium

All the bivalent cations in this series have the electronic configurations of inert gases.   Their chemical and physical properties vary systematically with increasing size, producing, for example, the differences in solubilities discussed in Chapter 9.   They are not significantly polarizable, nor do they show any visible or ultraviolet absorption.   Nevertheless, the ready solubility of anhydrous calcium chloride and calcium nitrate, in alcohols, ether, acetone, and anhydrous carboxylic acids suggests that some covalent bonding may occur in calcium salts.   This explains why, although this group of cations shows a preference for oxygen-containing anionic ligands such as those of rhodizonic acid, murexide, and o-cresolphthalein complexone, calcium (and magnesium) can also be determined spectrophotometrically with reagents containing unsaturated nitrogen groups as well as phenolic oxygens. Examples include eriochrome black T and 8-hydroxyquinoline. In all cases, irrespective of the type of ligand, the methods depend on spectral shifts produced in the ligand absorption spectra by the cations. Except for calcium with calcichrome (Chapter 6), most of these reagents are nonselective and prior separations are necessary.

These separations have included precipitation of calcium as its oxalate (magnesium also precipitates), its phosphate, its molybdate, or, in traces, as its oxinate with oxine as a collector. Barium has been precipitated as the sulfate or the chromate. The latter also serves as a collector for radium. Better separations should be possible using fractionations on ion-exchange columns; alternatively, mixtures of these cations should be separately determinable by careful titration using EDTA.

Cerium

See *lanthanum*.

Chlorine

By acquiring an electron, chlorine completes its outer electron shell and attains the electronic configuration of the inert gas, argon. This may be achieved by anion formation or by covalent bonding as in $TiCl_4$. The $3s$ and $3p$ electrons are then available for donation towards electron-deficient species, while it is also possible that some back-donation of electrons may also occur into the vacant $3d$ orbitals of chlorine, so that chloride ion readily forms chloro complexes with many metal ions. This can also lead to "bridging" by chlorine atoms in metal complexes and the formation of polynuclear complexes, especially with metals having filled or almost-filled d orbitals. This behavior is similar to, but less marked than, that shown by bromine, so that the chlorides of the monovalent ions of Ag, Cu, Hg, BiO, and SbO are not quite as insoluble as the bromides.

In the oxyanions ClO^-, ClO_2^-, ClO_3^-, and ClO_4^-, bonding can be thought of as involving electron donation from chlorine to oxygen, together with some back-bonding of the p_π electrons of the oxygens into the vacant d_π orbitals of the chlorine. There is very little tendency for perchlorate ion to form complexes with cations.

Chromium

The relative ease with which chromium can be inter-converted among the II, III, and VI oxidation states greatly simplifies the chemical separation of chromium from any potentially interfering species. For example, oxidation of Cr(III) to Cr(VI) in sodium hydroxide solution using hydrogen peroxide or bromine, followed by filtration, removes many metals. Further separation can be achieved (for example from Al and U) if the Cr(VI) is then reduced in a sodium hydroxide-sodium carbonate solution to give insoluble $Cr(OH)_3$ which, if only small amounts are present, can be collected using ferric iron.

Cr(VI) species include CrO_3, CrO_4^{2-}, and $Cr_2O_7^{2-}$, all of which have strong oxidizing properties, and the volatile CrO_2Cl_2. In alkaline solution the ultraviolet absorption of CrO_4^{2-} at 366 mμ serves for the direct determination of Cr. The most sensitive reaction for determining Cr is one between s-diphenylcarbazide and Cr(VI) in acid solution, but the nature of the resulting violet cation, which is extractable into organic solvents, is unknown. It is possibly a Cr(III)-diphenylcarbazone compound.

Except in Cr(VI) derivatives, which are tetrahedral, most Cr complexes have octahedral structures (which, in Cr(II), are distorted by a Jahn-Teller effect). Cr(II) (d^4) compounds are prepared by electrolytic or zinc reduction of Cr(III). They are readily oxidized, e.g. by air, back to Cr(III). Ligand-field stabilization effects favor complex formation with ligands such as α,α'-bipyridine, ethylenediamine, thiocyanate, and cyanide ion.

Cr(III) complexes are numerous and are distinguished for their chemical inertness (d^3 systems), so that different species such as $[Cr(H_2O)_6]Br_3$ and $[Cr(H_2O)_4Br_2]Br \cdot 2H_2O$ can be obtained. The hydrated Cr(III) oxide is amphoteric, giving $Cr(H_2O)_6^{3+}$ in acid solutions, and chromites (probably $Cr(OH)_6^{3-}$) in alkaline ones. Cr(III) complexes also readily exist in polynuclear forms which may be bridged through hydroxo and oxo groups. Like Cr(II), the most stable Cr (III) complexes are those formed with nitrogen- and sulfur-containing ligands. However, they have, to date, found little application in analysis.

Cobalt

Cobalt forms two series of salts and complexes, derived from Co(II) and Co(III). Whereas Co(II) is the stable state for salts, Co(III) exists mainly in low-spin, octahedral complexes, especially those with nitrogen donor atoms, although for electrostatic reasons anionic ligands also bond strongly to Co^{3+}. Thus, the tris complex of 2-nitroso-1-naphthol with Co(III) is stable because the metal-ligand bonds involve both a nitrogen donor atom and an anionic oxygen. Ligands with high ligand-field strengths favor Co(III) because of the large stabilization associated with a low-spin d^6 electronic configuration, so that Co(II) complexes readily oxidize to Co(III).

A low-spin d^6 configuration confers kinetic inertness on complexes; hence, once a species such as the tris complex of 2-nitroso-1-naphthol with Co(III) has been formed in weakly acid solution and extracted into an organic solvent such as chloroform, it is not readily dissociated even on shaking with strong hydrochloric acid. Under the same conditions most metals pass from the organic into the aqueous phase. Other polarizable ligands that have been suggested for the determination of Co(III) include diethyldithiocarbamate and di-1-naphthylketone monoxime, which forms tris complexes extractable into organic solvents, dimethylglyoxime, α,α',α''-terpyridyl, and a number of nitrosophenol derivatives containing the grouping

$$\underset{\displaystyle =\!\!\!\overset{\textstyle |}{C}\!\!-\!\!\overset{\textstyle |}{C}\!\!=}{\overset{\displaystyle \text{NO} \quad \text{OH}}{}}$$

including nitroso-R-salt which forms a water-soluble Co complex.

Cobalt (II) compounds can have square planar, tetrahedral, or octahedral stereochemistry. Tetrahedral species include the ions CoX_4^{2-} and $[CoX_3(H_2O)]^-$, where X = Cl, Br, I, SCN. The blue complex $(NH_4)_2Co(SCN)_4$ is extracted by oxygen-containing solvents from strong ammonium thiocyanate solutions buffered to about pH 3.5. This reaction separates Co from Ni. Alternatively, in the presence of large cations such as tetraphenylarsonium and triphenylmethylarsonium the cobaltothiocyanate ion can be extracted into chloroform. The anionic chloro complex of cobalt in strong hydrochloric acid can be separated by adsorption on to an anion-exchange column.

Copper

Copper forms two series of salts and complexes. Cu(I) complexes are usually linear or tetrahedral, depending on the nature of the ligand, whereas Cu(II) complexes are often square planar or distorted octahedral, the distortion being a consequence of the Jahn-Teller effect. Oxidation-reduction equilibria in copper (I) and (II) solutions are complicated by the ease of dismutation of Cu(I) into Cu(0) and Cu(II), so that Cu(I) complexes are usually formed only if they are insoluble (e.g. CuCN, CuI) or if the metal-ligand bond is largely covalent in character and steric considerations are favorable. The low charge on Cu^+, and its $3d^{10}$ electronic structure, lead to Cu(I) forming its most stable complexes with highly polarizable ligands, especially where back-double-bonding is possible. Common examples used in colorimetric methods include derivatives of α,α'-bipyridine and of 1,10-phenanthroline.

The common valence state for Cu is II, and Cu(II) forms many stable complexes. Its $3d^9$ configuration makes Cu^{2+} readily deformable, so that it bonds strongly to sulfur-containing anions such as diethyldithiocarbamate, and those of potassium ethyl xanthate, rubeanic acid, and dithizone, to give complexes soluble in organic solvents. Stabilities of complexes of the bivalent transition metals lie in the sequence Mn < Fe < Co < Ni < Cu > Zn, and differences are greatest with highly polarizable ligands, so that separation of Cu from other metals in the series is facilitated. For example, Cu can be extracted by dithizone in CCl_4 from 0.1–1N mineral acid solutions whereas, under the same conditions, most other metals are not significantly complexed by the reagent. Copper (II) also forms complexes with oxygen-containing ligands, especially in alkaline solution, and these are often polynuclear. Fehling's solution is a familiar example.

The tendency of Cu(II) towards covalent-bond formation is shown by the formation of insoluble copper sulfide when hydrogen sulfide is passed into a Cu(II) solution in dilute acid. (This reaction is applied in separations, and, if necessary, PbS is used as a collector.) Also, in strong hydrochloric and hydrobromic acids Cu(II) forms colored chloro and bromo complexes. In the presence of organic bases or of large organic cations, Cu(II) gives solvent-extractable thiocyanato complexes.

Fluorine

The F—F bond in the fluorine molecule is weaker than similar bonds for other halogens because its shorter length leads to greater repulsions between nonbonding electrons which, in the other halogens, are also partly reduced by the use of vacant outer d orbitals. Fluorine is the most electronegative and the most reactive of all the elements. Its analytical chemistry is concerned almost entirely with fluoride ion and hydrogen fluoride. In general, because fluoride ions are smaller than the other halide ions, fluorides have appreciably greater ionic character, so that bonding to Groups IA and IIA cations shows $F^- > Cl^- > Br^- > I^-$, whereas with more polarizable cations such as Zn^{2+}, Cd^{2+}, and Hg^{2+} the order is reversed. Fluorides show much less tendency than oxygen- or nitrogen-containing ligands to act as electron donors. It is not certain whether hydrogen bonding in the bifluoride ion $[FHF]^-$ should be regarded as an example; possibly it should be explained in terms of strong electrostatic interactions or of three-center bonds formed from two fluorine σ orbitals and the hydrogen $1s$ orbital, with two of the electrons in a bonding orbital and the other two in a nonbonding orbital. The formation of strong or insoluble fluoride complexes, leading to dissociation of metal complexes with chromophoric inorganic and organic groups, is the basis of almost all of the colorimetric, fluorometric, potentiometric, and volumetric methods for determining fluoride. The volatility of fluorosilicic acid, H_2SiF_6, is important as a means of separating fluoride ion from interfering species.

Gallium

The ion Ga^{3+} differs from Al^{3+} in its chemical properties mainly by its larger size and, more particularly, because it has ten outermost electrons filling the $3d$ orbitals. Like Al(III), Ga(III) is amphoteric, giving rise in alkaline solutions to anionic hydroxy complexes, and in neutral or weakly acid solutions its salts are extensively hydrolyzed. Gallium forms mainly octahedral complexes, but some tetrahedral complexes are known, including $GaCl_4^-$ and addition complexes formed by neutral donors with GaX_3. The free chlorogallic acid, $HGaCl_4$, is extracted from $6M$ hydrochloric acid by ethyl or isopropyl ether; under the same conditions its colored and fluorescent ion pair with rhodamine B is extractable into a 3:1 mixture of chlorobenzene and carbon tetrachloride. Similarly, a Ga thiocyanate complex is extracted by ethyl ether from a Ga solution $7M$ in ammonium thiocyanate and $0.5M$ in hydrochloric acid.

Because of its high charge, Ga^{3+} forms its most stable complexes with anionic ligands, especially those containing oxygen. Examples include the water-soluble tris cupferron complex, a lake with quinalizarin, and a complex with aluminon. Anionic ligands which form chelate rings through neutral nitrogen atoms also bind Ga, but less strongly. Thus the 8-hydroxyquinolinate anion gives a yellow fluorescent, chloroform-extractable, tris complex with Ga. The method is more sensitive, and the complex is more stable, if 5,7-dibromo-8-hydroxyquinoline is used instead of 8-hydroxyquinoline. In the same way, Ga forms colored fluorescent complexes with eriochrome red and black.

Traces of Ga in a solution can be collected by precipitation in the presence of aluminium hydroxide.

Germanium

Germanium dioxide is weakly acidic, and even more weakly basic. Thus, meta- and orthogermanates, analogous to the corresponding silicates, are known, and covalent $GeCl_4$ is formed in strong hydrochloric acid. $GeCl_4$ (boiling point 86°) can be distilled from $6M$ hydrochloric acid, or from a sulfuric acid-hydrochloric acid mixture, or it can be extracted from 8–9M hydrochloric acid into carbon tetrachloride or other nonpolar solvents. It is rapidly hydrolyzed by water. In ammoniacal or weakly alkaline solutions, Ge is quantitatively coprecipitated with ferric and aluminium hydroxides.

Ge, like Sn(IV) and Zr, forms slightly soluble, colored complexes with suitable oxygen-bonding ligands such as quinalizarin, 2,3,7-trihydroxy-9-phenyl-6-fluorone, and its 9-(4-dimethylaminophenyl) analog, all of which are o-diphenols. The reactions with the last two reagents are carried out in $1M$ hydrochloric acid and probably result in an octahedral bis complex of the type $Ge(OH)_2L_2$, which can be extracted into carbon tetrachloride.

Gold

In aqueous solution, the simple cation Au^+ undergoes a dismutation into Au and Au(III), so that Au(I) species are stable only in complexes, such as $Au(CN)_2^-$ and $AuCl_2^-$, or in very insoluble substances such as AuCN and AuI which precipitate from Au(III) solutions when cyanide or iodide ions are added. The slightly soluble red complex formed by gold in slightly acid solution with p-dimethylaminobenzylidene-rhodanine is probably also an Au(I) complex in which bonding is through the ring nitrogen atom. It can be extracted into benzene-chloroform mixture. Au^+ has a d^{10} electronic configuration and a preference for linear complexes. Complex formation is greatly favored with polarizable ligands, especially where back-bonding can occur.

Au(III) exists mainly as complexes that are powerful oxidizing agents, so that gold can be estimated indirectly by measuring the extent to which Au(III) oxidizes organic species such as o-tolidine, leuco-malachite green, and o-dianisidine. Conversely, Au(III) solutions are readily reduced to the free metal, so that gold can be separated, for example, by shaking with solid Hg_2Cl_2. Alternatively, stannous chloride can be used as reductant in the presence of tellurium tetrachloride which is reduced to Te, the latter, in turn, serving as a collector for gold. Au(III) forms well-defined complexes with the halide ions. $HAuCl_4$ can be extracted from upwards of $0.3M$ hydrochloric acid solutions by oxygen-containing solvents such as ethyl acetate. Its colored ion pair with rhodamine B can be extracted by isopropyl ether or benzene. Similarly, orange-colored bromoauric acid can be extracted from HBr, and $HAuI_4$ from $6.9M$ HI. Ethyl ether also extracts $HAu(NO_3)_4$ from $8M$ nitric acid. Au(III) has a strong tendency to covalent-bond formation, and forms a tris complex with dithizone in $0.5N$ sulfuric acid.

Hafnium

Hafnium and zirconium are almost identical in their atomic and ionic radii. They are also closely similar in their chemistry, as would be expected from their similar electronic configurations. For the tetra-valent ions these are Zr, [Kr], and Hf, $[Xe]4f^{14}$. In hafnium the $4f$ electrons lie too deeply in the ion to exert significant chemical effects. Chemical methods for the determination of zirconium also determine hafnium, except that zirconium and hafnium give different colors with rufigallic acid in strong hydrochloric acid solution. This may be due, in part, to the fact that hafnium is slightly more basic than zirconium.

In theory, it may be possible to devise analytical methods for separating hafnium and zirconium, based on techniques such as fractional crystalliza-tion, fractional precipitation, distillation, ion exchange, or solvent ex-traction. In recent practice, however, physical methods of determination, such as arc or spark emission or x-ray spectra, appear to have been pre-ferable.

Indium

Indium (III) differs from Ga(III) and Al(III) because its oxide and hydroxide are not amphoteric. Like these metals, however, its salts are extensively hydrolyzed in solution, and like Ga it forms well-defined complexes with halide ions. On the other hand, extraction conditions are different. Thus Ga, but not In, is extracted from $6M$ HCl by ethyl ether, where In (mainly as $HInBr_4$), but not Ga, is extracted when a solution $3M$ in HBr is shaken several times with ethyl ether. Similarly, the iodo complex can be extracted from $0.5–2M$ HI (or from KI and H_2SO_4). Indium can be adsorbed as its chloro complex on an anion-exchange resin from $4–5M$ HCl, and eluted using $0.1M$ HCl. Formation of colored ion pairs between these anionic complexes and an organic cation such as rhodamine B would be expected to be a useful reaction for determining In, but this does not seem to have been investigated.

Indium (III) forms octahedral complexes, particularly with anionic ligands. It has a moderate tendency to covalent-bond formation because of its $4d^{10}$ electronic configuration. Thus, it forms an insoluble sulfide in weakly acid solutions, gives a yellow, chloroform-extractable tris complex with 8-hydroxyquinoline in the pH range 3.2–4.5, and is extracted by dithizone in chloroform from weakly alkaline solution. Like the Ga complex, the In complex with 8-hydroxyquinoline is fluorescent. Indium forms complexes, but not of very great stability, with oxygen-containing anionic ligands such as citrate and tartrate.

Iodine

Its large size and small charge make I^- easily polarizable, so that iodide ion readily forms covalent bonds. Where metal-halide bonds are largely covalent this leads to the stability sequence I > Br > Cl > F; in essentially ionic complexes the order is reversed.   In alkaline solutions iodine rapidly disproportionates, through the unstable IO^-, into iodate and iodide ions.   Iodine also gives rise to periodic acid and periodates, which are powerful oxidizing agents.   Periodates, derived from H_5IO_6, show many resemblances to tellurates derived from H_6TeO_6.

Iridium

Although Ir also forms higher-valent fluoro complexes, its chemistry is mainly concerned with oxidation states III and IV, which are represented by many octahedral complexes.   In its cationic, neutral, and anionic complexes Ir(III) resembles Rh(III), but this valence state finds little analytical application.

Ir(IV) is represented by $IrO_2(H_2O)_x$, which is precipitated by neutralizing an acid solution containing bromate (as oxidizing agent) with sodium bicarbonate, and by the complexes IrX_6^{2-} (X = F, Cl, Br).   Although Ir(IV) is a d^5 system, these complexes are low-spin and, like cationic and neutral Ir(III) complexes (but unlike anionic Ir(III) complexes) they are kinetically inert.   This low-spin state confers considerable ligand-field stabilization on their octahedral complexes with amines.

Adsorption of Ir(IV) complexes on anion-exchange resins can be used to secure separations from other metals.   The brown tetraphenylphosphonium chloroiridate can be extracted from dilute hydrochloric acid using chloroform.   Alternatively, the oxidizing power of Ir(IV) can be used for indirect determinations based on the oxidation of suitable organic substances such as p-nitrosodimethylaniline, o-anisidine, benzidine, leuco-crystal violet and leuco-malachite green to give colored products.

Iron

The usual valence states for iron are II and III.   Iron is usually octahedral in its complexes, but it can also be tetrahedral, for example in $FeCl_4^-$ and $FeCl_4^{2-}$.   Many ferrous salts and complexes are known and, except where the complexes are formed by species which preferentially stabilize Fe(II), they are all more or less susceptible to aerial oxidation to Fe(III).   The spin states of Fe(II) and Fe(III) complexes have been discussed in Chapter 3, where it was pointed out that stable ferrous complexes are formed by ligands having sufficiently strong ligand fields to bring about electron pairing in the $3d$ orbitals.   This also confers kinetic inertness on the resulting complexes.   In practice, the choice of possible types of ligands is restricted essentially to those where bonding is through nitrogen atoms as in the analytically useful reagents based on 1,10-phenanthroline and α,α' bipyridine. Oxygen-containing anionic ligands (which form high-spin ferrous complexes) bind Fe(II) much less firmly, so that EDTA can be used as a masking reagent in the estimation of Fe(II) with, say, 1,10-phenanthroline. Anionic ligands such as those from nitroso-R-salt, isonitrosoacetophenone, and salicylaldoxime show, as expected, intermediate behavior, and it is possible that in some cases low-spin complexes are formed.

Fe(III) has appreciable covalent character, so that Fe_{aq}^{3+} is very readily hydrolyzed and hydroxo complexes exist in solutions of pH > 1. Anionic complexes are common, so that in hydrochloric acid solutions Fe(III) is adsorbed as a chloro complex on anion-exchange resins. More often, however, use is made of the extractability of chloroferric acid, $HFeCl_4$, from 5–7M HCl into methyl isobutyl ketone, ethyl ether, or some other oxygen-containing solvent. Similar behavior is shown by Fe(III) in 5M HBr solutions.

The charge-transfer absorption spectrum of Fe^{3+} with chloride ion is of limited use in determining Fe(III), but the analogous complexes with thiocyanate ion find much wider application. The stability constants of the thiocyanate complexes are small, so that high ligand concentrations are required, and a series of complexes differing progressively in their absorption maxima and intensity are formed, making standardization of conditions essential: Complex formation is enhanced by addition of acetone and other miscible solvents of low dielectric constant, or by extraction into oxygen-containing organic solvents. An anionic Fe(III) complex with thiocyanate ion can also be extracted as its ion pair with large organic cations such as triphenylmethylammonium and tributylammonium ions.

The favorable energy associated with the symmetrical, singly occupied d orbitals in the high-spin d^5 electronic configuration explains why Fe(III) is high-spin in almost all of its complexes. (The few exceptions include the low-spin, kinetically inert $Fe(CN)_6^{3-}$ and tris complexes with 1,10-phenanthroline and α,α'-bipyridine.) This is why Fe(III) is much less like other transition metal ions and why it forms its strongest complexes with anionic, rather than nitrogen-containing, ligands.

Thus, ligands used in colorimetric determination of Fe(III) may bind through two oxygen anions (as in pyrocatechol, tiron, and salicylic acid), through an oxygen and a sulfur anion (as in thioglycollic and sulfosalicylic acids), through an oxygen atom and an oxygen anion (as in acetylacetone and cupferron), or through a nitrogen atom and an oxygen anion (as in 8-hydroxyquinoline, ferron, and salicylaldoxime). Similarly, Fe(III) forms a very stable complex with EDTA, while citric, oxalic, and tartaric acid can be used to mask Fe(III) or maintain it in weakly acid or neutral solutions.   Fe(III) also forms complexes with fluoride and pyro-phosphate ions.

In the presence of ligands that stabilize Fe(II), ferric iron can also be determined by its oxidation of dimethyl-*p*-phenylenediamine to give a pink color.[8]

Lanthanum and the Rare Earth Elements

The La^{3+} ion has the electronic configuration of the inert gas Xe. The trivalent ions of the lanthanides from Ce to Lu differ significantly only in that the fourteen $4f$ electrons are successively added.   These electrons lie sufficiently deeply within the cations that they play little part in chemical bonding.   However, the increasing nuclear charge from La to Lu causes a progressive contraction of the atomic and ionic radii.   The latter decrease from 1.4 to 0.85 Å.   Hence, because the binding is largely ionic, the stability constants of complexes of the lanthanides increase from La to Lu.   For the same reason, the basicity of the hydroxides $M(OH)_3$ decreases from La to Lu.

Well-defined salts are formed with acids.   Of these, the oxalates are only slightly soluble in excess oxalic acid, and the fluorides are very sparing-ly soluble in the presence of hydrofluoric acid.

Complex formation is strongest with oxygen-containing anionic ligands such as citrate, tartrate, and thenoyltrifluoroacetonate ions, EDTA, and NTA.   The size of the hydrated ions increases from La^{3+} to Lu^{3+} (compare Cs^+ to Li^+), so that bonding to ion-exchange resins decreases in that order.   This serves as the basis of methods for separating rare earth elements which depend on adsorption onto a cation-exchange column, followed by careful elution using a suitable complexing species such as buffered citrate solution.   Alternatively, differences in extractability of complexes into organic solvents are sometimes used.   The rare earths can also be split into two main fractions based on differences in solubility of the double sulfate with sodium sulfate: Salts of the group La–Eu are only sparingly soluble in sodium sulfate, whereas Gd–Lu and Y are appreciably soluble.

Similarly, reagents for colorimetric determinations of rare earth elements are usually anions bonding through oxygen atoms.   Examples include sodium alizarin sulfonate, quinalizarin, sulfosalicylic acid, xylenol orange, pyrocatechol violet[9] and bromopyrogallol red.[10]   Also, although in principle they might be expected to be less suitable, some complexing agents have been proposed that depend on bonding through nitrogens as well as anionic oxygens.   This group includes arsenazo[11] and PAN,[12] which gives a red precipitate extractable into ethyl ether.

8-Hydroxyquinoline and its 5,7-dichloro derivative have also been used because their complexes can be extracted by chloroform.

In this series, the trivalent state is much the most common one, but di- and tetravalent ions can be formed in some cases, especially where the resulting electronic configuration is f^0, f^7, or f^{14}: The f^7 configuration confers additional stability because all the f orbitals are occupied singly by electrons. The tetravalent state is important only in Ce(IV) (f^0), which shows chemical resemblances to Zr(IV) and Hf(IV).

Oxidation of Ce(III) to Ce(IV) using peroxydisulfate, sodium bromate in $9M$ HNO, or other powerful oxidizing agent, followed by precipitation of its insoluble phosphate, hydroxide, or iodate, serves to separate Ce from the trivalent lanthanides. Ce(IV) in sulfuric acid can be estimated spectrophotometrically using its absorption maximum at 320 mμ. The oxidizing action of acid solutions of Ce(IV) on organic compounds which include anthranilic acid, benzidine, brucine, morphine, and sulfanilic acid also serves as the basis of (indirect) colorimetric methods. Ce(IV) is more covalent in character than the trivalent ions so that its salts are much more readily extracted into organic solvents. Thus $H_2Ce(NO_3)_6$ is extracted by ethyl ether or methyl isobutyl ketone from Ce(IV) solutions in $8M$ nitric acid. Similarly, the Ce(IV) complex with thenoyltrifluoro-acetonate ion is extracted by xylene from $1N$ H_2SO_4.

The most important of the bivalent series is Eu(II) (f^7), which can be obtained by reduction of Eu(III) solutions, electrolytically, or using Al, Mg, Fe, or Zn. Eu^{2+} resembles Ba^{2+} in its chemistry, differing from the other lanthanides in forming a soluble hydroxide and an insoluble phosphate and sulfate. It also sometimes occurs in Nature with the Group II minerals.

Lead

The very considerable inertness of the $6s^2$ electrons in Pb^{2+} makes the bivalent state in lead compounds much more stable than Pb(IV), so that species such as lead tetraacetate are powerful oxidizing agents. This fact can be made the basis of an indirect method for Pb by measuring the color produced when suitable organic reagents such as tetramethyl-diaminodiphenylmethane are oxidized by Pb(IV) species. Pb(IV) is much less amphoteric than Sn(IV), so that the plumbate anion $Pb(OH)_6^{2-}$ is formed only under strongly alkaline conditions.

The electronic configuration of Pb^{2+}, $[Xe]4f^{14}5d^{10}6s^2$, indicates that it is readily deformable, even though the $6s^2$ electrons reduce the extent of back-double-bonding between metal and ligand, and suggests that Pb(II) should form its most stable complexes with highly polarizable ligands.

This is found. Thus Pb(II) combines only weakly with cupferron in 0.01M nitric acid, and oxygen-containing anions such as citrate or tartrate can be present when lead is extracted as its dithizonate in chloroform or carbon tetrachloride from alkaline, aqueous solutions. Reduction of back-bonding and the absence of ligand-field stabilization in Pb(II) complexes explains why cyanide ion can be added to mask Cu (by forming Cu(I) cyanide complexes) without interfering in the dithizone extraction of Pb. In general, Pb(II) complexes are less stable than those of Cu(II), and its dithizonate is dissociated in dilute mineral acid solutions. Similarly, lead diethyldithiocarbamate, extracted by amyl alcohol-toluene from a pH 7 citrate buffer, is decomposed on shaking with 0.5M HCl. The lead complex of diethylammonium diethyldithiocarbamate can, however, be extracted from 1.5–2M HCl into chloroform.

Except for the nitrate and the acetate, most Pb(II) salts are insoluble in water so that separation from other metals is not difficult. Thus Pb can be precipitated from weakly acid solutions as the sulfide (using Cu, Fe, or Ag as collectors, if necessary), as the sulfate (with Sr as collector), or as the carbonate or phosphate (with Ca as collector).

Lithium

The small size of Li$^+$ and its inert-gas electronic configuration account for its more important chemical properties. Thus, its small size gives Li$^+$ more polarizing power than any of the other alkali ions, and greatly increases its tendency toward solvation and covalent-bond formation. This is why lithium chloride is soluble in organic solvents such as ethanol and ethyl ether. In basic solution Li$^+$ forms an ether-extractable chelate with dipivaloylmethane. It also gives a fairly stable chelate with uramildiacetic acid, but both are of only limited analytical application. In a strongly alkaline solution that is also 70% in acetone, Li$^+$ forms an orange complex with thoron (o-(2-hydroxy-3,6-disulfo-1-naphthylazo)-benzene-arsonic acid): The sensitivity of the reaction is high but the selectivity is very poor, and separation from most other cations is necessary. One possible method of achieving this is by cation-exchange resin, the order of preference for hydrated alkali cations being Li$^+$ < Na$^+$ < K$^+$ < Rb$^+$ < Cs$^+$. The reason for this order, which is contrary to intuitive expectations, is that Li$^+$ is the most strongly hydrated of the alkali metal ions, the extent of hydration decreasing steadily with increasing atomic number.

It appears unlikely that organic reagents will be found that are both sensitive and selective enough to be used satisfactorily for directly determining traces of Li. This leaves spectrographic, flame photometric, and indirect methods (such as the determination of Fe in a precipitate of the slightly soluble salt $LiKFeIO_6$) as the best ways by which to estimate Li.

Magnesium

The small ionic radius of Mg^{2+} and its double positive charge cause it to show a strong tendency to covalent-bond formation, although this is less so than for Be^{2+}. Thus, $MgBr_2$, MgI_2, and $Mg(ClO_4)_2$ are soluble in alcohols, ketones, and ethers, while magnesium alkyls and Grignard species form complexes with oxygen-containing donor molecules. Similarly, Mg^{2+} and to a lesser extent Ca^{2+} form rather weak complexes with ammonia and amines. Most magnesium salts are water soluble and usually crystallize from water as rather stable hydrates.

Mg^{2+} forms its most stable complexes with oxygen-containing anionic ligands, but its complex-forming ability is not very great. Hence many other metal ions that would otherwise interfere can be removed from Mg solutions by extraction or precipitation, by exploiting differences in their stability constants with "wide-spectrum" reagents such as diethyldithio-carbamate, 8-hydroxyquinoline, cupferron, and acetylacetone. In the absence of interfering cations, Mg can be determined in low concentrations by spectrophotometric measurements on its 8-hydroxyquinoline complex at 400 mμ. Between pH 10.5 and 13.6, the ion pair formed by butylamine with the tris(8-hydroxyquinoline) magnesium complex is extractable into chloroform. Alternatively, between pH 10 and 12 the bis complex can similarly be extracted if some butyl cellosolve is present to fill the remaining coordination sites in the (octahedral) Mg complex.

The tendency of Mg towards covalent-bond formation explains why in strongly alkaline solution (pH > 12) Mg^{2+}, or more probably $Mg(OH)_2$, is adsorbed on to a number of dyes containing azo groupings, to give colored "lakes." These dyes include titan yellow, brilliant yellow, 4-(p-nitrophenylazo)-resorcinol and -1-naphthol. Many metals interfere. Similar lake formation, but involving bonding through oxygen, occurs with quinalizarin, curcumin, and eriochrome cyanine R. It is likely that both types of bonding occur in the soluble Mg complex with eriochrome black T.

At higher concentrations, Mg^{2+} can be determined conveniently by complexometric titration. (See Chapter 6.)

Manganese

The main valence states for manganese are II, III, and VII. Mn^{2+} has a d^5 electronic configuration, so that the ion is spherically symmetrical, ordinarily lacks ligand-field stabilization in its complexes, and shows many resemblances to cations, particularly Mg^{2+}, that have the electronic structures of the inert gases. These considerations indicate that bonding by Mn(II) is mainly ionic, so that there is little tendency to form complexes with neutral ligands. Even with oxygen-containing anions the stability constants of Mn(II) complexes are quite low. Thus $0.1N$ mineral acid is sufficient to prevent the formation and chloroform extraction of the Mn(II) complex with cupferron, and the bis(8-hydroxyquinoline) Mn(II) complex requires a pH of about 9 for its extraction into chloroform. The few known low-spin Mn(II) complexes include $Mn(CN)_6^{4-}$, $[Mn(CN)_5NO]^{3-}$, and $Mn(CNR)_6^{2+}$, where RNC is an isonitrile. Mn^{2+} forms tetrahedral ions such as $MnCl_4^{2-}$ but in most of its complexes Mn is octahedral. Mn(II) is the most stable oxidation state in acid or neutral solutions.

Mn(III) compounds are known, but most of them are unstable in aqueous solution. Ligand-field stabilization is likely to be important only in low-spin complexes: $Mn(CN)_6^{3-}$, readily formed by aerial oxidation of the Mn(II) complex, is the only known example. The major factor determining the stability of Mn(III) complexes is probably an electrostatic one— the attraction between a trivalent cation and anionic ligands. Known Mn(III) complexes include the acetate, the hydrated fluoride, the tris(acetylacetone) complex, and the reddish-brown $Mn(CH_2NO)_3$ formed by manganese ions with formaldoxime in alkaline solutions. Also, the readily dissociable tris(diethyldithiocarbamate) Mn(III) complex is extracted from weakly acid solution by chloroform.

Most commonly, however, manganese is oxidized to Mn(VII), preceded, if necessary, by precipitation as $MnO_2(H_2O)_x$ from weakly alkaline solution using iron or magnesium as a collector. Manganese can be separated by distillation as permanganic acid.[13] Permanganate is obtained by oxidizing manganese species with periodate ion in hot nitric acid or sulfuric acid, or with persulfate ion in a boiling phosphoricnitric acid mixture containing a trace of silver. Permanganate can then be determined by direct optical measurement or, more sensitively, indirectly by the oxidation of substances such as benzidine, leuco-malachite green, o-tolidine or 4,4'-tetramethyldiaminotriphenylmethane to give colored products.

Mercury

The fact that the resistance of mercury metal to chemical attack, as shown also by its first two ionization potentials, is greater than for zinc or cadmium, can be ascribed to the chemical inertness of its pair of $6s$ electrons. This explains, for example, why mercury vapor is monatomic. In Hg^{2+} the electronic configuration $[Xe]4f^{14}5d^{10}$ makes for a much increased cation deformability and a much greater tendency towards covalent-bond formation. For example, ethyl ether readily extracts $HgBr_2$ from water and H_2HgI_4 from $6.9M$ HI. Similarly, Hg(II) forms an insoluble sulfide in acid solution. The ultraviolet absorption of the iodide complex in isoamyl alcohol and of the thiocyanate complex in water or butyl alcohol have been suggested as methods of determining Hg(II). Alkaloids such as strychnine form insoluble iodomercurates. In line with expectation, Hg(II) forms very stable complexes with highly polarizable ligands which provide opportunities for back-bonding. Reagents used in the colorimetric determination of Hg(II) include dithizone, its di-β-naphthyl analog, and diphenylcarbazone. Thus Hg(II) forms a very stable, orange-colored, photosensitive complex with dithizone, extractable by chloroform or carbon tetrachloride from $1N$ acid solutions. Alternatively, by using EDTA and thiocyanate ion as masking reagents, the reaction can be carried out in an acetate-buffered solution. As a check on the absorption measurements the Hg(II) dithizone complex in the organic solvent can later be readily dissociated by shaking with 6% KI in a buffer at pH 4: The stability constant of HgI_4^{2-} is approximately 10^{30}.

Formation of complexes by the mercurous ion, Hg_2^{2+}, may possibly be due to a mixing of d_{z^2} and s orbitals, with electron promotion, to form a linear complex such as O_3I—Hg—Hg—IO_3, in the same way that Orgel[14] has explained linear complex formation by Cu(I). In many cases, Hg_2^{2+} species probably owe their stability to their insolubility in water. The equilibrium, $Hg_2^{2+} \rightleftharpoons Hg + Hg^{2+}$, is readily displaced to the right by many covalent complex-forming species, with disproportionation of mercurous ion. Examples are cyanide and sulfide ions. Where bonding is more ionic, as in oxalate, succinate, and pyrophosphate, Hg_2^{2+} complexes are favored. Coordination of Hg_2^{2+} through sulfur and nitrogen is also important. Examples include the insoluble complexes with p-dimethylaminobenzylidenerhodanine, 4,4'-bis-(dimethylamino)thiobenzophenone, thiobenzophenone, and thiobenzamide, and the yellow dithizone complex which can be extracted from $1N$ acid.

Low concentrations of Hg can be separated from solution by precipitation as the sulfide, using Cd, Cu, or As as collectors, or by coprecipitation with tellurium in the presence of a strong reducing agent.

Molybdenum

Molybdenum derivatives exist in many stereochemistries and valence states. The more important valence states are III, IV, V, and VI. Mo(VI) is represented by the trioxide MoO_3, which dissolves in alkaline solutions to form molybdate ion, MoO_4^{2-}, distinguished from CrO_4^{2-} by having very little oxidizing ability. On acidification and standing, such solutions deposit "molybdic acid," $MoO_3 . 2H_2O$. However, less acid solutions undergo polymerization to yield isopolymolybdates, such as the para-molybdate ion $Mo_7O_{24}^{6-}$ formed at pH 6.

Acidification of molybdate solutions in the presence of oxyanions such as PO_4^{3-}, SiO_4^{4-}, and similar anions of As(V), Ge(IV), Ti(IV), Zr(IV), Ce(IV), Th(IV), Pt(IV), Mn(IV), Te(IV), I(VII), Co(III), Al(III), Cr(III), Fe(III), Rh(III), Ni(II), Co(II), Mn(II), Cu(II), Se(IV), P(III), and As(III) yields heteropolymolybdates which are extractable into oxygenated organic solvents. The acids are soluble in water, but their salts with large cations are insoluble. In these heteropoly anions each Mo is at the centre of an octahedron of six oxygen atoms which are also joined, singly or in pairs, to form tetrahedra or other structures containing the hetero atom.

In strong hydrochloric acid Mo(VI) forms chloro complexes such as MoO_2Cl_2 that can be extracted by oxygen-containing solvents and then readily taken back into water. Optimum extraction into ethyl ether is from $6M$ HCl, whereas $1–2M$ HCl is suitable if tributyl phosphate is used. The corresponding bromo complexes are only partly extracted from $6M$ HBr by ethyl ether.

In mineral acids, Mo(VI) reacts slowly with toluene-3,4-dithiol (the reaction is catalyzed by Fe(II)) to form the neutral, sparingly soluble dark green tris complex which is extractable into polar and nonpolar solvents. If the reaction is carried out in the presence of citric acid, tungsten does not interfere. It is likely that the ion MoO_2^{2+} is first formed and then, as sulfur atoms are coordinated to it, the oxygen atoms are progressively removed. The ion MoO_2^{2+} occurs in the bis(acetylacetone) complex, $MoO_2(acac)_2$, in $MoO_2F_4^{2-}$, and in MoO_2SO_4 which is made by dissolving MoO_3 in concentrated sulfuric acid. It is probably this Mo(VI) species that reacts with chelating agents in acid solutions. Its expected preference for oxygen-containing anionic ligands would explain the formation, under these conditions, of water-insoluble, chloroform-extractable complexes with α-benzoinoxine and cupferron. Similarly tiron, morin, chloranilic acid, quercetin, diethyldithiocarbamate, and thioglycollic acid have been suggested for use in the determination of molybdenum. Conversely, Mo(VI) does not form very stable complexes with reagents such as dithizone.

In the presence of Fe(II) or (III), in $1M$ HCl containing thiocyanate ion, stannous chloride reduces Mo(VI) to form a series of Mo(V) complexes, the most important of which is $MoO(SCN)_3$, which is the main species at high thiocyanate concentrations. This amber-colored complex can be stabilized by adding acetone to the solution, or by extracting it into oxygen-containing solvents such as isoamyl alcohol.   Alternatively, the related ion pair formed with tetraphenylarsonium ion can be extracted into chloroform.   In the absence of iron or copper, stannous chloride reduces Mo(VI) to Mo(IV), which then dismutes to Mo(III) and Mo(V).   Other Mo(V) complexes include MoF_6^-, $MoOX_5^{2-}$ (X = Cl, Br, CNS), and $MoOBr_4^-$. Neutralization precipitates $MoO(OH)_3$.

Lower-valent molybdenum complexes include the Mo(IV) species $Mo(CN)_8^{4-}$, and the Mo(III) anions MoX_6^{3-}, where X is halogen or pseudohalogen.   The Mo(III) complexes are strong reducing agents.

Insoluble molybdenum species include lead molybdate and molybdenum sulfide.   The latter may be gathered from solution using Cu or Sb(V), and the precipitate is uncontaminated by tungsten if tartaric acid is present.

Neptunium

In the gaseous state, the neptunium atom probably has the electron configuration $[Rn]5f^46s^26p^66d^17s^2$ or $[Rn]5f^56s^26p^67s^2$.   However, the difference in energy levels between $5f$ and $6d$ orbitals is small enough for $5f$ electrons to be promoted into $6d$ orbitals and take part in chemical bonding, so that Np(V) is the most stable oxidation state.   Thus Np(III) has two intense bands (molecular extinction coefficients = 2295, 1593) in the ultraviolet that are probably Laporte-allowed f–d transitions. These are much more intense than the very sharp absorption bands ($\epsilon \sim 10$–50) which arise in the visible from "forbidden" f–f transitions.[15] In the trivalent state, neptunium shows many resemblances to the lanthanides, whereas the tetravalent ion, Np^{4+}, is like Zr^{4+} and Th^{4+}.   Higher-valent neptunium is like uranium in forming oxoions NpO_2^+ and NpO_2^{2+}. This is nicely shown in the relation between the type of neptunium cation and the nature of the collector used in its coprecipitation. NpO_2^{2+} is precipitated with sodium uranyl acetate, whereas zirconium (IV) phosphate collects only Np^{4+}.   Similarly LaF_3, $Th(C_2O_4)_2$, and $LaK(SO_4)_2$ bring down Np^{3+} and Np^{4+} but not NpO_2^+ or NpO_2^{2+}.

Ease of interconversion of oxidation states facilitates separations through differences in ion exchange, complex formation, coprecipitation, and solvent extraction.   Stabilities of complexes lie in the sequence $Np^{4+} >$ $NpO_2^{2+} > Np^{3+} > NpO_2^+$.   In general accord with simple electrostatic predictions, the sequence for anions is $CO_3^{2-} > C_2O_4^{2-} >$ $SO_3^{2-} > SO_4^{2-} > F^- > NO_3^- > Cl^- > Br^- > I^- > ClO_4^-$.

Np(IV) readily forms anionic complexes so that, in the presence of reducing agents such as ferrous sulfamate and semicarbazide (which reduce Pu and higher transuranides to the trivalent state) Np(IV) is adsorbed from nitric and hydrochloric acid solutions onto a strong anion-exchange column from which it can later be displaced by ceric sulfate.[16] Similarly, using xylene, Np(IV) is extracted as neutral complexes with thenoyltrifluoroacetone from hydrochloric[17] and nitric[18] acids. Mono(2-ethylhexyl)orthophosphoric acid in toluene extracts Np(IV) from strong hydrochloric acid.[19] From acid solutions, neptunyl(VI) nitrate can be extracted into organic solvents as its tributylphosphate and hexone complexes. Extraction of neptunyl nitrate as the tetrapropyl ammonium nitrate complex into hexone, with subsequent extraction into thenoyltrifluoroacetone-acetone-xylene mixture has been suggested for the separation of neptunium from mixtures of uranium fission products.[20] In all cases, these complexes can be stripped from the organic phase by changing the valence state of the metal. The very stable Np(IV) complex with EDTA is not extractable from water.

As expected by analogy with thorium, Np(IV) forms a colored complex ($\epsilon \sim 15{,}000$) with thoron in solutions between pH 1 and 4. Arsenazo reacts under the same conditions ($\epsilon \sim 25{,}000$), but also gives colored complexes with Np(V) and Np(VI) in neutral solutions.[21] 1-Nitroso-2-naphthol at pH 9–10 gives a colored complex with Np(V) that extracts into isoamyl alcohol.[22] In general, however, neptunium is still usually determined by radiochemical techniques.

Nickel

The stable valence of nickel is II, but Ni(III) and Ni(IV) are known in a small number of complexes. The hydroxide $Ni(OH)_2$ is definitely basic and many Ni(II) salts are known. Ni(II) can form tetrahedral and octahedral complexes, as in $NiCl_4^{2-}$ and $Ni(H_2O)_6^{2+}$, $Ni(NH_3)_6^{2+}$, $Ni(bipy)_3^{2+}$, respectively, but especially where strong ligand fields are involved Ni(II) complexes are usually square planar in four-coordinate complexes. Where ligand fields are weak, as in oxygen-containing reagents such as acetylacetone, octahedral complexes are found. Some examples are known in which temperature effects are sufficient to bring about a transition from low-spin square planar to octahedral stereochemistry.

The ion Ni^{2+} is a d^8 system so that the stability of its complexes is determined both by ligand-field stabilization effects and by the ability of the ligand to permit back-bonding of d electrons from the metal. Examples where the latter effect is the more important are the stable complexes formed by sulfur-containing anionic ligands such as diethyldithiocarbamate, dithiooxalate, β-mercaptopropionate, β-isothioureidopropionate, and the dianions of rubeanic acid and quinoxaline-2,3-dithiol. Ligand-field stabilization is the decisive factor in the Ni(II) bis complexes with dioximes, such as dimethylglyoxime, that provide the most important gravimetric and spectrophotometric methods for nickel. Bonding in these complexes is through four nitrogen atoms, and their strong ligand fields lead to considerable stabilization energy for the resulting square planar complex. The weakness of coordination to any further sites round the metal atom leads to the extractability of the complexes into nonpolar solvents such as chloroform and provides a means of separation from metal ions such as Co^{2+} that form octahedral complexes.

Ni(III) and NI(VI) complexes are uncommon. They are formed only in those cases where oxidation of a Ni(II) complex results in stronger metal-ligand binding: The ligand is generally an anion.

Niobium

The important valence state for Nb is V, in which Nb resembles phosphorus and arsenic. The halides NbX_5 (X = F, Cl, Br, I), $NbOCl_3$, and $NbOBr_3$ are covalent, volatile, and easily hydrolyzed, even in acid solutions. The insoluble hydrated oxide $Nb_2O_5(H_2O)_x$, obtained in this way, dissolves in strong base to form "niobates," or in hydrofluoric acid to form fluoro complexes such as NbF_6^-, NbF_7^{2-}, and $NbOF_5^{2-}$ (which is insoluble). The ion $NbCl_6^-$ probably exists in concentrated hydrochloric acid solutions containing Nb(V), and it likely that $HNbCl_6$ is the form in which Nb is extracted from such solutions by diisopropyl ketone. This solvent also extracts Nb from a sulfuric acid ($6M$)-hydrofluoric acid ($9M$) mixture. Ion-pair formation probably explains the ability of tribenzylamine in chloroform to extract $HNbOCl_4$ and H_2NbOCl_5 from strong hydrochloric acid. (Tantalum complexes are not extracted under these conditions.)

Lower, unstable valencies of Nb are known, for example by electrolytic reduction of niobic acid. Reduction of Nb (but not Ta) by stannous chloride in strongly acid thiocyanate solutions gives a yellow, ether-extractable Nb(III) complex that is used as a colorimetric method for Nb.

Niobium lacks properties likely to confer specificity in chemical reactions. Like tantalum (and many other elements) it shows some affinity for vicinal phenolic groups, so that it forms precipitates with morin and quercetin and gives color reactions with quinalizarin, pyrocatechol, pyrogallol, tribromogallol, and xylenol orange. One of the best methods of separating Nb and Ta is based on fractional precipitation of niobic and tantalic acids as adsorption complexes on tannin, from oxalate solutions. (Tantalum, which is the more basic, forms stronger complexes and hence precipitates from more acid solutions. This pH effect is found for most Nb and Ta complexes.)

The preference of Nb and Ta for oxygen-type ligands is also shown in the use of N-benzoyl-N-phenylhydroxylamine as a precipitant for them.[23] Both Nb and Ta form soluble tartrate, citrate, oxalate, and ascorbate complexes. Similarly, Nb (but not Ta) gives a soluble yellow complex in $1.6M$ hydrochloric acid with tiron, and at pH 5.8, a blue color with bromopyrogallol red that can be extracted into organic solvents in the presence of suitable amines. This reaction is made more selective by using a tartrate buffer containing EDTA and cyanide ion as masking agents. Another sensitive reagent of the same type is 4-(2-pyridylazo)resorcinol. Niobium does not form a very stable complex with 8-hydroxyquinoline, and it is necessary to work at about pH 9 if the chloroform-soluble complex is to be obtained.

Other nonselective reagents are hydrogen peroxide, with which Nb and Ta form peroxy complexes in strong sulfuric acid, and phosphomolybdic acid which, on reduction with stannous chloride, yields a "molybdenum blue" with niobium. In concentrated sulfuric acid niobium and tantalum give a yellow color with hydroquinone.

Nitrogen

Nitrogen is covalent in its compounds, which usually involve three single bonds, leaving one "lone pair" of electrons available for "donation" in complex formation. Multiple-bond formation is also possible, as in the azo ($-N\!\!=\!\!N-$) and nitro ($-N\!\!\overset{\displaystyle O}{\underset{\nearrow}{=}}\!\!O$) compounds. The sp^3 hybridization in forming NH_4^+ is analogous with that for CH_4 and gives nitrogen a maximum coordination number of 4 and a tetrahedral stereochemistry. The amines themselves approximate the same stereochemistry, and the lone-pair electrons are located in an orbital with a definite spatial orientation; this orbital may be visualized as an s orbital with an appreciable p-orbital component which greatly enhances the electron-donor properties of the molecules. Similar remarks apply to the base hydrazine N_2H_4, which has lone-pair electrons on each N. The polarizability of nitrogen and the high ligand-field strengths associated with ligands bonding through nitrogen explain why the metal ions forming the strongest complexes with amines either are those of the transition series or else have filled d shells. The radius of the ammonium ion is comparable with those of K^+ and Rb^+, and all three cations form salts having comparable solubilities. The symmetrical linear azide ion N_3^- behaves rather like a halide ion.

The stereochemistries of nitrogen oxides and oxyacids are very much as expected. For example, the nitrate ion is planar and symmetrical, in agreement with the formation by nitrogen of three σ bonds using sp^2-hybrid orbitals, leaving the p_z orbitals of nitrogen and the three oxygen atoms to combine to form a π-molecular orbital which then contains two electrons. The stability of this system weakens the tendency of the nitrate ion to act as a monodentate ligand in complex formation.

Osmium

The most common osmium compounds are octahedral complexes of valence IV and VI, and the volatile Os(VIII) oxide OsO_4. This oxide is extractable by carbon tetrachloride and chloroform from acid solutions, a highly selective reaction which separates Os and Ru from other platinum metals. The greater stabilization of higher-valence states in Os than in Ru is an example of an effect common to pairs of elements in the third and second transition series. Thus, in aqueous $5M$ nitric acid osmium species are oxidized to OsO_4, which distils readily from the solution, whereas ruthenium is not oxidized to RuO_4. Similarly, in acid solution RuO_4 is reduced much more rapidly than OsO_4 by ferrous ion. Osmium can be determined by means of the colored oxidation products from the action of OsO_4 on substances such as o-tolidine, benzidine, and tetramethyl-p-phenylenediamine. OsO_4 reacts with potassium thiocyanate in acid solution to give a blue complex that is extractable into ether or amyl alcohol: The valence of Os in the complex is probably less than VIII. Thus, thiourea reacts with OsO_4 or chloroosmate ion in acid solutions to give the soluble red Os(III) complex, $Os(NH_2CSNH_2)_6^{3+}$. Derivatives such as o,o'-ditolylthiourea and 1,4-diphenylthiosemicarbazide behave similarly, although a reducing agent such as stannous chloride is necessary.

Os(IV) is slowly formed by reaction of OsO_4 with ferrous ion in acid solution. It forms the stable complexes OsX_6^{2-} (X = F, Cl, Br), and also, with tetraphenylarsonium ion, the ion pair, $[(C_6H_5)_4As]_2OsCl_6$, extractable into chloroform. Trivalent osmium is known in low-spin complexes with ammonia, α,α'-bipyridine, oxygen-containing ligands such as the acetylacetonate and oxalate ions, and nitrite ion in $[Os(NO_2)_5]^{2-}$.

Oxygen

The oxygen atom requires two electrons to complete its electron shell, and to do this it may exist as a dianion, a monoanion such as OH^-, or (covalently bonded) as a neutral species such as R—O—R. All three types are electron donating, the order of effectiveness being $O^{2-} >$ $OH^- >$ R—O—R. Oxides range from those that are essentially ionic, such as BaO, to those that are essentially covalent, as in CO_2 and OsO_4, but the oxide ion, O^{2-}, is unstable in aqueous solution, in which it forms hydroxyl ion.   In ions and molecules oxygen can usually donate only one pair of electrons because the resulting charge displacement involves too great a coloulombic work term to permit a second pair to be donated in the same way.   The donor properties of oxygen are important.   One consequence is the strong hydrogen bonding that occurs in aqueous solutions.   Another is the strong solvation of cations in water: This is usually pictured as an electrostatic ion-dipole interaction.   Oxyanions, in complex formation, approximate reasonably to the requirements of simple electrostatic theory, forming their strongest bonds to cations of small size and high charge, and these two factors are of more importance than the type of electronic configuration in the cation.

Palladium

Pd(II) usually shows a coordination number of 4 in its complexes giving square planar complexes such as $Pd(NH_3)_4^{2+}$ and brown-colored PdI_4^{2-}. This preference of palladium for square planar structures distinguishes it from most of the other transition metals.   Palladium chloride readily coordinates many ligands such as amines, phosphines, and sulfides to fill two of the sites round the metal.   Thus, coordination of two molecules of p-aminoacetophenone (through the amino groups) to palladium in $PdCl_2$ gives the water-insoluble complex $[(NH_2C_6H_4COCH_3)_2PdCl_2]$, whereas metals that form octahedral complexes still have water molecules coordinated to them and are soluble.   For the same reason, platinum behaves like palladium.

The bis complexes of the type $Pd[NOC_6H_4N(CH_3)_2]Cl_2$, formed by p-nitrosoaniline and its derivatives in weakly acid solutions, are used for the colorimetric determination of Pd; the nitrosodiphenylamine complex can be extracted into organic solvents such as butyl alcohol.   This preference for polarizable ligands of high ligand-field strength (especially where back-double-bonding is also possible) is characteristic of Pd(II) and is clearly seen in the reagents used in its isolation and colorimetric estimation.   These include dithizone (which forms a palladium complex, extractable from $1M$ HCl by carbon tetrachloride), thiocyanate ion (forming $H_2Pd(SCN)_4$ which is extracted by butyl and isoamyl alcohols), thiourea, thioglycollic acid, 2-mercapto-4,5-dimethylthiazole, and diethyldithiocarbamate ion (which forms a benzene-extractable complex).   So, too, it forms water-insoluble complexes with diethylaminobenzylidenerhodanine, 1-nitroso-2-naphthol and 2-nitroso-1-naphthol.   (The nitrosonaphthol complexes can be extracted into toluene.)   Like nickel, palladium forms an insoluble bis(dimethylglyoxime) complex that can be extracted into chloroform. Other dioximes also give this reaction, and α-furildioxime is a better reagent. Salicylaldoxime also forms a colored complex with palladium. The main difference between Pd(II) and the corresponding Ni(II) complexes lies in the greater kinetic inertness of the former.

Palladium also forms octahedral Pd(IV) complexes, $PdX_6{}^{2-}$, where X = F, Cl, Br, but they are not very important.

Palladium can be precipitated as the sulfide using lead as a collector. it is also readily precipitated along with tellurium when a tellurite is added to the solution and then reduced by sulfurous acid or stannous chloride. Alternatively, it can be reduced and adsorbed on to Hg_2Cl_2 when the latter is shaken with Pd(II) solutions.

Phosphorus

Phosphorus, like nitrogen, is covalent in its chemistry. However, the availability of empty $3d$ orbitals for hybridization enables phosphorus to exhibit coordination numbers up to 6, as in octahedral $PF_6{}^-$. The most important classes of phosphorus compounds are the oxides and the oxyacids. In these compounds, and also where PS bonding is involved, the d orbitals on phosphorus may be used in d_π–p_π bonding with the oxygen (or sulfur) so that multiple-bond character results. There is no tendency to p_π–p_π bonding. The structures of phosphorus oxides and oxyacids comprise tetrahedral arrangements around the phosphorus atoms. These units, by sharing oxygen atoms, give rise to condensed phosphates which may be linear or cyclic.

Platinum

The chemical properties of platinum and palladium are very similar, except that Pt(IV) complexes are more numerous and stable than those of Pd(IV). The preferred ligands in the square planar Pt(II) complexes are highly polarizable, have high ligand-field strengths, and often make back-double-bonding possible with the metal. Thus, in the presence of stannous chloride to ensure reduction of any Pt(IV) present, dithizone reacts in $4M$ HCl with Pt(II) to form a carbon tetrachloride-extractable complex. Pt(IV) is not extracted as a dithizonate. Other reagents that can be used with both Pd(II) and Pt(II) include p-nitrosodimethylaniline, p-nitrosodiphenylamine and diethyldithiocarbamate ion. (The last two form complexes extractable into organic solvents.)

In its tetravalent state, platinum forms a large number of octahedral complexes such as $[PtL_xX_{6-x}]$ where x varies from 0 to 6, L = NH_3,

N_2H_4, NH_2OH, or $\frac{1}{2}$(en), and X = Cl, Br, SCN, OH, or NO_2. Complexes of Pt(IV), like those of Pt(II) and Pd(II), are kinetically inert. The red iodoplatinate ion, PtI_6^{2-}, has limited application for colorimetric determination of platinum, and anions of this type can be used with anion-exchange columns to separate platinum from many other metals. Oxidation of platinum to Pt(IV) at pH 8 using bromate ion, followed by boiling, precipitates any palladium that may be present (as the hydrated oxide), but Pt(IV) remains in solution. Otherwise, the methods described for precipitating palladium from solution apply also to platinum. Thiosemi-carbazide and phenylthiosemicarbazide form colored complexes with Pt(IV) in weakly acid solutions; in the latter case the complex can be extracted into ethyl acetate.

Plutonium

The chemistry of plutonium (gaseous atom $[Rn]5f^66s^26p^67s^2$) corresponds closely to those of neptunium if corresponding valence states are compared. However, the increased nuclear charge and resulting orbital contractions make it more difficult to promote $5f$ electrons to $6d$ orbitals for bond formation so that Pu(IV) is the most stable oxidation state. (Contrast Np(V).) The plutonium ions Pu^{3+}, Pu^{4+}, PuO_2^{2+} are similar to the neptunium series, but PuO_2^+ disproportionates in weakly acid solutions, and Pu^{3+} and Pu^{4+} are less readily oxidized than Np^{3+} and Np^{4+}. The ultraviolet spectrum of Pu^{3+} has not yet been reported but strong bands due to f–d transitions are likely to lie at shorter wavelengths than in Np^{3+}.

Because of their small radii, plutonium ions form more stable complexes than the corresponding neptunium ions. The Pu(IV) complex with EDTA is sufficiently stable for complexometric titration to be possible (log $K = 25.1$) using alizarin red S as indicator and back-titrating with thorium nitrate.[24] Coprecipitants for plutonium ions are the same as for neptunium, and include the organic zirconium salts, zirconium benzene sulfinate, and zirconium phenyl arsonate, which collect Pu(IV). Bismuth phosphate, in moderately concentrated nitric or sulfuric acids, collects Pu(III) and Pu(IV).

The complex-forming tendencies of plutonium ions lie in the sequence $Pu^{4+} > PuO_2^{2+} > Pu^{3+} > PuO_2^+$. This is also the sequence for the coordination of molecules such as tributyl phosphate, thenoyltrifluoroacetone, and tri-n-octylamine[25] used in extracting plutonium complexes from acid solutions. The TBP-nitric acid extraction of Pu^{4+} as $Pu(NO_3)_4 \cdot 2TBP$ is important.[26,27] Where solvent coordination is weaker, as with diethyl ether and hexone (which is used in analytical separations[27]), the sequence becomes Pu(VI) > Pu(IV) ≫ Pu(III) > Pu(V).[28]   Extraction coefficients are often improved by salting out.

Ion exchange affords analytically useful separations of plutonium. This may be with cation-exchange columns, using hydrochloric acid for progressive elution of metals as their chloride complexes; or anion-exchange columns to adsorb anionic chloride and nitrate complexes, followed by reduction and elution.   Thus Pu(IV), adsorbed onto an anion-exchange column from $12M$ HCl, is reduced to Pu(III) and eluted if $12M$ HCl–$0.25M$ HI is run through.[30]   The analytical chemistry of plutonium is rendered more complicated by the diversity of elements resulting from nuclear-fission processes.   Anion exchange has been used to separate Pu from such systems.[31]

The oxidation-reduction potential of Pu(III)–Pu(IV) in $1M$ HCl is 0.97 v; in $1H$ HClO$_4$, 0.98 v; and in $1M$ H$_2$SO$_4$, 0.75 v; so that Pu(III) can be titrated with ceric(IV) sulfate, using the ferrous 1,10-phenanthroline complex as indicator.[32]

Colorimetric methods for plutonium (IV) have used reagents such as sodium alizarin sulfonate,[33] which gives a complex having $\epsilon = 9870$ at 530 mμ and pH 3; thoron,[34] for which $\epsilon = 11,000$ at 540 mμ; and arsenazo,[35] which gives a 1:1 complex with $\epsilon = 21,000$ at 580 mμ in $0.1M$ nitric acid.   Pu(III) (at pH 5.5–6.5) and Pu(IV) and Pu(VI) (at pH 8.5–9.5) also form colored complexes with arsenazo.   None of these reagents is very selective, so that prior removal of interfering metal ions, and also some anions, is necessary.

Polonium

The intense α radiation arising from the nuclear disintegrations makes the study of polonium chemistry difficult.   Polonium is metallic in character, and the inertness of its $6s^2$ electrons ordinarily limits its valency to 4. Its chemical bonding is still highly covalent, so that polonium tetrahalides are volatile above 150°C and are soluble in organic solvents.   These tetrahalides closely resemble their tellurium analogues.   They can be formed by dissolving PoO$_2$ in halogen acids, and they readily give rise to anionic complexes such as PoBr$_6{}^{2-}$, which can be precipitated as insoluble salts of the larger cations such as cesium and tetraethylammonium ions. Polonium dioxide is much less acidic than tellurium dioxide.   Polonium forms salts such as the disulfate, tetranitrate, phosphate, oxalate, and acetate, as well as a number of basic salts resembling their tellurium counterparts.

Analytical applications of organic reagents for polonium determinations have not been investigated.

Potassium

See *sodium*.

Protoactinium

Protoactinium is the first of the actinide elements, named from their resemblance to actinium.   The actinides, like the lanthanides, occur because of the progressive filling of f orbitals (in this case $5f$) which, in all but the early members, play little part in bonding.   Filling is complete in No and Lw.   Protoactinium has the electronic configuration $[Rn]5f^{2}6d^{1}7s^{2}$ or $[Rn]5f^{1}6d^{2}7s^{2}$, and, as the energies of electrons in the $5f$, $6d$, $7s$, and $7p$ orbitals are not very different in this atom, covalent-hybrid bonding involving $5f$ electrons can occur, leading to the oxidation states IV and V.   Pa(V) resembles Nb(V) and Ta(V) but is more prone to hydrolysis.   Anionic complexes are formed with fluoride, chloride, nitrate, sulfate, thiocyanate, and citrate ions, but Pa(V) does not form a simple cation.   Reduction using titanous sulfate or zinc amalgam affords Pa(IV), which is rapidly oxidized by air.

Radium

See *calcium*.

Rhenium

The commonest valence states of rhenium are III, IV, V, and VII; Re(III) and Re(IV) complexes are usually low-spin.   The oxide Re_2O_7 is volatile and can be distilled from strong sulfuric acid solutions.   The corresponding acid, perrhenic acid, can be extracted from acid solutions using butyl or isoamyl alcohol.   Its anion, ReO_4^-, is stable in aqueous solution and is obtained when rhenium compounds are oxidized by strong oxidizing agents such as nitric acid or hydrogen peroxide.   Conversely, ReO_4^- is reduced by HBr and HI.   Perrhenate ion resembles perchlorate in the solubilities of its salts.   For example, whereas most Re(VII) species are soluble in water, tetraphenylarsonium perrhenate is not.   This permits a separation of rhenium from molybdenum: The tetraphenylarsonium perrhenate is extractable into chloroform.   Re(VII) has a strong affinity for sulfur, and the sulfide Re_2S_7 is precipitated by hydrogen sulfide from 4–7M HCl or 3M H_2SO_4.   (Trivalent arsenic can be used as a collector.) Similarly, toluene-3,4-dithiol and 4-hydroxy-3-mercaptotoluene form colored complexes with Re(VII).   When perrhenic acid is heated in 5–7M HCl with 2,4-diphenylthiosemicarbazide a red product, extractable by chloroform, is produced.   Its nature is unknown.

Reduction of Re(VII) with stannous chloride or titanous chloride in the presence of thiourea or diphenylthiourea gives colored Re(V) complexes, $ReO_2L_4^+$. In the presence of thiocyanate ion, stannous chloride reduces acid solutions of perrhenic acid to give a yellow Re(V) complex which may be $ReO(SCN)_3$ or $ReO(SCN)_4^-$ (compare molybdenum). The complex is extractable into ethyl ether.

If dimethylglyoxime (or, better, α-furildioxime) is used instead of thiocyanate ion, a red complex, possibly containing Re(IV) as $ReOL_2^{2+}$, is formed and can be extracted into chloroform. In hot, strong hydrochloric acid, hydrazine reduces perrhenic acid to the Re(IV) complex ion, $ReCl_6^{2-}$. When the corresponding iodo complex, ReI_6^{2-}, is treated in methanol with potassium cyanide it gives the stable, water-soluble $[Re(CN)_8]^{3-}$ ion, whereas TcI_6^{2-} forms $[Tc(CN)_6]^{2-}$, which is rapidly hydrolyzed by water. Reduction of Re(VII) in hot $10M$ HCl with chromous chloride leads to Re(III) species.

Rhodium

Rhodium forms no oxyanions or high-valent oxides, its chemistry being mainly concerned with the valence states III and IV, the former being most stable of the oxidation states. Both Rh(III) and Rh(IV) complexes are usually octahedral. Rhodium, in the form Na_3RhCl_6, can be separated from palladium, platinum, and iridium as Na_2MCl_6 (M = Pd, Pt, Ir), because of the solubility of the latter, but not the former, in ethanol. $Rh(H_2O)_6^{3+}$ resembles Co_{aq}^{3+} and forms salts such as the sulfate, perchlorate, and chloride, as well as a series of ammine complexes. Rhodium is the only element in the second or third transition series that forms a well-defined, stable, trivalent cation. Hydrated Rh_2O_3 is precipitated above pH 6 when alkali is added to solutions of some of these salts, for example $Rh_2(SO_4)_3 \cdot 14H_2O$. In some cases, such as $Rh_2(SO_4)_3 \cdot 6H_2O$, the anion appears to be coordinated to the metal. In weakly acid solutions, hydrolysis of Rh(III) salts occurs, giving hydroxy complexes.

Rh(III), like cobalt, forms complexes of the types $[M(CN)_6]^{3-}$ and $[M(NO_2)_6]^{3-}$, but there are no cobalt analogs of $[RhX_6]^{3-}$ and $[RhX_5H_2O]^{2-}$, where X = Cl, Br, and SCN. All Rh(III) complexes and salts are low-spin, so that, because d^6 systems are concerned, there are high ligand-field stabilization energies, especially with ligands such as CN^-, ethylenediamine, and α,α'-bipyridine.

Because it is a trivalent cation, Rh^{3+} forms stable complexes with anionic ligands; typical examples of reagents used for its precipitation include 1-nitroso-2-naphthol, 2-mercaptobenzoxazole, 2-mercaptobenzothiazole, thionalide, and thiobarbituric acid. The use of sulfur rather than oxygen binding increases the ligand-field contribution to the stability of the complexes.

The most commonly used method for the colorimetric determination of rhodium, based on reduction of Rh(III) by hot stannous chloride or stannous iodide, is empirical, and the nature of the products is unknown. When Rh(III) in acid solution is heated with 2-mercapto-4,5-dimethylthiazole an amber-to-red color, possibly due to a Rh(II) complex, $Rh(C_4H_6NSCS)_2$, is produced. Other spectrophotometric methods depend on solution in acetone of the rhodium complexes with 2-mercaptobenzoxazole and 1-nitroso-2-naphthol. Use of the bis complex with sym-diphenylcarbazone, in methanol or N,N-dimethylformamide, has also been proposed.[36]

Rubidium

See *sodium*.

Ruthenium

The common valence states for Ru are II, III, and IV, and its complexes are usually octahedral. Ru(VIII) occurs in the volatile oxide RuO_4, which is formed when acid solutions of the Ru species are heated with powerful oxidizing agents. Like OsO_4, RuO_4 is extractable by carbon tetrachloride and chloroform from acid solutions, thereby providing a convenient separation of Os and Ru from other platinum metals. Shaking the extract with a reducing agent such as sulfurous acid returns the ruthenium to the aqueous phase. The anions RuO_4^- and RuO_4^{2-} show resemblances to MnO_4^- and MnO_4^{2-}. For example, perruthenate ion is formed when ruthenium compounds are fused with alkali containing an oxidizing agent, but, in alkaline solution, the ruthenate ion is the more stable. Complexes of Ru(IV) include RuX_6^{2-}, where X = F, Cl, Br, but they are readily hydrolyzed.

Most of the analytically important reactions of ruthenium involve Ru(III). Although Ru(III) is a d^5 system, all of its complexes are low-spin. It forms stable complexes with polarizable ligands such as ammonia and also with anions, especially those containing sulfur. Thus, in strong hydrochloric acid solutions, $RuCl_3$ reacts with the monoanions of thiourea and its derivatives, including thiosemicarbazides, to form colored species such as $Ru(HNCSNH_2)^{2+}$ and $Ru(HNCSNH_2)_3$. Dithiooxamide also gives colored complexes, and the tris (2,4-diphenylthiosemicarbazide) complex is extractable by chloroform. Ru(III) forms colored complexes with halide and thiocyanate ions and, in weakly acid solutions, with p-nitrosodimethylaniline, probably by coordination through the nitroso group (compare Pd(II) and Pt(II)). It reacts with 8-hydroxyquinoline, but not very strongly, so that acetate buffers are used in forming the tris oxine complex which is extractable into chloroform.

Like its homolog Fe(II), Ru(II) slowly adds α,α'-bipyridine or 1,10-phenanthroline (if necessary, in the presence of a reducing agent such as hydroxylamine) to form coloured, low-spin, kinetically inert tris complexes.

Scandium

Scandium forms salts and complexes only in the trivalent state. The ion Sc^{3+} has the electronic configuration of argon, while its radius is comparable with, but slightly less than, those of the later members of the lanthanide series, which it closely resembles chemically. It is more basic than aluminium, but less so than the lanthanides, so that it forms a hydrated oxide, $Sc_2O_3(H_2O)_x$, and also $ScO(OH)$, rather than $Sc(OH)_3$. The hydrated oxide can be coprecipitated with cobalt hydroxide, using ammonia. Scandium can be separated from the lanthanides by its greater ease of complex formation, including $Sc(NCS)_3$ (which can be extracted into ether). A similar separation can be achieved by extracting scandium from strong hydrochloric acid solutions as a chloro complex, using tributyl phosphate. Scandium differs from the trivalent lanthanides in forming an insoluble double sulfate in potassium sulfate solution. The trifluoride ScF_3 is insoluble but redissolves in excess fluoride ion to form ScF_6^{3-}. Scandium can also be separated from aluminium by precipitation as the tris(8-hydroxyquinaldine) complex, scandium, but not aluminium, being big enough to allow tris complex formation without excessive steric interaction between ligands. The corresponding complex of scandium with 8-hydroxyquinoline, precipitating in near-neutral solutions, is extracted by chloroform or benzene. Its concentration in the extract can be determined by ultraviolet spectrometry.

By its nature, Sc^{3+} forms its strongest complexes with oxygen-containing anionic ligands. For example its tris(thenoyltrifluoroacetone) complex is extracted at pH 1.5–2.0 into benzene containing excess ligand. For this reason, reagents for colorimetric estimation of scandium are lake-forming types such as alizarin red S and quinalizarin: The quinalizarin complex is extractable into isoamyl alcohol. Similarly, quercetin and anthrarufin-2,6-disulfonic acid[37] have been suggested as colorimetric reagents for scandium.

A related substance, morin, is used in a fluorimetric method for scandium. These reagents are very unselective, so that a great deal depends on the efficiency of the prior separation of scandium from other metals, for example by ion exchange.

Selenium

The electronegativity of selenium is much less than for oxygen, so that it forms mainly covalent bonds.

The chemistries of sulfur and selenium show many similarities. For example, the most important valence states for selenium are IV and VI, although volatile H_2Se is produced by strong reducing agents.

Oxidizing agents such as nitric acid or bromine convert selenium to the volatile oxide SeO_2, which dissolves readily in water to give selenious acid, $OSe(OH)_2$. This acid is a moderately strong oxidizing agent, undergoing reduction by reagents such as ferrous sulfate, stannous chloride, hydrazine, and glucose, with precipitation of selenium. Selenious acid is converted by more powerful oxidizing agents to selenic acid and selenate ion, SeO_4^{2-}. Selenic acid is comparable with sulfuric acid in strength, and it is less easily reduced than SeO_2.

Silicon

Silicon is essentially nonmetallic in chemistry. Its coordination number is usually 4, so that the basic units in the structures of silica and polymeric silica anions consist of four oxygen atoms tetrahedrally disposed about silicon atoms, the units being linked by shared oxygen atoms. The zeolites, used as ion exchangers and "molecular sieves," are built up into porous three-dimensional frameworks from AlO_4 and SiO_4 tetrahedra, each aluminium atom requiring one proton or monovalent cationic charge for electronic neutrality. However, because of its empty $3d$ orbitals, silicon can also form octahedral complexes by sp^3d^2 hybridization, as in SiF_6^{2-} and in the tris(acetylacetone) complex.

Silver

The usual valence state for silver is I, but Ag(II) and Ag(III) are known in complexes. Ag^+ has a d^{10} electronic configuration so that complex formation is greatly favored with polarizable ligands, especially where back-bonding can occur. This is why, for example, Ag(I), like Cu(I), gives the stability constant sequency $I > Br > Cl > F$. Possibly because of $d_{z^2}-s$ orbital hybridization with electron promotion, as discussed for Cu(I), the preferred coordination number of Ag(I) in its complexes is 2, giving linear complexes, so that chelating agents tend to be forced to form polynuclear complexes. The unfavourable stereochemistry and the fact that bonding is through carboxylic oxygens accounts for the weakness of EDTA complex formation with silver, making it a good masking reagent for use in methods where silver is determined. Conversely, the use of p-dimethyl- and p-diethylaminobenzylidenerhodanine as precipitants for silver (see Chapter 9) is possible because a linear complex is formed in which bonding is appreciably covalent. The same comment applies to the similar use of 2-thio-5-keto-4-carbethoxy-1,3-dihydropyrimidine and formazylcarboxylic acid. However, because of the strong π-acceptor character of the latter ligand, its Ag(I) complex is probably tetrahedral. This is also true of the silver dithizone complex which, in the absence of high halide concentrations, is extracted into carbon tetrachloride from strong acid, and the silver dithio-β-isoindigo complex which is extractable into n-butyl alcohol. Both of these complexes are used in colorimetric methods for silver.

Silver coprecipitates with tellurium, mercurous chloride, and as the sulfide with copper or mercuric sulfide, in the same way as palladium. Insoluble silver salts include the halides, cyanide, and thiocyanate, all of which redissolve in the presence of excess of the complexing species to form anionic complexes. Ag(I) also forms cationic complexes with monoamines.

Examples of Ag(II) complexes, which appear to be square planar and isomorphous with their Cu(II) analogs include $[Ag\ py_4]^{2+}$, $[Ag(bipy)_2]^{2+}$, and $[Ag(o\text{-phen})_2]^{2+}$, which are formed by persulfate oxidation of Ag^+ in the presence of the ligand. Under the same conditions a 1:1 Ag(III) complex is formed with ethylenedibiguanide.

Sodium, Potassium, Rubidium, and Caesium

Cations in this series have the electronic configurations of the inert gases, neon to xenon, so that they are spherically symmetrical and not readily deformable. The stabilities of these electronic configurations lead to an absence of color in such cations because of the very large energies that would be needed to excite electrons into the lowest unfilled orbitals.

The chemistry of these cations is governed by essentially electrostatic considerations, the series Li–Cs showing many well-defined gradations of properties with increasing size. Relevant quantities are radius ratios and lattice energies, so that the larger cations form the more stable salts with larger anions. The larger the cation, the more numerous are its insoluble salts. Bonding is ionic, even in the small number of chelate complexes these cations form with oxygenated ligands such as salicylaldehyde and benzoylacetone. The stability constants of these complexes are, almost always, too small for analytical applications. Limited use can be made of ion pair association for some solvent extractions. For example, cesium can be extracted into a solution of dipicrylamine in nitrobenzene. For the estimation of these elements, atomic absorption spectra, flame photometry, or similar spectrographic techniques are much more useful.

Where chemical methods of analysis are used they depend, in general, on the formation of sparingly soluble salts. These may be determined gravimetrically or, alternatively, colorimetric methods may be used if the precipitate contains a species able to yield a colored product with a suitable reagent. Some examples are given in Chapter 9. Others include potassium as $K_2AgCo(NO_2)_6$ (using silver cobaltinitrite), rubidium and cesium as their salts with $Bi(NO_2)_6^{3-}$, and caesium as $Cs_3Bi_2I_9$ (using iodobismuthous acid) and as caesium tungstosilicate.

Strontium

See *calcium*.

Sulfur

By adding two electrons, sulfur can attain the same electronic configuration as argon. However, the resulting dianion is so large (radius 1.84 Å) that it is very readily polarized by cations, leading to covalent-bond formation, especially where the cations are, themselves, readily deformable. Comparing O^{2-} and S^{2-}, the smaller radius of the former will lead to stronger ionic bonding with "hard" cations such as Na^+, Mg^{2+}, and Al^{3+}, whereas the electron-donor properties of S^{2-} will be greater, so that oxygen will be more ionic, and sulfur will be more covalent, in metal bonding. This is true also of oxygen and sulfur in their neutral species such as ethers and thioethers. Under favorable conditions, the vacant $3d$ orbitals on sulfur are also probably of low enough energy for some "back-bonding" of electrons into them to be possible from metals with filled, or almost filled, d shells. Multiple bonding can thus result from $d_\pi-p_\pi$ interaction between sulfur and oxygen, as in SO_4^{2-}. Use of d orbitals explains why sulfur can be six-coordinate, as in SF_6. However, this coordination number is not common because the energy required to promote the sulfur atom from its $[Ne]3s^23p^4$ ground state to a $[Ne]$ $3d^13p^33d^2$ state is usually too great to be offset by the energy of formation of six bonds.

The reducing power of sulfite ion arises from the readiness with which sulfur accepts another oxygen to complete the disposition of its eight $3s$ and $3p$ electrons, in pairs, tetrahedrally around it. Instead of oxygens, further sulfur atoms can be coordinated, to give ions such as $S_2O_3^{2-}$ (analogous with SO_4^{2-} but less stable) and others containing two or more sulfur atoms. Large anions such as SO_4^{2-} have relatively weak metal-complexing ability, but, because of the peripheral sulfur atoms, this property is important in anions such as $S_2O_3^{2-}$ with cations such as Cu^{2+}.

Sulfur is a rather poor hydrogen bonder, so that the solubility in water of ligands and complexes containing sulfur is lower than for the corresponding substances where oxygen is present.

The analytical chemistry of sulfur-containing species is to some extent simplified by the ease with which valence states can be changed, as in the reduction of sulfate to sulfide, or in the oxidation of sulfide to sulfur, or sulfide to sulfate, so that a good method for the estimation of, say, sulfide can be adapted to the determination of sulfate, while the oxidation-reduction behavior can be made the basis of qualitative tests and quantitative procedures.

Tantalum

The chemistries of tantalum and niobium are very similar, except that tantalum compounds are more weakly acidic. Tantalum compounds readily undergo hydrolysis, even in acid solutions, to give insoluble $Ta_2O_5(H_2O)_x$, which dissolves in strong bases to form "tantalates" and in hydrofluoric acid to form fluoro complexes such as TaF_7^{2-} and TaF_8^{3-}. Oxo complexes corresponding to $NbOF_5^{2-}$ and $NbOF_6^{3-}$ have not been described, but covalent $TaOCl_3$ and $TaOBr_3$ are known. Tantalum complexes are more easily extracted than niobium ones by organic solvents such as diisopropyl ketone.

Like niobium, tantalum forms soluble complexes with tartrate and gives coloured complexes with reagents such as morin, pyrogallol, gallic acid, and fluorone derivatives, all of which contain vicinal phenolic groups. Recent additions to this list include arsenazo,[38] 2,3,7-trihydroxy-9-phenyl-6-fluorone,[39] and quercetin.[40] Tantalum can be separated from niobium by differential extraction with butyl alcohol of their catechol complexes formed at pH 3 in the presence of oxalate.

Tantalum complex halides give colored precipitates with rhodamine B, brilliant green, gentian violet, and methylene blue. It seems likely that these complexes could be extracted into organic solvents and used as the bases of colorimetric methods, similarly to the recent benzene extraction of the methyl violet-tantalum fluoride ion pair.[41]

Technetium

Technetium resembles manganese, but the increased stabilization of higher-valence states observed in descending the periodic table makes the IV and VII states the important ones. Technetium is recovered from waste radioactive fission products by precipitation as tetraphenylarsonium pertechnetate, $(Ph_4As)TcO_4$, with the corresponding perchlorate as carrier, followed by solution in alcohol and separation on an anion-exchange column. The oxide Tc_2O_7 can be separated from rhenium because of its volatility when acid solutions containing TcO_4^- are evaporated. Pertechnetic acid and pertechnetates are formed in solution by oxidizing technetium compounds by strong oxidizing agents such as nitric acid or hydrogen peroxide. Like ReO_4^-, TcO_4^- is reduced by HCl, HBr, and HI. Pertechnetic acid is a strong acid, and its salts have solubilities resembling the perchlorates.

Technetium (V) can be estimated as its thiocyanate complex,[42] thus resembling its neighbor molybdenum, and Tc(VII) forms stable complexes with thioglycolic acid[43] and toluene-3,4-dithiol.[43a]

Tellurium

Tellurium is more metallic than selenium and shows weakly basic and acidic properties. Its oxide, TeO_2, is less acidic than is SeO_2, although it forms soluble salts with alkali metal hydroxides. It is also more readily reduced to the element. Telluric acid, $Te(OH)_6$, is a very weak acid, prepared when Te or TeO_2 is oxidized by strong oxidizing agents such as chromic acid. Tellurium also forms tetravalent anionic complexes such as $TeBr_6^{2-}$, which are prepared by reacting TeO_2 with the appropriate halogen acid. The usual coordination number in tellurium complexes is 6.

Thallium

In aqueous solutions the Tl(I) state is much more stable than Tl(III). Tl^+ shows resemblances to Rb^+, which has a comparable ionic radius, in forming a water-soluble strong base and also some salts that are isomorphous with alkali metal salts. Because of its electronic configuration, $[Xe]4f^{14}5d^{10}6s^2$, Tl^+ is much more deformable, and in most respects it resembles Ag^+ more closely. However, whereas back-bonding is often important in silver complexes, the "inert pair" of 6s electrons that are responsible for the lower-valent state, Tl(I), greatly reduce any tendency in thallium complexes for the 5d electrons to back-donate from Tl^+ into suitable ligand orbitals. This is why, for example, Tl(I) forms much less stable complexes with cyanide ion than Ag(I) does, and why thallous sulfide can be precipitated only from neutral or ammoniacal solution whereas silver sulfide is precipitated in acid solution. Similarly, Tl(I) requires a weakly alkaline (pH 9–12) solution for the extraction of its dithizone complex into carbon tetrachloride, and for the formation of its insoluble complex with thionalide. The selectivity of the latter reaction can be improved by using as masking agents cyanide and tartrate ion, Tl(I) showing little tendency to form complexes with oxygen-containing anionic ligands. For the same reason, complexing species such as cupferron, 8-hydroxyquinoline, and diethyldithiocarbamate can be used for the extraction of other metals from Tl(I) solutions.

Oxidation of Tl(I) to Tl(III) occurs when bromine or chlorine water is added to Tl(I) solutions in hydrochloric acid. Tl(III) is mildly oxidizing. It is reduced to Tl(I) by iodide ions, and it can also be determined colorimetrically by the oxidation products it gives with azo derivatives of chromotropic acid and with p-aminophenol. Tl(III), probably as $HTlCl_4$, is readily extracted by oxygen-containing organic solvents such as isopropyl ether from strong hydrochloric acid solutions. Under the same conditions Tl(I) is only partly extracted. The ready extraction of Tl(III) by ethyl ether from $0.1-1M$ HBr solutions enables a separation from Fe(III) and most other metals except Au(III). Unlike the chloro complexes, Tl(I) bromo complexes are quantitatively extracted by ethyl ether from $1-4M$ HBr solutions. So, too, Tl(I) and Tl(III) iodo complexes are extractable from $0.5-2.5M$ HI, using ethyl ether. The ion pairs of $TlCl_4^-$ with p-dimethylaminoazobenzene and with methyl orange are insoluble. The corresponding ion pairs with rhodamine B, methyl violet, and malachite green are also insoluble in water, but, extracted into nonpolar organic solvents such as benzene, they find application in colorimetric methods for thallium. The ion pairs of methyl violet and brilliant green with $TlBr_4^-$, extracted into amyl acetate, have also been used in this way.

Thorium

The only valence state that is important in thorium chemistry is IV, and Th^{4+} has the electronic configuration of the inert gas radon. Thorium complexes are eight-coordinate, as in the tetrakis acetylacetonate, which has a square antiprism structure. Th^{4+} forms salts with strong mineral acids, but at pH values greater than about 3 its salts are increasingly hydrolyzed to give polynuclear hydroxy or oxo bridged species. The hydroxide is precipitated by ammonia or hexamethylenediamine at about pH 5, and aluminium or ferric hydroxides can be used as collectors. The insolubility of its fluoride, iodate, oxalate, and phosphate, even in strongly acid solutions, is also useful in separating thorium from other elements. Thorium nitrate, which is very soluble in water, also dissolves in oxygen-containing solvents such as alcohols, esters, ethers, and ketones. Similarly, thorium in nitric acid can be extracted by tri-n-butyl phosphate, thenoyltrifluoroacetone in carbon tetrachloride, cyclohexanone, mesityl oxide, methyl isobutyl ketone, and related solvents, especially in the presence of the nitrates of lithium and other strongly hydrated cations. The solvent coordinates to the nitrato-thorium complex. The effects of many undesirable complexing species can be overcome by adding a swamping excess of aluminium nitrate.

Thorium forms its most stable complexes with polyanionic, oxygen-containing ligands, usually with the formation of bidentate chelates. Examples of such reagents that are used in the colorimetric determination of thorium include morin (which gives a bis complex in slightly acid solution), alizarin red S, quercetin, quinalizarin, and catecholsulfone-phthalein. It is likely that thoron (1-(o-arsonophenylazo)-2-naphthol-3,6-disulfonic acid) and o-arsonophenylazochromotropic acid form tetra-dentate thorium complexes by coordination through two oxygens of the arsono dianion, the phenolic oxygen, and an azo nitrogen. Because of the increased stability of such structures, the chelate complexes can be formed in fairly strongly acid solutions, so that selectivity is improved. Arsenazo (neothoron) is also a sensitive and selective reagent for thorium.[44] Although other types of reagent, such as nitroso-R-salt, 8-hydroxyquinoline and indo-oxine, have been proposed for the determination of thorium, theoretical considerations suggest that they are likely to be less suitable.

Tin

Tin forms the two cations $Sn^{2+}([Kr]4d^{10}5s^2)$ and $Sn^{4+}([Kr]4d^{10})$. The existence of the first cation is a result of the chemical "inertness" of the $5s^2$ electrons, so that the oxidation reduction of $Sn(II)$–$Sn(IV)$ is due to their removal or restoration. Whereas $Sn(II)$ is essentially basic in its properties (although it is extensively hydrolysed in solution and can form "stannites" in strongly alkaline solutions), $Sn(IV)$ is amphoteric, forming stannates containing the anion $[Sn(OH)_6]^{2-}$, which is analogous with the series of ions $[SnX_6]^{2-}$ ($X = F, Cl, Br, I$), as well as complexes such as $SnCl_4$. In $Sn(II)$, and very much more so in $Sn(IV)$, complexes, the bonding is mainly covalent, so that tin can be extracted as bromo complexes from $4M$ HBr by ethyl ether, and $Sn(II)$ is extracted as an iodo complex from $6.9M$ HI. Benzene extracts SnI_4 from $Sn(IV)$ solutions in sulfuric acid containing high iodide concentrations. Similarly, $Sn(IV)$ is extracted quantitatively as its thiocyanate complex, using ethyl ether, from 1–$10M$ ammonium thiocyanate made $0.5M$ in hydrochloric acid. The stannic halides $SnBr_4$ and $SnCl_4$ distil readily when the appropriate halogen acid is added to hot sulfuric or perchloric acid solutions containing tin. Further separation of tin from other metals can be achieved by its sulfide precipitation in strong acid, using copper as a collector.

Sn(II) and Sn(IV) differ in the types of ligands with which they form their most stable complexes. Although the inert pair of electrons in Sn(II) complexes greatly reduce the extent of back-double-bonding from the metal, the filled d orbitals in Sn(II) lead to the strongest complex formation being with polarizable ligands, but the absence of ligand-field stabilization (because tin is a d^{10} system) results in neutral amines being less effective than anions. The higher electronic charge on Sn^{4+} makes electrostatic effects more important, favoring complex formation with anionic, oxygen-containing ligands such as pyrocatechol violet.[44a] Thus Sn(II), but not Sn(IV), is extractable by dithizone. Sn(II) forms an insoluble, red bis complex with toluene-3,4-dithiol that can be extracted (with a color change to yellow) into organic solvents. The reaction, which is used as a colorimetric method for tin, is usually followed in the aqeuous phase in the presence of a dispersing agent. Dithiocatechol and 4-chloro-1,2-dimercaptobenzene react similarly. Sn(II), but not Sn(IV), is extracted from an acid solution by diethylammonium diethyldithiocarbamate in chloroform.

By contrast, Sn(IV) forms sparingly soluble, colored complexes with reagents such as gallein, haematoxylin, morin, phenylfluorone, and quinalizarin, and fluorescent complexes with carminic acid and purpurin. The Sn(IV) cupferrate, precipitated in $1N$ HCl or H_2SO_4, is extracted by chloroform. Sn(IV) also forms an 8-hydroxyquinoline complex (at pH 2.5–5.5) which is extracted by chloroform, and a diethyldithiocarbamate complex.

Some restriction on possible reagents is imposed by the oxidation-reduction behavior of Sn(II)–Sn(IV) systems. Conversely, the reducing action of Sn(II) has been used for its estimation. Examples include the formation of a violet color with cacotheline (a nitro derivative of brucine) and of a blue-fluorescent material when 6-nitro-2-naphthylamine-8-sulfonic acid is reduced in ammoniacal solution. Diazine green (Janus green), formed by coupling N,N-dimethylaniline and diazotized safranine, is reduced back to safranine by stannous chloride in acid solution. The color change in this sensitive reaction (which is also given by titanous chloride) is from bluish green to violet or red.

Titanium

The common valency of titanium is 4, and Ti(IV) compounds are generally covalent. For example, $TiCl_4$ is a distillable liquid which is readily hydrolyzed by water. The ion Ti_{aq}^{4+} is unknown. Instead, hydrolyzed species such as $Ti(OH)_3^+$ occur in aqueous solution or, in the presence of high ligand concentrations, anionic complexes such as TiF_6^{2-}

and $TiCl_6^{2-}$ are formed. Addition of sodium hydroxide to Ti(IV) solutions precipitates the hydroxide $Ti(OH)_4$. Powerful reducing agents convert Ti(IV) to Ti(III), the ion $[Ti(H_2O)_6]^{3+}$ being well known and much more basic than Ti(IV).

Ti(IV), lacking d electrons, forms its most stable complexes with oxygen-containing, anionic ligands. Its yellow cupferrate, which is precipitated in dilute acid, can be extracted by chloroform. Reagents used in the colorimetric determination of Ti(IV) are phenolic in character, and include the following, which give yellow to orange-red products: alizarin red S, chromotropic acid, 1,8-dihydroxynaphthalene, phenylfluorone, pyrocatechol, sulfosalicyclic acid, and tiron. In some cases colors are pH dependent because of the stepwise nature of complex formation, the highest complexes being formed in the least acid solutions. Titanium reacts with ascorbic acid to give a yellow complex: The reaction is non-specific, and prior separation, for example by ion exchange, is necessary.[45] The titanium complex with sulfosalicyclic acid forms an ion pair with the tributylamine cation which is extractable into chloroform. In acid solution, Ti(IV) gives a yellow color with hydrogen peroxide: This reaction, although less sensitive, is often used for titanium determinations.

Tungsten (Wolfram)

The chemistries of tungsten and molybdenum are very similar except that the higher-valence states are more stable in tungsten than in molybdenum, and tungsten is more basic (less acidic). The more important valencies of tungsten are IV, V, and VI. Tungsten (VI) is represented by the oxide, WO_3, that dissolves in alkali to form tungstate ion, WO_4^{2-}. Neutralization or acidification leads to the formation of polymeric tungstic acids that precipitate out. Like molybdate ion, tungstate ion can also give rise to heteropoly acids. Methods of separating W(VI) from species interfering in its analysis include its solution in alkali and coprecipitation of the oxide with $Fe(OH)_3$, $Al(OH)_3$, or lead arsenate by neutralization with ammonia or hexamethylenetetramine. Differences in stabilities of their tartrate complexes enable molybdenum to be separated from tungsten by precipitation of MoS_3 from acid solutions. Like molybdenum, tungsten forms precipitates with α-benzoinoxime (extracted by chloroform) and cupferron (extracted by isoamyl alcohol). In dilute hydrochloric acid, rhodamine B reacts with tungstic acid, giving a color change from yellow-red to violet. The same reaction may also be used in analysis by measuring the reduction in the fluorescence intensity of rhodamine B. Dithiol gives a blue-green color with W(VI) that is extractable into organic solvents: Presumably the tris complex is formed. Reactions producing color species of unknown composition occur in strong sulfuric acid between W(VI) (and also Mo(VI) and Ti(IV)) and hydroquinone.

The most extensive group of tungsten complexes derive from W(V) and ligands that include oxygen-containing, halide, thiocyanate, and cyanide ions. Examples are $WOCl_5^{2-}$, $WOCl_4^-$, $[WO_2(C_2O_4)_2]^{3-}$, and $W(CN)_8^{3-}$. One of the most important methods for determining tungsten depends on the formation of a yellow W(V) thiocyanate complex in acid solution, usually by the reduction of W(VI) with stannous chloride in the presence of thiocyanate ion. Until the reactants are mixed the W(VI) must be kept in alkaline or tartrate solutions to avoid the formation of colloidal or polymeric species. The colored complex can be read directly in the aqueous solution, which may be stabilized with acetone or extracted into isopropyl ether or some other immiscible oxygen-containing solvent.

Reduction of tungstic acid in hydrochloric acid by tin gives $[W(OH)Cl_5]^{2-}$. Another W(IV) complex is $W(CN)_8^{4-}$, which is oxidized by Ce(IV) or permanganate ion to $W(CN)_8^{3-}$. Tungsten complexes in this valence state do not, at present, find any analytical application.

Uranium

Uranium species can exist in aqueous solution in three well-defined valence states, U(III), U(IV), and U(VI), of which U(VI) is the most important. Complex formation and hydrolysis effects are often pronounced, the latter increasing in the order $U^{3+} < UO_2^{2+} < U^{4+}$. Because of its resemblances to the rare earth elements, uranium ($[Rn]5f^36d^17s^2$) forms stronger complexes, usually as UO_2^{2+}, with oxygen-containing reagents such as citrate and tartrate ions, acetylacetone and thenoyltrifluoroacetone, than with nitrogen-containing ligands. The energy needed to promote electrons from $5f$ to $6d$ in uranium is within the range of chemical binding energies, so that $5f$ electrons can be used in uranium complex formation.

Uranium compounds in fused salts (particularly fluorides) show a very sensitive fluorescence. In the presence of aluminium or ferric ions as collectors, uranium (VI) is precipitated by ammonia or phosphate ion. With these exceptions, the chemistry of uranium is dominated by complex formation. Thus, uranium (VI) gives soluble complexes with excess carbonate ion, whereas many other metals are precipitated. Uranyl ion forms complexes with nitrate ion which are readily extractable into oxygen-containing organic solvents that can coordinate with UO_2^{2+} as monodentate ligands. Solvents include dialkylethers, ketones, esters, trialkyl phosphates (coordinating through their phosphoryl group, $P \rightarrow O$), and trialkyl phosphine oxides. Factors in the choice of solvent include low solubility in water, a relatively high dielectric constant, stability, and, in the phosphoryl compounds, the basicity of the phosphoryl oxygen. Extractability of UO_2^{2+} is improved by inserting electron-donating groups into the organophosphorus molecule. In some cases, for example with tributyl phosphate, complex formation and extraction are so effective that it is necessary to use a diluent such as kerosene to increase the selectivity. The nature of the anions present must also be considered: Fe(III) and Al, but not U(VI), are extracted into ethyl ether as their chlorides, whereas the converse is true of the nitrates. Uranyl complexes in organic solvents become extractable back into water if they are reduced to U(IV).

In the solvated UO_2^{2+} ion, the oxygen-uranium-oxygen atoms probably lie on an axis while six ligands (including any inorganic anions) are disposed around uranium in a plane perpendicular to it. With large molecules, including tributyl phosphate, it may not be possible to fit as many ligands as this around the metal ion, so that complexes such as $UO_2(TBP)_2(NO_3)_2$ are formed. This stereochemistry is not very suitable for coordination to EDTA so that the UO_2^{2+}-EDTA complex has only a small stability constant, making EDTA a convenient reagent for masking other cations in uranium determinations. This coordination number explains the ready formation of anionic tris complexes with bidentate ligands such as glycollate ion and the 8-hydroxyquinoline anion. The stability of anionic complexes, including fluorides, makes it possible to remove potentially interfering cations by passing suitable uranium solutions through a cation-exchange column. Conversely, after precipitation of fluoride ion, interfering anions can be removed by anion exchange.

In acidic media, the cupferron complex with U(IV), but not with U(VI), is precipitated and can be extracted into ethyl ether or chloroform. Interfering metal ions can be removed from a U(VI) solution by extraction as their cupferrates. The U(VI) is then converted to U(IV), using a Jones reductor, and extracted, taking special precautions against oxidation. Other species used in solvent separations include U(IV) and U(VI) chelates with thenoyltrifluoroacetone and the U(VI) chelate with acetylacetone.

Uranium gives colored complexes with many organic reagents, but the reactions lack specificity. The strongest complexes are likely to be formed where bonding is through adjacent oxygen atoms, at least one of which is anionic. Examples include dibenzoylmethane, chromotropic acid, tiron, salicyclic acid, sulfosalicyclic acid, alizarin red S, thoron, morin, and cresotic acid. Thus dibenzoylmethane, as its monoanion, forms a yellow bis complex with uranyl ion, having a molecular extinction coefficient of about 20,000. In the absence of chromium (VI) (which must be reduced if present) and halides (which permit other ions to extract) the reaction with dibenzoylmethane can be made specific for uranium by using a prior extraction of uranium, for example as its tetrapropyl-ammonium trinitrate complex from a moderately acid solution containing ammoniacal aluminium nitrate (for salting out) with methyl isobutyl ketone as extractant. Of the few ions extracted, only UO_2^{2+} gives a coloured complex when dibenzoylmethane in an ethanol-pyridine buffer is added to the separated organic phase.[46] Alternatively, if much uranium is present, the color of its tetrapropylammonium trinitrate complex can be measured directly.

A widely used reagent for uranium is thiocyanate ion which forms the yellow complexes $[UO_2CNS]^+$, $UO_2(CNS)_2$, and $[UO_2(CNS)_3]^-$, the reaction generally being applied in aqueous solution. Azide ion also forms yellow complexes with U(VI). Another commonly used reaction for uranium (VI) is with hydrogen peroxide to give yellow peruranates in basic media.

Although they are potentially less likely to be selective, a number of reagents have been proposed for the spectrophotometric determination of uranium in which at least one of the metal-ligand bonds is not through oxygen. Their use generally entails prior separation of uranium (VI) from more reactive ions. Examples include arsenazo (3-(2-arseno-phenylazo)-4,5-dihydroxynaphthalene-2,7-disulfonic acid), 1-(2-pyridyl azo)-2-naphthol (PAN), salicylhydroxamic acid, thioglycollic acid, salicylamidoxime, 8-hydroxyquinoline, 1-nitroso-2-naphthol, and solochromate fast red 3G 200.[47] Diethyldithiocarbamate and benzylphenyl-dithiocarbamate ions also react with U(VI), giving colored complexes that are extractable into organic solvents.

Vanadium

Fusion of vanadium compounds with sodium carbonate, especially in the presence of oxidizing agents, produces soluble vanadates. These V(V) species are probably formed by the progressive loss of protons from hydrated V_2O_5. The resulting anions may aggregate by oxygen bridging. In acid solutions the pervanadyl ion, VO_2^+, is the main species. Such solutions are moderately strong oxidizing agents, and V(V) can be estimated by measuring the color produced by the oxidation of organic bases such as diphenylamine, diphenylaminesulfonic acid, benzidine, diphenylbenzidine, 3,3'-dimethylnaphthidine, strychnine, and variamine blue.

The most stable oxidation state is V(IV), so that aerial oxidation converts V(III) to V(IV), and mild reduction of vanadates, for example by sulfur dioxide, gives V(IV) species such as the hypovanadates. Almost all V(IV) complexes contain the vanadyl ion, VO^{2+}. Electrolytic reduction of V(IV) or V(V) leads to the trivalent ion, $V(H_2O)_6^{3+}$, and its hydrated salts such as $VX_3(H_2O)_6$ (X = F, Cl, Br, I). V(III) forms complexes with both oxygen-containing and nitrogen-containing ligands: It also gives a yellow color with thiocyanate ion in acidic acetone solutions, but these reactions are not used in chemical analysis.

In alkaline solutions, vanadate reacts with sulfide ion to form the colored thiovanadate ion. This reaction is not a very sensitive one. Most methods for determining V(V) are applied in acidic or weakly acidic solutions where cationic species, mainly VO_2^+ and $VO(OH)^{2+}$, respectively, are present. They form their most stable complexes with anionic ligands. In the pH region 3–5, V(V) combines with cupferron, 8-hydroxyquinoline, and diethyldithiocarbamate to form complexes, extractable into chloroform, that are used for separations and estimations. Other colorimetric reagents include salicylhydroxamic acid and benzoylphenylhydroxylamine. In more acid solutions, V(V) gives a colored product with hydrogen peroxide and also reacts with phosphotungstic acid to form the yellow, soluble phosphotungstovanadic acid.

Vanadyl ion, VO^{2+}, forms a colored complex with pyrocatechol in solutions between pH 4.5 and 6. V(IV) reacts only weakly with formaldoxime, to give a yellow complex in basic solutions.

Yttrium

The chemistry of yttrium closely parallels those of scandium and the lanthanides. Y^{3+} has the electronic configuration of krypton, and its radius lies within the lanthanide range. Like the lanthanides, yttrium forms its most stable complexes with oxygen-containing ligands. Yttrium can be separated from scandium by extraction of the latter into ethyl ether as its thiocyanate complex. Cation-exchange resins, with graded elution by anionic ligands such as citrate or nitrilotriacetate, are likely to find use in the separation of yttrium from the many other cations that interefere in current spectrophotometric methods based on reagents such as quinalizarin, alizarin red S, and pyrocatechol violet.[9]

Zinc

The only oxidation state found in zinc salts and complexes is II, and the ion, Zn^{2+}, has the electronic configuration $[Ar]3d^{10}$. The diffuse nature of the d orbitals makes Zn^{2+} readily deformable and makes for stable covalent complex formation with polarizable ligands such as ammonia, amines, and cyanide ion. Because there is no ligand-field stabilization energy involved in zinc complex formation (zinc having a filled d shell), ligands that also permit back-double-bonding probably form the most stable zinc complexes. The considerable covalent character of the bonding in zinc halides is shown by their solubility in alcohol, acetone, and similar solvents. In chloride solutions, zinc forms anionic complexes, so that separation from some metals is possible using anion-exchange resins. Because of ion pair formation, methyldioctylamine extracts zinc chloro complexes into trichloroethylene from $2M$ HCl. Zinc thiocyanate is extracted quantitatively by ethyl ether from $1-5M$ ammonium thiocyanate that is also $0.5M$ in hydrochloric acid. At low thiocyanate concentrations the extracted species is $Zn(SCN)_2$, but at higher concentrations it is $(NH_4)_2Zn(SCN)_4$. Similar ion-pair formation between anionic zinc thiocyanate complexes and a number of organic bases, including acridine, methylene blue, pyridine, and rhodamines B and C, followed generally by extraction into an immiscible solvent, has been used in spectrophotometric methods for zinc. Zinc hydroxide is amphoteric, dissolving in alkaline solution to form zincate ions such as $[Zn(OH)_3[H_2O]_3]^-$ or $[Zn(OH)_3H_2O]^-$.

The absence of ligand-field stabilization in zinc complexes means that the stereochemistry of such complexes depends only on considerations of size and electrostatic and covalent bonding forces. Thus, zinc complexes can be tetrahedral as in $[Zn(CN)_4]^{2-}$ or octahedral as in $[Zn(NH_3)_6]^{2+}$.

Zinc forms relatively weak complexes with ligands where only bonding to oxygen is involved, as in citrate or tartrate. Almost without exception, all useful organic reagents for zinc bind the metal through sulfur or nitrogen (or both). Thus, the currently most important reagents, dithizone and di-β-naphthylthiocarbazone, which are used for the extraction of zinc and for its spectrophotometric determination, form, with zinc, chelate complexes linked through sulfur and nitrogen. Even so, these complexes are reextracted from chloroform and carbon tetrachloride, with dissociation, on shaking with dilute aqueous acids. Complex formation with zincon probably involves bonding through two nitrogen atoms and two anionic oxygens, to give a tetradentate chelate. In the zinc complexes with 8-hydroxyquinoline and indo-oxine there is probably back-bonding through the (heterocyclic) nitrogen atom. This is less likely when 1-amino-2-naphthol-4-sulfonic acid is used as a colorimetric reagent for zinc. Zinc also forms extractable complexes with diethyldithiocarbamate and diethylammonium diethyldithiocarbamate.

Zirconium

Zirconium is tetravalent in its complexes, and its hydrated oxide $ZrO_2(H_2O)_x$ is insoluble in alkaline solutions. Because of the difficulties of removing four electrons from the metal, its bonding is usually appreciably covalent, so that $ZrCl_4$ sublimes at 330° and fumes in moist air. The atomic size of zirconium permits coordination numbers up to 8, for example in the tetrakis acetylacetonate and oxalate complexes. Partial hydrolysis of zirconium species gives the zirconyl ion, ZrO^{2+}, which forms a number of crystalline salts, and also other ions such as $[ZrO(OH)]^+$, $[Zr(OH)_3]^+$, and $[Zr_2O_3]^{2+}$. Zr^{4+} would have the electronic configuration of the inert gas krypton and hence would not be readily deformable (an effect greatly reinforced by the higher formal positive charge on the cation). For this reason, zirconium forms its most stable complexes with oxygen-containing and other anionic ligands, such as fluoride, sulfate, and phosphate ions, that form ionic rather than covalent-type bonds, giving soluble ions such as ZrF_6^{2-} and $[Zr(SO_4)_4]^{4-}$. The low solubility of zirconyl phosphate in $1N$ hydrochloric or sulfuric acids is useful in helping to separate zirconium from other metals.

Almost all of the organic reagents complexing with zirconium (usually as ZrO^{2+}) do so by forming five- or six-membered chelate rings in which the metal is bonded through two oxygen atoms. Examples include cupferron which, in strong acid solution, precipitates zirconium as a tetrakis complex that is extractable into chloroform, and α-thenoyltrifluoroacetone which forms a complex extractable by xylene from $6M$ hydrochloric acid. As expected, EDTA, tartrate, and citrate ions form very stable complexes with zirconium. p-Dimethylaminoazophenylarsonic acid is a good precipitant for zirconium in acid solution: Presumably, the metal-ligand bonding involves two of the arsono oxygens, with formation of a four-membered ring. Other useful precipitants for zirconium are mandelic acid and its p-bromo and p-chloro derivatives, which give insoluble tetrakis complexes which can be weighed or determined by oxidative titrations. It is probable that each of the ligand anions is also bonded to the metal through the alcoholic oxygen atom to form a chelate complex. The same type of ligand atom is seen in the reagents used in the spectrophotometric determination of zirconium as a slightly soluble, strongly colored "lake." Examples include alizarin red S, chloranilic acid, haematoxylin, morin (fluorescence), phenylfluorone, purpurin, pyrocatechol violet, quercetin, quinalizarin, SPADNS, and thoron.

The chemical properties of zirconium and hafnium are so closely similar that these metals are ordinarily determined together as "zirconium" unless use is made of physical methods such as arc or spark emission spectra. Recently, however, it has been suggested[48] that zirconium and hafnium can be determined separately using xylenol orange or methylthymol blue, if, following spectrophotometric measurement of the zirconium plus hafnium complexes in acidic medium, hydrogen peroxide is added to mask zirconium. An analytical procedure has been developed for the separation of zirconium and hafnium as their sulfate complexes on an anion-exchange resin.[49]

References

1. Sandell, E. B., *Colorimetric Determination of Traces of Metals*, 3rd ed., Interscience, New York, 1959; Kolthoff, I. M., and P. J. Elving (eds.), *Treatise on Analytical Chemistry*, Interscience, New York, 1959–1964.
2. Kraus, K. A., F. Nelson, and G. W. Smith, *J. Phys. Chem.*, **58**, 11 (1954).
3. Horton, A. D., and P. F. Thomason, *Anal. Chem.*, **28**, 1326 (1956).
4. Magnusson, L. B., and M. L. Anderson, *J. Am. Chem. Soc.*, **76**, 6207 (1954); Schneider, R. A., and K. M. Harmon, *U.S. At. Energy Comm. Rept.*, HW–53368 (1957).
5. Choppin, G. R., B. G. Harvey, and S. G. Thompson, *J. Inorg. Nuclear Chem.*, **2**, 66 (1956).
6. Phillips, G., and E. N. Jenkins, *J. Inorg. Nuclear Chem.*, **4**, 220 (1957); Smith, H. L., C. I. Browne, D. C. Hoffman, J. P. Mize, and M. E. Bunker, *J. Inorg. Nuclear Chem.*, **3**, 93 (1956).
7. Capelle, R., *Anal. Chim. Acta*, **24**, 555 (1961).
8. Ceriotti, G., and L. Spandrio, *Clin. Chim. Acta*, **6**, 233 (1961).
9. Young, J. P., J. C. White, and R. G. Ball, *Anal. Chem.*, **32**, 928 (1960).
10. Herrington, J., and K. C. Stead, *Anal. Chim. Acta*, **22**, 180 (1960).
11. Kuteinikov, A. F., and G. A. Lankoi, *Zh. Anal. Khim.*, **14**, 686 (1959).
12. Shibata, S., *Anal. Chim. Acta*, **28**, 388 (1963).
13. Strickland, J. D. H., and G. Spicer, *Anal. Chim. Acta*, **3**, 543 (1949).
14. Orgel, L. E., *J. Chem. Soc.*, **1958**, 4186.
15. For spectra, see Sjoblom, R., and J. C. Hindman, *J. Am. Chem. Soc.*, **73**, 1744 (1951).
16. Roberts, F. P., *U.S. At. Energy Comm. Rept.*, HW–59032 (1959).
17. Moore, F. L., *Anal. Chem.*, **29**, 941 (1957).
18. Murray, B. B., *U.S. At. Energy Comm. Rept.*, DP-316 (1958).
19. Peppard, D. F., G. W. Mason, and R. J. Sironen, *J. Inorg. Nuclear Chem.*, **10**, 117 (1959).
20. Maeck, W. J., G. L. Booman, M. C. Elliott, and J. E. Rein, *Anal. Chem.*, **32**, 605 (1960).
21. Bergstresser, K. S., unpublished work, Los Alamos Scientific Laboratory (1959).
22. Alimarin, I. P., Y. A. Zolotov, and E. L. Pal'shin, *Dokl. Akad. Nauk SSSR*, **124**, 328 (1959).
23. Majumdar, A. K., and A. K. Mukherjee, *Anal. Chim. Acta*, **21**, 245 (1959); **23**, 246 (1960); Moshier, R. W., and J. E. Schwarburg, *Anal. Chem.*, **29**, 947 (1957).
24. Milner, G. W. C., and J. L. Woodhead, *Analyst*, **81**, 427 (1956).
25. Kader, W. E., J. C. Sheppard, and A. S. Wilson, *J. Inorg. Nuclear Chem.*, **12**, 327 (1960).
26. McKay, H. A. C., *Proc. Intern. Conf. Peaceful Uses At. Energy, Geneva*, 1955, Paper 441, **7**, 314 (1956); Nairn, J. S., D. A. Collins, H. A. C. McKay, and A. G.

Maddock, *Proc. Intern. Conf. Peaceful Uses At. Energy Geneva*, 1958, Paper 1458, **17**, 216 (1958).

27. Schneider, R. A., and K. M. Harmon, *U.S. At. Energy Comm. Rept.*, HW–53368 (1957).

28. For further extraction systems, see Stewart, D. C., *U.S. At. Energy Comm. Rept.*, CN–3905 (1945).

29. Diamond, R. M., K. Street, and G. T. Seaborg, *J. Am. Chem. Soc.*, **76**, 1461 (1954).

30. Browne, C. I., D. C. Hoffman, W. T. Crane, J. P. Balagna, G. H. Higgins, J. W. Barnes, R. W. Hoff, H. L. Smith, J. P. Mize, and M. E. Bunker, *J. Inorg. Nuclear Chem.*, **1**, 254 (1957); Hoffman, D. C., "Plutonium," in J. Kleinberg, "Collected Radiochemical Procedures," *U.S. At. Energy Comm. Rept.*, LA–1721 (1954), pp. Pu 1.

31. See, for example, Ryan, J. L., and E. J. Wheelwright, *Proc. Intern. Conf. Peaceful Uses At. Energy, Geneva*, 1958, Paper 1915, **17**, 137 (1958).

32. Ashley, R. W., and G. M. Allison, *At. Energy Can. Ltd., Chalk River Project Rept.*, PDB–19 (1951).

33. King, G. L., *U.S. At. Energy Comm. Rept.*, LA–1197 (1951).

34. Healy, T. V., and P. E. Brown, *At. Energy Research Estab. (Gt. Brit.) Rept.*, AERE C/R–1287 (1953); Powell, R, *U.K. At. Energy Authority, Ind. Group Rept.*, IGO–AM/W–115 (1958).

35. Ockenden, D. W., *U.K. At. Energy Authority, Ind. Group Rept.*, IGO–RW–2 (1956).

36. Ayres, G. H., and F. L. Johnson, *Anal. Chim. Acta*, **23**, 448 (1960).

37. Macdonald, J. C., and J. H. Yoe, *Anal. Chim. Acta*, **28**, 264 (1963).

38. Nikitina, E. I., *Zh. Anal. Khim.*, **13**, 72 (1958).

39. Luke, C. L., *Anal. Chem.*, **31**, 904 (1959).

40. Popa, G., D. Negoiu and G. Baiulescu, *Z. Anal. Chem.*, **165**, 16 (1959).

41. Layer, R. S., and N. S. Poluektov, *Zavosk. Lab.*, **25**, 903 (1959).

42. Boyd, G. E., *J. Chem. Ed.*, **36**, 3 (1959).

43. Miller, F. J., and P. F. Thomason, *Anal. Chem.*, **32**, 1429 (1960).

43a. Miller, F. J., and P. F. Thomason, *Anal. Chem.*, **33**, 404 (1961).

44. Holcomb, H. P., and J. H. Yoe, *Microchem. J.*, **4**, 463 (1960).

44a. Ross, W. J., and J. C. White, *Anal. Chem.*, **33**, 421 (1961).

45. Korkisch, J., G. Arrhenius, and D. P. Kharkar, *Anal. Chim. Acta*, **28**, 270 (1963).

46. Maeck, W. J., G. L. Booman, M. C. Elliott, and J. E. Rein, *Anal. Chem.*, **31**, 1130 (1959).

47. Korkisch, J., and G. E. Januer, *Anal. Chim. Acta*, **25**, 463 (1961).

48. Cheng, K. L., *Anal. Chim. Acta*, **28**, 41 (1963).

49. Hague, J. L., and L. A. Machlan, *J. Res. Natl. Bur. Std*, **65A**, 75 (1961).

CHAPTER 14

On Seeking New Organic Reagents
for Use in Inorganic Analysis

Feigl[1] has discussed the factors that determine the analytical usefulness of chemical reactions by which a substance to be detected or determined is converted into a more readily characterized material. Because of the effects of variables such as temperature, pH, and reagent concentrations, and the presence of other species, including masking agents, it is often necessary that these conditions be carefully specified in any test or determination. These factors often profoundly modify the degree of sensitivity, selectivity, and specificity (in qualitative analysis), and of completeness of conversion to the species to be determined. Current chemical theory provides a rational interpretation of many of the methods, operations, and reactants used in analytical chemistry and, in turn, suggests some of the possibilities of new procedures and improved reagents. The realization that the selective action of many organic compounds can be ascribed to the presence of particular atomic groupings introduces the possibility of "tailoring" such molecules, to increase their utility in chemical analysis. For example, the introduction of suitable groups can raise or depress solubility, improve extractability, or modify color.

14.1 Organic Reagents for Metal Ions

For detecting and determining metal ions, it is necessary to consider the natures of the reagent and the metal ions concerned.

Bonding Groups in Reagents

If a substance is to be potentially useful as a complex-forming reagent with metal ions, it must have a sufficient number of acidic or basic groups, preferably so placed as to allow the formation, with metal ions, of stable five- or six-membered chelate rings. These groups have, to date, been drawn mainly from the following types: —COO$^-$, phenolic —O$^-$, —S$^-$,

—$\overset{|}{C}$=O, —N=O, —OR, —NH$_2$, —NR$_2$, =N(heterocyclic), —CR

=N—R, —N=N—, and —$\overset{|}{C}$=S. The size and orbital directions of sulfur atoms permit four-membered ring formation in complexes of dithio acid derivatives, such as the Ni and Cu complexes of diethyldithio-carbamic acid and the Ni complex of xanthic acid. Similar four-membered rings are formed in some carboxylic acid complexes, but they are much less stable.

Where multidentate chelates are formed in which ligand atoms serve as links between different portions of the complexing agent, the preferred ligand atoms are nitrogen (compare, for example, EDTA) and phosphorus. The other possibilities—ether sulfur and oxygen—are very weakly basic and have only a weak tendency to coordination.

One way of achieving increased selectivity would be to design ligands in which the coorrdinating atoms are phosphorus, sulfur, selenium, and arsenic, so that stronger complexing and bigger differences in stability constants would be expected among the transition metal ions in their lower valencies and among metal ions with filled d^{10} shells. However, most of the possible chelating groups are unstable in air or water so that progress in this direction is likely to be limited. Thus, simple mercaptans are readily oxidized, so that dithiol has to be stored in sealed ampoules. Similarly, diethyldithiocarbamic acid rapidly decomposes. However, the latter is stabilized by conversion to its alkali metal salt, and dithiol is stable as its covalent zinc complex. If related sulfur-containing ligands were similarly prepared, their use as reagents might be practicable. Rational development in this direction would be helped if sufficient quantative information was available about the stability constants of metal complexes with, say, 8-mercaptoquinoline (which is easily oxidized in air but forms insoluble complexes with Co, Ni, Cu, Pd, Pt, and Ag[2]) and 8-hydroxyquinoline.

It is not always necessary that the organic reagent used in a reaction with an inorganic species be stable. This is borne out by the behavior of salicylaldehyde and ammonia which, in the presence of Cu, Ni, Co, Pd, Fe, or Zn salts, precipitate the stable bis chelates of the Schiff's base, salicylimine, even though the latter is, in itself, unstable in aqueous solution. This reaction is possible because complex formation displaces the equilibrium between salicylimine and its hydrolysis products, sali-cylaldehyde and ammonia. Other o-hydroxyaldehydes and ketones behave similarly.[3]

THE NATURE OF THE METAL ION

Relevant factors are the electronic structure of the ion, its size, its preferred stereochemistry, and its valence state.

The preferences of metal ions for particular types of complexing groups were discussed in Chapter 3. For example, polyvalent cations bind most strongly with di- and higher-valent anions, and with increasing atomic number bonding to sulfur becomes stronger than to oxygen. This explains, in part, why it is that tiron (pyrocatecholdisulfonic acid) with two adjacent phenolic groups is a reagent for ferric ion, whereas dithiol (toluene-3,4-dithiol) with similarly placed thiol groups reacts with Mo(VI), Re(VI), and W(VI). (This reaction is not selective, but it can be made more so by using mineral acid solutions so that the tris complexes of only these three ions, all of which have high stability constants, can be formed.) Exploitation of such preferences is important in increasing the selectivity of reagents, particularly by using "masking" reactions (for example, organic hydroxy acids with iron (III) or cyanide ion with transition elements) which depend on differences in stability constants of metal ions with different types of complexing species.

The stability constants of complexes of transition metal ions with a given ligand form a regular and well-defined series. However, when the logarithm of stability constants of complexes with a given ligand are plotted against metal ion the slope of the plot depends on the type of ligand. Thus, the increase in stability from Mn(II) to Cu(II) is much greater when chelation involves nitrogen bonding than it is when bonding takes place through two oxygen atoms. This suggests, for example, that if it was desired to determine Mn(II) in the presence of Cu(II), it might be possible to use a nitrogen-type ligand to mask Cu(II) while Mn(II) forms a complex with an oxygen-type ligand. Conversely, the roles of these ligands would be reversed if Cu(II), and not Mn(II), was the species sought. Reasons for these differences have already been discussed.

This broad classification can be further refined. For example, heteroaromatic nitrogen is less basic than aliphatic nitrogen, as shown by proton dissociation constants of their cations (pK_a values). Hence, as a donor atom, the former might be expected to form less stable complexes with metal ions than aliphatic nitrogen-type ligands do. This weaker bonding is offset, however, in a greater or less degree by the possibility of additional bonding involving π orbitals of the heterocyclic ring and suitable orbitals of the metal ion. Where back-bonding of this type would be expected to be important, such as with the ion $Ag^+([Kr]d^{10})$, stronger complexes with heterocyclic ligands are likely. On the other hand, in ions such as $Tl^+([Xe]4f^{14}5d^{10}6s^2)$ and Pb^{2+} (also $[Xe]4f^{14}5d^{10}6s^2$) the inert pair of $6s$

electrons "screens" the d electrons, inhibiting $d-\pi$ bonding, so that aromatic ligands form relatively less stable complexes.

Considerations of such relative complexing ability with different types of metal ion can suggest likely types of reagent for particular applications. For example, comparison of 8-hydroxyquinoline and 8-aminoquinoline as complexing species leads to the expectation that the latter would favor cations belonging to Sidgwick's classes 2 and 3 (Chapter 3), particularly if ligand-field stabilization was likely to be important. This factor is probably one of the main reasons for the stability of the low-spin, square planar bis complex that 8-aminoquinoline forms with Pd(II) (d^8). The nitrogen-metal bond is so strong that when the insoluble, yellow bis complex $[Pd(NH_2\text{-quin})_2]Cl_2$ is made alkaline, protons are lost from the amino group to give the violet, chloroform-extractable, neutral species (CLXXVIII). This reaction has been suggested as a method for the

CLXXVIII

spectrophotometric determination of Pd.[4] The same factors that suggest the types of ligands to combine with particular cations also operate in the selection of masking agents, except that, in general, the resulting complexes are preferably colorless, soluble, and, perhaps, different in extraction behavior from the species sought.

The usual stereochemistry of the metal ion must also be considered. It must be such that complex formation will not be opposed by steric hindrance due to other groups in the ligand (although hindrance to the adoption of stereochemistries preferred by other cations may be desirable and may lead to increased specificity). Stereochemical differences can also be exploited in using masking reagents.

The size of the metal ion may be important. Aluminium forms an insoluble tris(8-hydroxyquinoline) complex. A similar reaction cannot occur if 8-hydroxyquinoline is methylsubstituted in the 2-position to give 8-hydroxyquinaldine because the Al^{3+} ion is so small that three ligand molecules cannot for steric reasons be packed around it to form an octahedral complex. This factor is unimportant for the larger Cr^{3+}, Fe^{3+}, or Ga^{3+} or for bis complex formation with the divalent metal ions and serves to effect the separation of aluminium from them.[5] Much greater specificity can be expected if three-dimensional ligands can be designed to form a rigid chelate "cage" around a metal ion, so that only cations of suitable size can enter the cage. In this restricted group there will be preferential binding of such cations as match best the stereochemistry imposed by the ligand. Calcium ion with calcichrome, discussed in Chapter 6, is an example.

Different valence states of a metal often differ in the stereochemistries, extraction behavior, and other properties of their complexes and in the types of ligand with which they form their most stable complexes. In such cases, extraction (preferably), ion exchange, precipitation, or some other technique, followed by oxidation or reduction and then reaction with an appropriate ligand, can be made the basis of highly selective analytical methods.

Finally, for any reaction to be suitable for use in chemical analysis it must proceed quickly and quantitatively. This latter requirement may also be expressed by saying that, if any equilibria are involved, the changes in free energy must be large enough for the reaction to go effectively to completion.

14.2   Metal Complexes as Reagents

The properties of an anion, a neutral molecule, or a metal ion can often be deliberately modified as a result of complex formation with a metal ion, to give an analytically useful species. For example, complex formation with Cd^{2+} to give the 1:1 complex converts EDTA into a monobasic acid of pK 2.6 that has been suggested as a primary standard for alkalimetry (and also for chelometry).[6] Coordination of a ligand, such as a large anion, to a metal ion may alter to a marked extent the reactivity of the ligand or the metal ion by:

1. Changing the electron distributions in the ligand and the metal ion. (For example, the metal ion catalyzed hydrolysis of amino acid esters.)

2. Binding a chemically active center of the ligand. (For example, "masking" by copper ion of the amino and carboxylic groups of α-amino acids, leaving other groups available for chemical reaction.)

3. Forcing the ligand molecules into a particular stereochemical form. (For example, stabilization of the enol form of ethyl acetoacetate by copper (II), facilitating bromination.)

4. Providing a conducting pathway for electron addition or removal. (This may be important either for oxidation and reduction of metal ions or for metal ion catalyzed oxidation or reduction of organic species. Examples include the ability of cuprous chloride in pyridine to catalyze the aerial oxidation of aniline to azobenzene, and copper (II) to catalyze the oxidation of phenols.)

5. Stabilizing an otherwise unstable organic species. (Precipitation of the copper (II)-salicylaldimine complex from solutions of salicylaldehyde and ammonia was discussed in Chapter 9.)

Other properties that can be exploited in chemical reactions include the utilization of stereospecificity arising from coordination in complex formation, and the bringing into juxtaposition of two or more reactive species. In general, however, the study of such reactions lies outside the present scope of analytical chemistry, except where the resulting metal complexes are stable.

Any such complexes, to be analytically useful, would usually need to be kinetically inert. This, in turn, restricts the metals and ligands that are suitable to certain types discussed in Chapter 5. Examples include the complex ions such as the tris(orthophenanthroline) iron (II) and tris (α,α'-bipyridine) iron (II) ions and their substituted derivatives that are used as oxidation-reduction indicators. Other metals, such as ruthenium, could replace iron. Thus, in $1M$ nitric acid the ruthenium (II)-ruthenium (III) complexes of 1,10-phenanthroline and α,α'-bipyridine have oxidation-reduction potentials of 1.29 v[7] and 1.25 v,[8] respectively.

In other cases, nonmetallic or metalloid elements can form the "core" of analytically useful reagents such as the tetraphenylarsonium and tetraphenylborate ions.

14.3 Some Promising Fields for Research in Analytical Methods

The range of organic extractants has been greatly extended by the introduction of amines and oxygenated phosphorus compounds. Variations in extraction behavior using these new materials should make possible the development of new analytical methods, especially those based on differential extraction. Related to this approach is the use of "liquid cation exchangers" such as dinonyl naphthalenesulfonic acid[9] as extractants. Also, the extractability of metal complexes varies considerably with valence state, so that extraction, followed by oxidation or reduction and reextraction, is potentially capable of providing highly selective separations. Although at present lacking a sound theoretical interpretation, synergistic effects are often observed using mixed types of extractants such as an amine and an organic phosphate. For example, a mixture of bis(2-ethylhexyl)phosphoric acid and 4-sec-butyl-2-(α-methylbenzyl)phenol in a kerosene-type diluent is a much better extractant of Cs (along with Sr and rare earth elements) from aqueous solutions at pH 4 than either is separately:[10] In the absence of the phosphoric acid it is necessary to work at pH values greater than 12.

Related to the improved extraction possibilities, and depending on them, are methods based on ion pair formation. By using suitably colored species as counter ions, a greater range of cations and anions should be able to be determined spectrophotometrically.

Another consequence of the greater range of extraction procedures is the possibility of direct nonaqueous colorimetry of trace elements. Advantages include the appreciable increase of concentration of the element sought and the improved separation from interfering species. Examples where this technique has already been used comprise several with tri-n-octylphosphine oxide as extractant. These include determinations, in the organic phase, of uranium with dibenzoylmethane,[11] zirconium with pyrocatechol violet[12] and PAN,[13] chromium with diphenylcarbazide,[14] titanium with thiocyanate,[15] and iron with 1,10-phenanthroline.[16] Similarly, zirconium has been determined colorimetrically with xylenol orange following the extraction of its anionic chloro complex into tri-n-octylamine as an ion pair.[17] Under comparable conditions, zinc can be determined by zincon.[18]

It is possible, in some cases, to devise methods of estimating one metal ion in the presence of others by exploiting differences in the rates of formation and dissociation of complexes; that is, by using kinetic rather than thermodynamic properties. This would require the analytical procedure used, or else some property such as physical separation by precipitation, liquid extraction, or ion exchange, to be fast relative to the rate at which coordination takes place. Such a procedure is most likely to be useful where ligands have high field strengths, as in cyanide ion and chelating amines, provided complex formation involves a change from a high- to a low-spin state. Alternatively, polydentate ligands such as EDTA often lead to slower reactions because of the extent to which they have to be orientated around the metal ion. (Dissociation of the Ni-EDTA complex is an example.) Bond making and breaking is also often slow if appreciable covalent character is involved.

Steric factors are important in designing ligands for particular ions. The preference of copper (II) and nickel for square planar structures, whereas most cations favor octahedral stereochemistries, explains why removal of two of the acetic acid residues from EDTA to give four-coordinating ethylenediamine-N,N'-diacetic acid increases the relative

$$^-O-C{=}CH-C{=}N-CH_2-CH_2-N{=}C-CH{=}C-O^-$$
$$|\phantom{C{=}CH-}|\phantom{C{=}N-CH_2-CH_2-N{=}}|\phantom{C-CH{=}}|$$
$$CH_3CH_3CH_3CH_3$$

CLXXIX

selectivity of the reagent for these ions.[19] So, too, ethylenediamino-bis(acetylacetone) dianion (CLXXIX) is especially adapted to fit four coordination sites around a metal ion forming a square planar complex, such as Ni^{2+}, Pd^{2+}, Pt^{2+}, and Cu^{2+}. In complex formation with an ion preferring an octahedral stereochemistry the remaining two sites on the metal ion (*trans* to each other) are filled by water molecules or some other unidentate ligand. Increased selectivity for cations forming square planar complexes could be achieved by modifying the ligand so as to include groups that would interfere sterically with ligands in either of these two positions. Slight modifications in the chain length of (CLXXIX) should also, by altering the ease with which it can be fitted as a girdle around the metal ion, produce significant differences in relative ease of complex formation with different metal ions. Stereochemical effects have already been shown to be important in the analogous *cis* and *trans* 1,2-diaminocyclohexane-bis(acetylacetones).[20]

Another example where steric effects are important concerns the metallochromic indicator, glycine thymol blue, ((CLXXX), R = —NHCH$_2$COOH). This reagent consists of two glycine residues, each

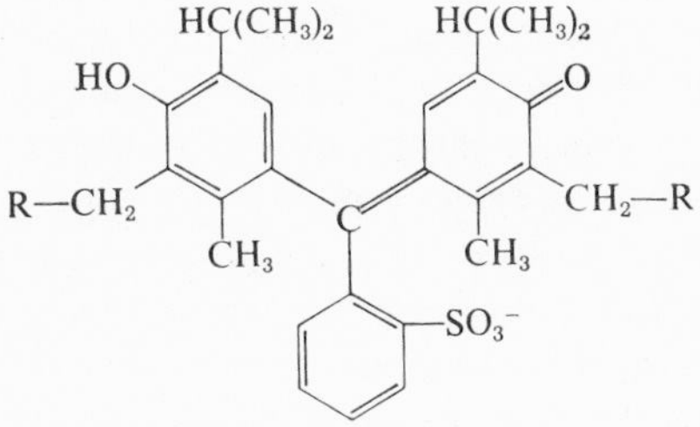

CLXXX

of which is attached, through a methylene group, to a benzene ring with an ortho phenolic substituent. This makes it possible for a copper (II) ion to be coordinated to the amino nitrogen and carboxylate oxygen of a glycine portion and also to the phenolate oxygen, the three ligand atoms occupying three of the four square planar sites about the metal ion. The rest of the molecule functions, essentially, as a chromophoric group. The configuration of the complex favors metal ions such as copper that usually form square planar complexes, and the size of the metal ion is also important in determining the strength of the metal-ligand bonding (because of steric limitations imposed by the rigidity of the benzene ring and the directions in which its substituents must point). This makes glycine thymol blue a sensitive and selective (but not specific) reagent for copper. Most of the other cations react only weakly, and many cause no detectable interference. The effect of replacing the glycine portions by other amino acids has been examined; proline appeared to be the most suitable.[21] Considerations such as these suggest possible directions in which to seek new reagents, both as indicators for particular metal ions in complexo-metric titrations and also as more selective species for the direct colori-metric determination of these metal ions.

With the major part now played by complexometric titrations in analyti-cal chemistry, it has become apparent that ligands showing true specificity for individual cations are unlikely to be found. Instead, improvement in existing methods, and development of new ones, will call for increased selectivity in three different directions—in the selectivity of the titrant, the selectivity of the masking agents, and the selectivity of the indicator if visual methods are used.

Sufficient qualitative and quantitative information is now available for it to be practicable to design metal indicators having stability constants that would make them suitable for use in complexometric titrations. Their color changes can be modified by introducing chromophoric groups. Further, depending on the nature of complexing groups, these indicators can be so designed that the logarithms of their stability constants with different metal ions will vary in a parallel fashion to similar constants with, say, EDTA. Conversely, by using nitrogen-type ligands they can show relatively much stronger metal binding towards $Cu(II)$ and $Zn(II)$. For greatest sensitivity, metal-indicators should have high extinction coefficients: This generally leads to the ligand being chosen because of its resemblance to dyestuffs. Some latitude in design is possible if the chromogenic and metal-binding parts of the ligand are more or less separate. This has been achieved in molecules such as metalphthalein and catechol violet in which a metal-complexing group is appended to a conventional dyestuff molecule.

Nevertheless, if indicators are used for visual rather than photometric endpoint detection, physiological factors depending on the response of the human eye to different colors become important. For this reason, indicators must be considered not only in relation to indicator error (arising from differences in stability constants of metal indicator and metal titrant complexes), but also in terms of sharpness of color change and its brightness, intensity, and contrast. Similar comments apply to fluoro-metric indicators. The "screening" of indicators arises from attempts to improve visual acuity, but discussion of such effects lies outside the province of this book.

Schwarzenbach[22] has pointed out the lack of complexometric methods for alkali metals; for small or highly charged cations of Be, B, Ti, Ge, Nb, and Ta; for the platinum metals; and for As, Sb, Sn, Mo, and W. Bonding of alkali metal ions is essentially electrostatic, so that anionic ligands are necessary; but, to date, stability constants of complexes of the alkali metals have failed to reach values of at least 10^7, which is the minimum needed for analytical usefulness in complexometric titration. The main hope of producing a ligand to meet this requirement appears to lie in finding one with a cagelike structure in which anionic groups are disposed tetrahedrally about the cavity in which the metal ion is accommodated: a tendency towards these conditions has been invoked in Chapter 6 to explain results with uramildiacetic acid. Difficulties with Be, B, Ti, Ge, Nb, and Ta arise from the small sizes of their cations, so that carboxylate ions do not pack well around them, from their proneness to hydrolysis, and from their strong tendency towards covalent-bond formation. The making and breaking of covalent bonds is usually a slow process, so that even when the ligands are diphenols derived from catechol (with which these cations form stable complexes) reaction proceeds only slowly. These considerations suggest that this group of cations can best be determined by other methods.

Some of the complexometric reagents derived from EDTA have been discussed in Chapter 6, but in general resulting differences in stability constants are small or unfavorable. Lengthening the ethylene chain in EDTA by replacing it with the ether grouping $-CH_2CH_2OCH_2CH_2-$ increases its affinity for barium relative to magnesium, whereas the group $-CH_2CH_2NHCH_2CH_2-$ would be expected to favor cations bonding more strongly to nitrogen than to oxygen. Similarly the corresponding thioether grouping should enhance the stability of complexes with cations having filled d shells. Use of polyamines rather than aminopolycarboxylic acids, to increase differences in stability constants between, say, copper (II) and manganese (II) complexes has the disadvantage that with many of the transition metal ions, especially of the second and third rows, the high ligand-field strength leads to spin pairing and very slow reaction rates. Attempts to devise better reagents for As, Sb, Sn, Mo, and W by replacing oxygen and nitrogen atoms in the complexing species by sulfur and phosphorus (with which they form much stronger bonds) are unlikely to be practicable if mercaptans and substituted phosphines are used, because of sensitivity to atmospheric oxidation. In this respect, the properties of anions of the thioacid analogs of nitrilotriacetic acid and EDTA would probably repay study.

The higher coordination numbers of the heavier elements of the periodic table suggest that ligands having up to eight suitably placed binding groups are likely to be useful in analysis.

Most organic precipitants contain a polar group linked to a large hydrophobic molecule, so that metal complex formation, by reducing the extent of hydrogen bonding by water, leads to a sparingly soluble product. The performance of such reagents might be improved if the molecule was "doubled up;" e.g. if p-tolylarsonic acid (CLXXXI) was replaced by ethylene-1,2-bis(p-phenylarsonic acid) (CLXXXII). The advantage of such a reagent lies in the ability of each molecule to act as a complexing species to two different metal ions, leading to the formation of large, much less soluble polynuclear complexes. Such coordination polymers have been described by Berg and Alam[23] using 8,8'-dihydroxy-5,5'-biquinolyl (CLXXXIII) with bivalent metal ions and also 1,6-dihydroxy-phenazine (CLXXXIV) with bivalent Cu, Zn, Ni, Co, and Hg. The latter

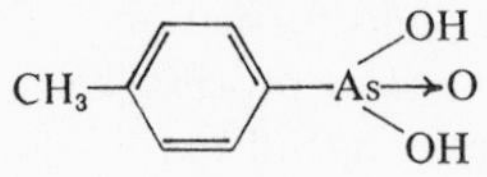

CLXXXI

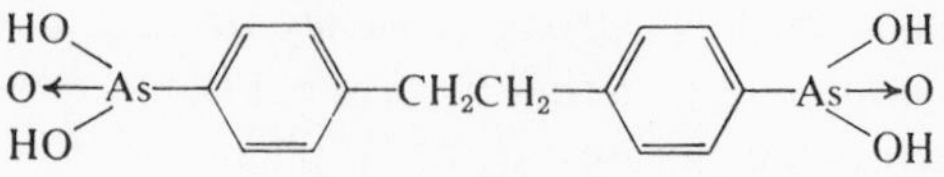

CLXXXII

has been suggested as a spot test for many metal ions, with which it gives colored precipitates, but the reaction proved to be neither very sensitive nor selective. 5,8-Dihydroxyquinoxaline (CLXXXV) also behaves in this way but is more readily oxidized.

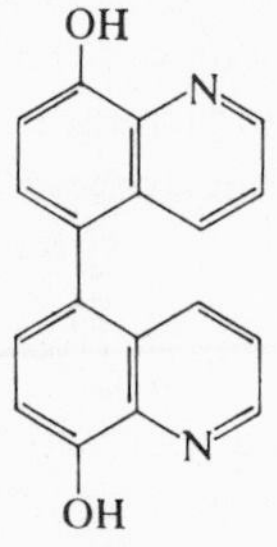

CLXXXIII 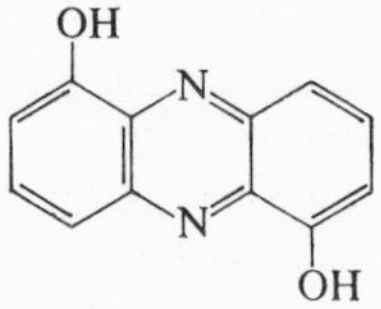   CLXXXIV 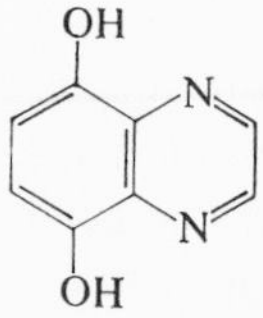   CLXXXV

Similarly, the chelating properties of bis(8-hydroxy-2-methyl-5-quinolyl)methane (in which two 8-hydroxyquinaldine molecules are linked through a methylene group) have been studied.[24]

Such precipitates cannot be used directly in gravimetric determinations because the metal-to-ligand ratio varies with the size of the polynuclear complexes formed.

The profound effect of complexing species on oxidation-reduction potentials such as ferric-ferrous and cupric-cuprous leads to the expectation of their increasing use to obtain in this way agents having carefully controlled oxidizing and reducing capabilities.

The discussion in this book has aimed to show how groups can be introduced or modified to alter solubility, color, and other properties, and hence to improve organic reagents for specific purposes. It has also endeavored to provide a framework within which to understand and predict chemical behavior. Nevertheless, chance will undoubtedly continue to play a part, although probably a diminishing one, in the discovery of new analytical procedures. The highly selective and sensitive reaction of the cerous alizarin complex with fluoride ion (Chapter 11) is a recent example of the initial observation being unexpected, although the result could be explained readily in terms of current chemical theory. No claim can be made that the present treatment is exhaustive, and I freely accept the charge that

There are more things in heaven and earth, Horatio,
Than are dreamt of in your philosophy.

References

1. Feigl, F., *Chemistry of Specific, Selective and Sensitive Reactions*, Academic Press, New York, 1949.
2. Taylor, J. R., *Virginia J. Sci.*, 3, 289 (1943).
3. Duke, F. R., *Ind. Eng. Chem.* (*Anal. Ed.*), 16, 750 (1944).
4. Gustin, V. K., and T. R. Sweet, *Anal. Chem.*, 35, 44 (1963).
5. Irving, H., E. J. Butler, and M. F. Ring, *J. Chem. Soc.*, 1949, 1489.
6. Powell, J. E., J. S. Fritz, and D. B. James, *Anal. Chem.*, 32, 954 (1960).
7. Dwyer, F. P., J. E. Humpoletz, and R. S. Nyholm, *Proc. Roy. Soc. N. S. Wales*, 80, 212 (1946).
8. Brandt, W. W., and G. F. Smith, *Anal. Chem.*, 21, 1313 (1949).
9. White, J. M., P. Tang, and N. C. Li, *J. Inorg. Nucl. Chem.*, 14, 255 (1960).
10. *Chem. Eng. News*, May 27, 1963, p. 46.
11. Horton, C. A., and J. C. White, *Anal. Chem.*, 30, 1779 (1958).
12. Young, J. P., and J. C. White, *Talanta*, 1, 263 (1958).
13. Crawley, R. H. A., *Anal. Chim. Acta*, 26, 281 (1962).
14. Mann, C. K., and J. C. White, *Anal. Chem.*, 30, 898 (1958).
15. Young, J. P., and J. C. White, *Anal. Chem.*, 31, 393 (1959).
16. Hibbits, J. O., W. S. Davis, and M. R. Menke, *Talanta*, 6, 28 (1960).
17. Cerrai, E., and C. Testa, *Anal. Chim. Acta*, 26, 204 (1962).
18. Scroggie, L. E., and J. A. Dean, *Anal. Chim. Acta*, 21, 282 (1959).
19. Chaberek, S., and A. E. Martell, *J. Am. Chem. Soc.*, 74, 6228 (1952).
20. Honda, M., and G. Schwarzenbach, *Helv. Chim. Acta*, 40, 27 (1957).
21. Koch, M., V. Svoboda, and J. Körbl, *Talanta*, 5, 141 (1960).
22. Schwarzenbach, G., *Complexometric Titrations*, Interscience, New York, 1957, Chapter 7.
23. Berg, E. W., and A. Alam, *Anal. Chim. Acta*, 27, 454 (1962); 28, 126 (1963).
24. Philips, J. P., and J. T. Leach, *Anal. Chim. Acta*, 26, 572 (1962).

Index